PUBLICATIONS OF RUSSELL SAGE FOUNDATION

Russell Sage Foundation was established in 1907 by Mrs. Russell Sage for the improvement of social and living conditions in the United States. In carrying out its purpose the Foundation conducts research under the direction of members of the staff or in close collaboration with other institutions, and supports programs designed to develop and demonstrate productive working relations between social scientists and other professional groups. As an integral part of its operations, the Foundation from time to time publishes books or pamphlets resulting from these activities. Publication under the imprint of the Foundation does not necessarily imply agreement by the Foundation, its Trustees, or its staff with the interpretations or conclusions of the authors.

The Individual, Society, and Health Behavior

Andie L. Knutson, Ph. D.

Professor of Behavioral Sciences
School of Public Health

Research Behavioral Scientist
Institute of Human Development

University of California, Berkeley

Russell Sage Foundation • New York • 1965

© 1965
RUSSELL SAGE FOUNDATION
Printed in the United States
of America

*Library of Congress
Catalog Card Number: 65–21057*
5/74

CONNECTICUT PRINTERS, INC.
HARTFORD, CONNECTICUT

To Ruth,
Ann, and Alan

Foreword

THOSE OF US who have been privileged to be colleagues of Dr. Andie Knutson since Russell Sage Foundation established a Behavioral Science Unit in the School of Public Health, at the University of California in Berkeley, now share our fortunate experiences with you, the readers, in this book, *The Individual, Society, and Health Behavior.* You, too, will expand your horizons as you and Dr. Knutson explore new concepts. These concepts are exemplified by salient public health problems that are familiar and couched in words with which one is comfortable. One is neither led nor patronized but recognized as an understanding colleague with whom both knowledge and problems are shared. These problems are treated as limitations of present knowledge and not as frustratingly hopeless barriers. Dr. Knutson portrays them as challenging research problems which, when scaled, will lead us to new programs of health. Thus in this book, as in his leadership of our Behavioral Science Unit, Dr. Knutson exemplifies the behaviorist's precepts upon which he focuses his professional career.

Never has public health been as excitingly strenuous. With exponential increase in scientific knowledge each decade, the conquest of epidemic disease has been a major achievement. However, the resultant dramatic reduction in deaths has produced our equally familiar population explosion which, of itself, is creating environmental and emotional problems even more difficult of solution than pneumococcal pneumonia, tuberculosis, malaria, or typhoid fever. Industrialization and urbanization so compress the nation that one-half reside in its 184 metroplitan areas and the proportion will rise to two-thirds by 1970. No longer are individuals, families, and communities protected by barriers of distance. As never before, society becomes vulnerable to the individual, be he an autoist whose engine emits the hydrocarbon ingredients of smog, a careless or ignorant applier of insecticides or weed killers so essential to our agricultural productivity, or a charlatan whose nostrums may fatally delay the treatment of curable disease. Thus the interaction of the individual with the society of which he constitutes a part becomes ever more crucial.

5

In this setting and to these problems, Dr. Knutson brings to bear his skills as a behavioral scientist and his comprehensions of these complex modern problems of health. He analyzes and studies man as an individual, underscoring his social needs as one of his major traits. Dr. Knutson identifies these social concepts and from them proceeds logically to a consideration of the behavior of society as related to health. Current health problems are used as models wherein society determines the patterns of the individual and in which the individual decides the pattern of society. Only a generation ago the individual physician focused on his patient while public health dealt with the community. Now these differences become increasingly blurred and community programs can be effective only if they deal with individuals, whether in control of cervical cancer by Pap. screening or of congenital heart disease by open heart surgery made possible by socially supported crippled children's services. As Dr. Knutson appraises these health problems of the individual and of the community, appropriate measures evolve logically. However, eventually these applications of our knowledge lead to as yet unsolved questions. Then, together with Dr. Knutson, we identify the research that will be necessary to provide these answers and further extend health programs.

We see as especially crucial the role of communication. The press, radio, and television make conversation pieces of health topics. Moreover, like education and freedom, health is deemed a *right* in our democratic society. Thus the individual must be informed, persuaded, and motivated into health patterns for his own protection and for that of society. On the one hand, he must be convinced to approve controlled fluoridation of his water in order to protect the teeth of his children. On the other, he must be educated to deny himself the pleasure of smoking cigarettes in order to protect himself and, by example, his children from illness and death. These are only two illustrations of a whole array of pressing health measures which we must achieve despite the clamor and din of pseudo-scientific "jamming." Here, especially, the careful research which Dr. Knutson identifies and underscores is crucial to our public health programs.

We members of the public health family can only hope that Dr. Knutson's portrayal of health research problems will be equally challenging to his confrère behavioral scientists. Individuals and their social aggregations urgently need this melding to achieve our goals of health behavior. Through the years Russell Sage Foundation has been one of society's most effective implementers of these concepts. This publication will serve as a valuable instrument in achieving these indispensable goals.

CHARLES E. SMITH, M.D., D.P.H.

Berkeley, California

Preface

THIS BOOK deals with man as a member of society, and with his behavior of concern to public health. Its aim is to impart in an organized fashion some of the conclusions, of potential significance to public health, that may be drawn from man's studies of himself as an individual and as a member of society. What is presented represents an attempt to unite theory, research, and practice in a way meaningful to the public health practitioner.

In presenting this description of man as a unified social being, attention has been drawn both to the current state of knowledge and theory and to many areas of uncertainty that demand research attention. The constructs employed to interpret man's health-related actions have been examined from different points of view and illustrated in various ways in the hope that this approach will contribute to a better understanding of these conceptual tools and of the findings obtained through their use. It may also facilitate the more efficient use of these organizing or analytical tools in public health research and practice.

Each chapter contains material that has been pretested with public health colleagues in lectures, seminars, consultations, and discussions. My colleagues have been a perceptive, critical, and practical audience whose questions and responses have served as valuable feedback. On the basis of these pretests, I have included content that might otherwise have been left out, reorganized and revised content, searched long and hard to find appropriate laboratory and field examples, and critically examined the public health validity and significance of each illustration used.

The reader is urged to remember that social psychology is a broad and rapidly growing field of study, and includes in its fold scientists with widely divergent points of view. What is included here is my own theoretical orientation, and represents my own judgment of appropriateness and significance regarding a limited part of this field. It is my hope that readers will be led by this presentation to examine other approaches.

Less reference has been made to original research findings and theoretical discussion than might be true of a text prepared for students of a specific discipline. An attempt has been made to identify general sources that are more likely to be available in local libraries. Particular attention has been given to research and review articles that seem to be meaningful for public health people with diverse professional orientations.

Acknowledgments

This book was prepared under grants by Russell Sage Foundation to the University of California, School of Public Health, for the purpose of developing a Behavioral Science Unit in the School. My interest in such a task grew out of nine years' research experience in the United States Public Health Service, to which I was attracted by Dr. Mayhew Derryberry. The interest was stimulated by discussions with Drs. Hadley Cantril and John C. Eberhart.

I consider myself especially fortunate to have been invited by Dean Charles E. Smith and Professors Dorothy B. Nyswander and William Griffiths to initiate and develop this project, and deeply appreciate the warm and staunch backing they have given.

The many opportunities provided by the faculty, particularly by Professors Jessie Bierman, Ruth Huenemann, Walter Mangold, Beryl Roberts, Edward S. Rogers, and Jacob Yerushalmy, to test ideas and approaches with their student groups have helped me in the difficult task of translating behavioral concepts into public health illustrations. The wise counsel and steadfast encouragement of Drs. Donald Young, Leonard S. Cottrell, Jr., Esther Lucile Brown, and, more recently, of Dr. Orville G. Brim, Jr., all of Russell Sage Foundation, have been of immeasurable value.

I am indebted to many writers and publishers who have permitted the use of their material. Their cooperation is deeply appreciated. Specific credit for quotations and illustrations borrowed from the literature has been given at points of citation. It is hoped that readers will be enticed by the brief mention given in the text to examine these primary sources.

Parts of this book have been presented elsewhere in lectures and articles. Much of the material in Part One, General Characteristics of Man, was presented in abbreviated form at the annual meeting of the Western Branch, American Public Health Association, Denver, Colorado, May 26, 1960, and published as "The Psychological Basis of

Human Behavior" in the *American Journal of Public Health,* vol. 51, November, 1961, pp. 1699–1708. Chapter 29, Interpersonal Communication Within Organizations, was presented at the Health Education Institute, Asilomar, in 1957 and published in *California's Health,* vol. 15, May 1, 1958, pp. 161–165. Both are reproduced here with permission of the publishers. In addition, I have drawn upon many previously published papers of my own for illustration, and credit to the original sources has been given in the text.

Chapter 28, The Role of Mass Media in Public Health, was previously published with William Griffiths as co-author in the *American Journal of Public Health,* vol. 50, April, 1960, pp. 515–523. Both he and the publisher have granted permission to reproduce it here. I thank Ronald C. Dillehay for preparing, especially for this book, Chapter 19 on Attitudes and Beliefs.

Many readers helped me improve my original manuscript. Dorothy B. Nyswander and William Griffiths reviewed it from a public health education point of view, and Eugene Hartley and David Glass gave it a critical reading from the standpoint of social psychology. Their suggestions have led me to make important additions and revisions. Mildred Glacken has helped significantly through library search and editing, as well as in the typing. The illustrations were prepared by the Audio-Visual Department of the School of Public Health under the direction of William T. Larkins. The direction received from Margaret R. Dunne, editor for Russell Sage Foundation, is deeply appreciated. Above all, I wish to acknowledge the active guidance and support of my wife, Ruth R. Knutson, whose ideas have been merged with my own in many hidden ways.

My behavioral science colleagues, particularly those in the United States Public Health Service and in the School of Public Health at the University, have stimulated my thinking in ways that cannot adequately be expressed.

I am sensitive that sources of ideas often become lost after the ideas themselves have been accepted, integrated, and acted upon. To my many colleagues who find here evidence of their influence: please accept my thanks.

A. L. K.

Berkeley, California
January 15, 1965

Contents

FOREWORD BY CHARLES E. SMITH, M.D.   5

PREFACE   9

PART ONE
GENERAL CHARACTERISTICS OF MAN   27

1. MAN AS PART OF ENVIRONMENT   29
   The Meaning of Transaction   29
   Man's Permeable Boundaries   31
   Geography and Behavior   32
   Geography and Psychological Life   33
   Effects of Environmental Change   34
   Public Health Illustrations   35

2. THE UNITY OF MAN   38
   Inner Balances   38
   Psychosocial Balances   39
   Objective-Subjective Totality   40
   Centralizing Psychological Effort   41
   Public Health Illustrations   42

3. MAN AS A SOCIAL ANIMAL   44
   Man's Slow Development   44
   Man's Group Ties   45
   Social Definitions of Health Status   47
   Illustrations of Social Influences on Health   49

4. THE UNIQUENESS OF MAN   52
   Individuality in Other Societies   53
   Sources of Uniqueness   54
   The Intimate Nature of Health   55
   Leadership and Interpersonal Skills   56

Unique versus General Principles of Behavior 57
Communicating Unique and General Findings 58
Translating General Findings 59

5. PATTERNS OF INDIVIDUAL VARIATION 61
Diseases and Disorders 62
Vision and Hearing 63
Touch 65
Taste and Smell 65
Kinesthetic Senses 66
Intelligence 66
Constitutional and Glandular Differences 68
Conclusions 70

6. THE BEHAVIORAL CYCLE 72
Children and Youth 73
Anticipating Crises in Adults 75
Program Planning and Research 75
Tuberculosis Program Research 76
Pregnancy and Childbirth 79
Conclusions 82

PART TWO
MAN IN HIS SOCIAL ENVIRONMENT 87

7. SOCIETY AND CULTURE 91
Human Society 92
Common Features of Societies 92
Inequalities in Social Placement 93
Effects of Unequal Placement 93
Culture as Man's Way of Life 94
Varying Influences of Culture 95
Man Internalizes Culture 96

8. PLACING MAN IN HIS SOCIAL HABITAT 98
Social Class 99
The Use of Class Terms 102
Implications of Social Class for the Practitioner 103
Measuring Social Class 103
The Use of Indices of Social Class 104
Distinguishing Caste and Class 105

Other Reference and Membership Groups ... 106
   Ethnic Groups ... 107
   Professional Membership and Reference Groups ... 109
   The APHA as a Membership-Reference Group ... 110

9. POSITION, STATUS, AND ROLE ... 117
Position and Status ... 117
Roles as "Sets of Expectancies" ... 119
Line and Staff Positions and Roles ... 120
Role Dilemmas ... 122
Role Definition ... 122
Role Sets ... 126
Role-Taking ... 126
Role Conflicts ... 128
Transactional Ties with the Community ... 129

10. THE MEANING OF FOOD ... 132
Some Definitions of Food ... 133
Food and the Life Cycle ... 134
Food and Religion ... 135
Food, Work, and Social Organization ... 136
Food and Personality Development ... 138
Changing Food Practices ... 138
Food as Incentive for Social Change ... 139
Symbolic Uses of Food ... 140
Other Social and Emotional Meanings ... 141
Implications ... 142

PART THREE
PERCEIVING THE WORLD ... 147

11. MAN'S KNOWLEDGE COMES FROM EXPERIENCE ... 149
The Nature-Nurture Question ... 149
Learning to Perceive ... 151
   Research Difficulties ... 152
   Insights from Observation ... 153
   Studies of Chimpanzees ... 154
Possible Implications ... 156
   Perception of Pain and Physiological Changes ... 156
   Can Perceptual Abilities Be Changed? ... 157

12. THE FUNCTION AND PROCESS OF PERCEPTION 159
    Perceptions Guide Actions 159
    Perception as a Dynamic Selective Process 161
    Perceiving Constancy and Stability 162
      Constancy in Perceiving Things 163
      Constancy in Perceiving Persons 164
      Ignoring Constant Stimulation 164
    Giving Meaning to Environment 165
    The Perceptual Process 166
      Components of the Perceptual Process 168
      Steps in Acquiring Meaning 169
    The Efficiency of the Sense Organs 170
    Factors Contributing to Error 171
      Sensory Factors 171
      Influence of Ego-Defense Mechanisms 172
      Personality Factors 174
    Dealing with Cognitive Strain 175
      Narrowing Range of Observation 175
      Grouping and Stereotyping 176
      Recording Observations 177
      Expectations Guide Efforts to Reduce Strain 177

13. MAN'S PRIVATE WORLD 180
    The Approach of Field Theory 181
    Objective and Subjective Facts 183
    Applying the Approach of Field Theory 184
      Application in Dental Health 185
      Application in Program Development 186
      Communicating Health Concepts 187
      Diagnosis and Treatment 188
      Patient Instructions 189
      Other Implications 191
    Summary 191

PART FOUR
SOCIAL MOTIVATION 197

14. THE SEARCH FOR THE SOURCES OF MAN'S ENERGY 199
    Instincts and Instinctual Tendencies 200
    Homeostasis 201
    Homeostasis and Social Motivations 202

Biogenic and Sociogenic Motives   203
Are Some Motives "Basic"?   204
Motivation in Infancy   205
Diffused Character of Infant Behavior   207
Conclusions and Implications   208
   Is the Concept of Motivation Necessary?   208
   Implications   209

15. MOTIVATION RESEARCH: AN ELUSIVE CHALLENGE   212
Problems of Definition   213
Conflicting Motives   214
Inferring Motives   214
Motive-Response Relationships   215
The Value Quality of Experience   216
Validity of Responses   217
Indirect Methods   217
   A Study of Attitude Formation   218
   The Study of Rumor   218
   Marketing Research   219
   Uses in Public Health Research   219
   Limitations   221
Implications   222

16. MOTIVATION IN HEALTH ACTION   225
An Overview   227
The Future Orientation of Behavior   228
The Self or Ego   230
   Ego-Involvement versus Egotism   231
   Ego-Involvement and Health Behavior   231
Changes in the Self or Ego   232
   Changes During Adolescence   233
   An Illustration: The Various Meanings of "Hospital" 233
   Major Identifications as Anchorages   237
Consistency-Inconsistency   238
Health Goals and Personal Relevance   239
Other Ego-Satisfactions and Threats   240

17. PATTERNS OF STRIVING   243
Deficiency and Growth Motives   243

Maslow's Hierarchy 246
Patterns of Security-Insecurity 249
Changes in Strivings During Starvation 251
Possible Implications for Public Health 253

PART FIVE
VALUES, ATTITUDES, AND BELIEFS 259

18. VALUES AND VALUE PATTERNS 261
Problems of Definition 262
Values Guide and Limit Action 264
Values Give Life Meaning 264
The Early Acquisition of Values 265
Values Are Inferred from Behavior 266
Difficulties of Research on Values 267
Studies of American Values 268
The Process of Identifying a Social Value 269
Influence on Public Health Programs 270
Comparing the Values of Groups 270
A Self-Anchoring Scale 271
Spranger's Value Types 273
A Scale of Personal Values 274
Values of Women and Public Health 275
Values of Health Team 275
Top Level Bias 276
"Basic Value Orientations" 277
Orientation to Human Nature 278
Value Orientation to Man-Nature 280
Orientation to Time 281
Orientation to Activity 283
Orientations to Relationships 283
The Values of Health and Life 284
Prenatal and Infant Care 285
Family Planning 286
Value of Animal and Insect Life 287
Other Life Value Influences 287
Death and Its Meanings 288
General Implications 289

19. ATTITUDES AND BELIEFS
        By Ronald C. Dillehay   293
        The Concept of Attitudes   294
        Attitude Measurement   298
        The Formation and Maintenance of Attitudes   299
        The Motivational Bases of Attitudes   302
        Attitudes, Beliefs, and Psychological Processes   303
        Attitudes and Action   305
        Persuasion and Attitude Change   307

PART SIX
THE PROCESS OF SOCIALIZATION   313

20. ACQUIRING SOCIAL BEHAVIORS   315
        Early Socializing Agents   316
            Identification and Imitation   316
            Reward and Punishment   317
        Personal Identity, Self, and Self-Image   318
            Dealing with Oneself   318
            Observing Responses of Others to Oneself   319
        Indirect Nature of Social Learnings   320
            Indirect Sources of Attitudes   320
            Learning "Must" Behaviors   321
            Learning Rules versus Learning "Whys"   322
        An Experimental Study of Socialization   323
            The Contact Comfort Hypothesis   324
            The Experiment   324
            Experimental Findings and Conclusions   325
        The Learning of Social Roles   326
        Socializing Agents and Social Change   328
            Socializing Agents as Barriers to Progress   328
            Unchallenged Assumptions   329
            Stabilizing Influences   330
            Implications for Change   331
            Education for Child Rearing   331

21. PERCEPTUAL DEVELOPMENT AND DEPRIVATION   334
        The Unstable World of Infancy   334
        Discovering the World   336
        Acquiring Concepts   338
        Acquiring Language   339

Experimental Studies of Children   340
    Other Experience and Intelligence   343
    Follow-up Studies   343
Experiments with Dogs   346
The Epidemiology of Reading Disabilities   348
Implications for Public Health–Mental Health   350

PART SEVEN
HUMAN LEARNING AND HEALTH ACTION   357

22. LEARNING THEORIES AND HEALTH ACTION   359
Experimental Studies of Learning Processes   359
    Classical Conditioning   359
    Rote Learning or Memorizing   361
    Trial and Error Learning   362
    Instrumental or Operant Conditioning   364
    Other Research Examples   366
Problems of Definition and Generalization   367
    Learning and Maturation   368
    Learning and Experience   369
    Learning as Improvement   370
Learning and Social Values   372
    The Value of Resistance   374
    Textbook Weaknesses   374
    Other Theories of Learning   375
Conclusion   376

23. LEARNING COMPONENTS OF PUBLIC HEALTH PROGRAMS   380
Typical Learning Situations in Public Health   380
    Programs with Required Outcomes   382
    Programs with Recommended Outcomes   383
    Self-Directed Learning Situations   387
Learning as a Subjective, Irregular, Perceptual Process   387
Learning Begins with Interest or Concern   389
    Perceptual Curiosity   389
    How Much Concern?   391
    Role of Education in Arousing Interest   392
    Illustration from Public Health Nursing   394
    Psychological Readiness in Tuberculosis Case-Finding   395
    Illustration from Maternal and Child Health   397
    Lack of Professional Concern   398

Exploratory Behavior as Part of Learning 399
Types of Exploratory Responses 400
Discursive Beginnings 401
Approaching Solution from Learner's Point of View 402
Identifying Barriers to Action 403
Learning Through Solving Problems 404
Effects of Thwarting 405
Thorndike's "Law of Effect" 405
The Timing of Effect 406
Delayed Rewards May Not Be Seen as Effects 407
Possibilities of Early Reinforcement 407
"Inappropriate" Behaviors May Relieve Concerns 408
"Learning by Doing" 409
Ego-Involvement in the Task 410
Gaining Acceptance of Participation in Learning 411
Importance of Participation in Change Processes 412
Social and Emotional Support for Learning 412
Support from Social Groups 413
Expectations of Others' Reactions 413
Personal Concerns May Block Discussions 414
The Transfer of Learning 417
Public Health Examples 418
Conditions Fostering Transfer 419
Conclusions 421
The Integration of New Learnings 421
The Growing Edge 423

24. VERBAL CONDITIONING 428
Awareness in Verbal Conditioning 429
Awareness and Learning 429
Experimental Study of Awareness 431
The Meaning of Awareness 432
Public Health Implications of Verbal Conditioning 433
Verbal Conditioning in Therapy 433
Opinion Surveys 434
Diagnostic Interview 435
Awareness in Experimental Research 437
Unsettled Issues 438
Conclusions 438

PART EIGHT
THE COMMUNICATION PROCESS 445

25. THE CRISIS IN MEDICAL COMMUNICATION 449
The Public Health Communication Chain 450
   The Research Scientist 450
   The Public Health Practitioner 451
   Expert Communication "Gatekeepers" 452
Conclusions 453

26. THE COMMUNICATOR FOR PUBLIC HEALTH AGENCIES 455
Representing Agency Policies 456
Clarifying Intentions 457
Defining the Image of the Audience 459
   Consideration of Special Factors and Conditions 461
   Audience Understanding of Health Jargon 462
   Basic Orientation to Authority 464
Maintaining a Trustworthy Image 465
The Order and Manner of Presentation of Issues 467
   The Laws of Primacy and Recency 467
   Commitment 468
   One-Sided versus Two-Sided Presentation 468
   Implications for Action 470
The Use of Feedback 470
   Potential Barriers in Communication 471
   Types of Feedback 472
Conclusions 474

27. FRAMES OF REFERENCE IN PUBLIC HEALTH
    COMMUNICATIONS 477
The Influence of Preparedness-Unpreparedness 478
The Search for Cognitive Clarity 480
   Theory of Social Comparison 480
   The Influence of Anxiety 481
   Experimental Studies of Anxiety and Affiliation 482
The "Autokinetic Phenomenon" 485
Impressions of Other People 486
Value and Attitude Climates 487
The Persistence of Frames of Reference 489
   Public Health Illustrations 490

Experimental Findings   491
Influence on Council Activities   493
Implications for Public Health   495

28. THE ROLE OF MASS MEDIA IN PUBLIC HEALTH
    By William Griffiths and Andie L. Knutson   498
    Mass Media Tend to Reach Select Audiences   499
    Effects May Be Specific and Limited   501
    Personal Appeals May Influence Effects   504
    Psychological Set Influences Interpretation   506
    Trusted Informal Leaders Can Serve Key Function   506
    Tinker to Evers to Chance?   507

29. INTERPERSONAL COMMUNICATION WITHIN
        ORGANIZATIONS   511
    Physical Situation   512
    The Web of Relationships   513
    The Unique Qualities of the Communicator   515
    The Unique Qualities of the Communicant   517
    Words Are Perceptions   519
    Summary   521

INDEX   523

Figures and Tables

FIGURES

1. Cross-section of Artichoke: A Representation of Man in, and as Part of, His Social Groups   46

2. Increasing Job Demands for Human Skills Over Technical Skills During Professional Advancement   57

3. Typical Behavioral Cycle of Tuberculosis Patient Passing Through Case-Finding Treatment, and Rehabilitation Program—Preliminary Planning Outline, 1949   77

4. Typical Behavioral Cycle of Tuberculosis Patient Passing Through Case-Finding, Treatment, and Rehabilitation Program—Completed Outline   78

5. The Behavioral Cycle of a Typical Middle-Class American Mother During Marriage and First Pregnancy   80

6. Diagrammatic Schematization of the Perceptual Act   169

7. Rumble Strip Experiments—South of Rodeo, California   173

8. Asymtote Decay Curve Illustrating Scientific Progress Toward a Naturalistic Interpretation of Man's Social Behavior   206

9. Mobile X-Ray Unit Employed as Projective Device   220

10. Schematic Portrayal of the Progressive Changes in Relative Saliency, Number, and Variety of Wants as Described by Maslow   248

11. A Self-Anchoring Scale   272

12. Mean Frequencies of Vocalizing and Mean Numbers of Types of Sounds in the Vocalizing of Infants in Homes and Institutions   342

13. Mean Length of Response by Chronological Age, by Sex, by Paternal Occupation, and by Single and Multiple Births   343

14. Young Lady   492

15. Old Lady   492

16. Composite   492

TABLES

1. An Outline of the Order of Psychosocial Development in Children   74

2. The Indirect Nature of the Perceptual Process   167

3. The Human Motives   245

4. The "Other" of the Anticipated Interaction Prior to Seeking Professional Medical Care for Specific Conditions   417

Part One

General Characteristics of Man

Part One

General Characteristics of Man

EACH OF US, while sensitive to his own uniqueness, tends to observe sameness in other men. Social distance seems to foster this observation of sameness: when we first meet people from other cultures, they look alike and act alike; members of neighboring social groups appear to have somewhat greater variability; members of one's own family have distinct personalities. We ourselves are unique individuals.

Our first observations of strange or foreign peoples tend to be of their group characteristics. These modal customs and behaviors may screen from view rare personal qualities. Some common experience with others in a familiar setting, within which we can better judge individual differences, seems to be a necessary step toward observing and understanding the details of personality. In this way we become most sensitive to the particular characteristics of those with whom, and within whom, we live.

Strangeness that may thus conceal uniquenesses in behavior may also conceal basic similarities among peoples everywhere. Group and individual differences in ways of perceiving, feeling, striving, and acting may distract our attention from those patterns of perception and response that are common to all humans. One who observes striking differences in cultural patterns and individual personality may be led to assume even greater innate variance than actually exists.

Kluckhohn, Murray, and Schneider tell us that:

Every man is in certain respects
    a.   like all other men,
    b.   like some other men,
    c.   like no other man.[1]

They note that among the determinants of personality are some factors that are universal, some that are limited to men who live alike or belong to similar groups, and others that are unique to each man. Certain common features of environment which distinguish man's life

27

from that of other animals are so obvious we tend to overlook them. From these general features of environment we need to distinguish the effects of specific sociocultural background, caste, class, occupational and membership groups, common sources of income and support, or patterns of life, and the like that foster common ways of behaving among groups of people. Then we may better identify the specific personal capacities, patterns of development, and experience which contribute to individuality.

As we consider some of the general, group, and personal characteristics of man as related to his health actions, it is essential to bear in mind that the same pattern of hereditary, experiential, and situational determinants of behavior, differentially applied, account for both the likenesses and uniquenesses of mankind.

NOTE TO INTRODUCTION TO PART ONE

1. Kluckhohn, Clyde, and Henry A. Murray, with the collaboration of David M. Schneider, editors, *Personality in Nature, Society, and Culture.* 2d ed., rev. and enl. Alfred A. Knopf, Inc., New York, 1956, p. 53.

Chapter 1

Man as Part of Environment

MAN is at once both part and product of environment. We cannot safely speak of man and environment nor of man interacting with environment. Dewey and Bentley suggest that the relationship is one of transaction rather than interaction.[1] Any change in either man or environment, of which he is a part, is *ipso facto* a change in the other.

Man's existence as an organized unit or central point of physical environment depends upon his being constantly attuned to essential features of that environment—the air, water, food, heat, light, and chemicals. Either insufficient or excessive transactions regarding any one of a wide range of elements directly affect the functioning of man as a physiological organism. Minor imbalances may be reflected in minor insufficiencies or ill health; more extended or drastic imbalances may find expression in death.

As Gardner Murphy puts it,

> The organism has *a practical boundary* for some purposes—for example, the skin and mucous membranes. From other standpoints, however, the skin makes by no means an absolute barrier. The air we breathe is "within us" not when it passes valve-like barriers, but by degrees as it passes through nostrils, bronchi, the red blood cells and, with chemical reshuffling, back through veins and breath to the windowpane or to the people around us. To find a sharp barrier between self and non-self is a nice metaphysical task. If this is true of the simplest facts of biological existence, it is hard to see how people can be considered solely from the point of view of internal structure, of the personality that lies within the skin.[2]

The Meaning of Transaction

Dewey and Bentley note that in dealing with man-environment relationships, scientists studying human behavior have employed three different approaches as "levels of organization" in conceptualizing their data:

> *Self-action:* where things are viewed as acting under their own powers.
> *Inter-action:* where thing is balanced against thing in causal interconnection.
> *Trans-action:* where systems of description and naming are employed to deal with aspects and phases of action, without final attribution to "elements" or other presumptively detachable or independent "entities," "essences," or "realities," and without isolation of presumptively detachable "relations" from such detachable "elements."[3]

The concept of self-action with its assumptions of free will and independence and the vital principle commands less attention of the behavioral sciences today than formerly. "Organisms do not live without air and water, nor without food ingestion and radiation. They live, that is, as much in processes across and 'through' skins as in processes 'within' skins. One might as well study an organism in complete detachment from its environment as try to study an electric clock on the wall in disregard of the wire leading to it."[4]

"Interaction" has been widely used as a principle of inquiry and organization. Some who employ this approach do so in accord with the definition above. Their ecological descriptions tend to treat organisms and objects as separate things which can be adequately described prior to, or independent of, interactions taking place. Others who employ interaction as a principle of organization have found it necessary to extend their definition of the term far beyond that given by Dewey and Bentley. They note that organisms and objects vary in definition in accord with changing conditions. For them, perceptions are guided by expectancies, which grow out of assumptions gained from previous experience. A high degree of interdependence thus exists between person and person, or person and thing, observed. The term "transaction" seems more appropriate than interaction for describing such a dynamic interplay.

"Transaction" thus suggests a high degree of fusion between persons, objects, or factors entering into any event observed. Since man is ever part of any observation concerning man's behavior, Dewey and Bentley hold that "manifestly the subject matter of behavioral inquiries involves organism and environmental objects jointly at every instant of their occurrence, and in every portion of space they occupy. . . . The behavioral inquiries . . . fall into difficulties the very moment they depart from the transactional, except for the most limited minor purposes; their traditional unsolved puzzles are indeed the outcome of their rejecting the transactional view whenever it has suggested itself, and of their almost complete failure to allow for it in any of their wider constructions."[5]

Man's Permeable Boundaries

The skin that binds the flesh confines neither psyche nor soma. Man's self or ego, the center of his psychological activities, knows no boundaries. It may become extended through identification with persons, places, or things far removed in time and space. The things with which man identifies may be real or imagined, tangible or intangible, nearby or infinitely removed. Yet whatever affects the object of man's identification affects man himself, for psychologically his identifications are part of himself.

This applies whether the object of man's identification or loyalty is a friend or leader, a country or city, an idea or principle, or some social or religious value. It may be a symbol out of the distant past that retains personal significance for him. Even the self-image with which man identifies may bear only the slightest relation to this physical self. The invisible scars left by the surgeon who removes a tumerous breast may have far greater significance to the patient than the scars left by his knife.

So accustomed are we to thinking and dealing with man as an independent and distinct unit in the constellation of inner and outer forces that make him what he is that we are often blind to the permeable nature of his boundaries, and to his network of value-laden extensions. We tend to identify ourselves as well as others as fairly independent agents in a more or less ordered environment. Yet as Lawrence K. Frank in an excellent discussion of "Society as the Patient" observed, "The individual, except when uniquely endowed, cannot escape from his culture and the peculiar climate of opinion of his age; he is immersed in it, like the fish in water, and as unaware of this surrounding medium."[6]

Even in our strivings for cognitive freedom—in perceiving, in thinking, in imagining and reasoning—we are dependent primarily on the symbols provided by fellow men. Like Thoreau, who borrowed an axe in his attempt to escape all social influence, we borrow symbols and logic in attempts to think creatively.

Geography and Behavior

Since Darwin's emphasis on factors contributing to the survival of the fittest, there has been growing awareness of the significance of man's geographical environment to his physical and social well-being. Topography, climate, rainfall, soil, plant and animal life, sources of power—all these features of man's physical and biological environment—help to shape the pattern of his social and personal life. Customs, occupations, values, beliefs, and behaviors of peoples the world over seem intimately knit to his efforts to deal with nature.

The kind and amount of food available to man for himself and his herds, and the food relationships developed between man and other creatures, have as much to do with his social life as with his nutritional status. The ways of gathering, storing, distributing, and preparing food became the central focus of much social activity. Society must of necessity be different in areas that are barren and frozen, dry and sparse, or rainsoaked and fertile. The area required to sustain a family unit is of compelling significance to the size of communities and the pattern of community life. It influences also the type of family unit, the form of marital system, the relationships between husbands and wives, and even the value placed on the number and sex of children.

To a considerable degree, conditions of geography govern both the availability of safe waters in adequate supply for purposes of consumption and cleaning and the accessibility of suitable means of disposing of water used as a carrier of human and other waste. The problems of water control and waste disposal are strikingly different in torrid, temperate, and frigid geographic zones, as well as in mountain, desert, and fertile lowland areas.

The ways people clothe and house themselves, and their manners of sanitary and hygienic practice, are closely bound by matters of terrain, climate, and rainfall. Materials for implements of service and ritual are usually drawn from native sources. Natural terrain and water routes help to shape the flow of commerce in goods and services, women and children, ideas and disease.

Few would question that geography ranks high in the configuration of forces that result in some people being "haves" and others "have-nots" in terms of food, water, products, and power. The manifold diversity of man's cultural achievements also reflect in no small part nature-defined possibilities and limitations. Yet man, as part of this geographic environment, is not everywhere a blind, yielding dependent. The river that blocks one man's progress may be turned by another man into a means of commerce or a source of power.

As man has gained strength as a social creature, he has joined with fellow men to attune many features of physical environment to his needs. His success in modifying geography to serve his social purposes has freed him from many natural forces. Today he is becoming more master than slave to nature. Yet the customs, characteristics, beliefs, and values acquired during early struggles with natural forces linger on in his personal and institutional life. They are revealed in patterns of social interaction and social organization, class structure, property ownership, manner of dress, food habits, social and personal rituals, beliefs, and values.

Geography and Psychological Life

The significance of geography to man's psychological life becomes paramount when we recognize the extent to which this fusion of physical and social environment is reflected in cultural learnings. Hallowell reminds us that:

> . . . the very existence of varying cultural patterns carries with it the psychological implication that the individuals in these societies live in different orders of reality.
>
> Human beings . . . never live in a world of bare physical objects and events. They live in a meaningful universe. And the traditional culture patterns to which they become habituated define the specific meanings of that universe. Man's psychological responses to the physical objects of his external environment and to other human beings can only be understood, therefore, in terms of the traditional meanings which these latter have for him. He never views the outer world freshly or responds to his fellows entirely free from the influence which these meanings exert upon his thought and conduct.[7]

Cross-cultural studies yield many evidences of the relationship of modes of thought and expression to man's way of life and to the challenges and vicissitudes of the settings in which people strive. It is not surprising that Eskimos think of many snows rather than one snow, that they have several different words to refer to snow in its varied forms—falling snow, packed snow, slushy snow, and so on; whereas Aztecs, for whom snow has minor daily significance, use but one word to speak of snow, ice, and cold.[8] The accident of time alone can scarcely explain why written records of social heritage tend to be more extensive for sociocultural groups living in stable and temperate circumstances than for those who live nomadic lives. On the other hand, nomadic peoples have some of the most highly developed spoken languages.

Perhaps modern man's strongest ties to primitive nature reside in his symbolic life—in his modes of thought and expression. Alfred North Whitehead observed: "Language arose with a dominating reference to an immediate situation. Whether it was signal or expression, above all things it was *this* reaction to *that* situation in *this* environment. In the origin of language the particularity of the immediate present was an outstanding element in the meaning conveyed."[9]

Interpretation of many phenomena of culture requires understanding of the continual transaction between man, his physical environment, and his sociocultural environment. While symbols and modes of man's expression and thought bear relationship to his physical environment, the physical world is perceived in terms of the symbolic frame of reference acquired by the perceiving individual from his culture. In truth we do, as Whorf suggests, "dissect nature along lines laid down by our native languages."[10]

Effects of Environmental Change

Environmental changes tend to sharpen our awareness of the intimate transactions of man as part of environment. Yet even insights regarding these transactions are less likely to come regarding our own culture than other cultures. In observing other sociocultural groups one sees most clearly how man, as part of environment, changes with that environment (although seldom in clearly definable ways), and how other parts of environment change under the impact of the behaviors of man and his groups.

The UNESCO report, *Cultural Patterns and Technical Change,* provides ample support for the thesis that:

> Man's being and function, his body, mind, activity, emotions, and social relations, are all one, and weakness of the person, the failure to take preventive measures or to strengthen one's person, may result in "illness" in any one of these areas.
> In many cultures throughout the world man is continuous with his environment. Therefore, he is not healthy unless his environment is "healthy," or, conversely, the well-being of his environment depends on his acts.[11]

Technical and industrial progress may seriously disrupt the social and economic structure of a community. Families are deeply injured by rapid changes in occupational status and by the realignments of social and economic forces that accompany what we call progress.

Changes in the manner of living brought about by river control, power development, mechanization, urbanization, and other aspects of technological change deeply concern the lives of the people involved. Man's cultural, mental, and moral life—as well as his economic and physical well-being—are affected. Technical and industrial change brings with it changes in occupational, economic, and social status; changes in property values and property rights; changes in transportation, communication, and social interaction. What personal tragedies may be wrought by the sudden impact of these changes on traditional ways of eating, sleeping, working, playing, and worshiping!

The population explosion which alarms many leaders is in part a by-product of effective public health, welfare, and educational effort. Improving sanitary conditions, harnessing contagious diseases, and inculcating values regarding the worth of every individual have helped to disrupt population balances maintained through infant deaths resulting from pestilence, starvation, and infanticide. Serious problems arise when such early forces in population control are influenced without either supplementing them by current methods of control or developing adquate means to feed and care for the new members of society.[12]

The impact of environmental change on the health of the individual and his family is dramatically evident when we view the awesome effects of fires, floods, droughts, and other disasters. Unemployment or unsuitable employment opportunity, occupational stress, accidents, and the impact of injury, illness, or death in the family, and many other critical experiences of human life leave their mark on man's physical or emotional well-being. There is ample evidence that such events do affect man's health. The crucial question concerns why similar crises affect individuals and families in dissimilar, often contrary ways. Man, as part of environment, influences the nature and order of even such environmental changes as they apply to himself. Hence the effects of any specific change can seldom be predicted with certainty.

Public Health Illustrations

To say that man is at once part and product of environment is to say that we cannot expect to take man from his environment, change him through treatment or therapy, return him to an unchanged environment, and expect him to function effectively. Personal and social difficulties are almost certain to arise.

A rehabilitated heart patient, for example, may have difficulties learning and carrying out new occupational and family roles when those about him expect another pattern of action from him. The duties, responsibilities, and privileges that were once his may have been taken over during his absence by those who may not know how to give them up or may not be eager to do so. Yet these roles, duties, responsibilities, and privileges *are part* of what he was before he became ill. Acquiring a new role and function means becoming a new person within a setting in which others expect him to be the person he once was. Role expectations must change if the new role enactments are to be successful.

The mentally ill patient who has been reclaimed by society and returned to an unchanged locale faces almost insuperable problems. The social forces that once helped to shape his behavior in unhealthy ways are likely to do so again unless new opportunities for action exist and are perceived as existing. Preparation for a new job or new social role go for nought unless members of the community are prepared to accept him in the new roles. In short, his relationship with the rest of his environment must be a new and different relationship if he is to be a new and different person—a secure and effective social being.

Nor can one expect to change an environment as in a slum clearance or urban renewal project without having impact on the economic, social, and emotional lives of the families involved. The family lifted from slum life into modern low-cost housing may suffer greatly from the loss of intimate ties fostered by overcrowding and shared misfortunes. While some social ills may be mitigated by the change, others may emerge from new imbalances created. How man's housing affects man's health remains a riddle to researchers whose best efforts are clouded by the difficulties of identifying stable boundaries of man and stable boundaries of housing as separate parts of a total environment.[13]

NOTES TO CHAPTER 1

1. Dewey, John, and Arthur F. Bentley, *Knowing and the Known*. Paperback edition. Beacon Press, Boston, 1960, pp. 107–109. Dewey and Bentley draw upon evidence from many scientific areas to illustrate their discussion regarding the differences between the approaches of self-action, interaction, and

transaction. For a more extended discussion of the implications of the transactional approach in the study of human behavior, and for illustrations of research employing this approach, see Kilpatrick, Franklin P., editor, *Explorations in Transactional Psychology,* New York University Press, New York, 1961.

2. Murphy, Gardner, *Personality: A Biosocial Approach to Origins and Structure.* Harper and Bros., New York, 1947, p. 4.

3. Dewey, John, and Arthur F. Bentley, *op. cit.,* p. 108.

4. *Ibid.,* p. 128.

5. *Ibid.,* p. 130.

6. Frank, Lawrence K., *Society as the Patient.* Rutgers University Press, New Brunswick, N.J., 1948, p. 181.

7. Hallowell, Alfred I., "Psychological Leads for Ethnological Field Workers" in Haring, Douglas G., editor, *Personal Character and Cultural Milieu.* Rev. ed. Syracuse University Press, Syracuse, N.Y., 1949, pp. 308–309.

8. Whorf, Benjamin L., "Science and Linguistics," *Technology Review,* vol. 44, 1940, pp. 229–231, 247, 248. Republished in Maccoby, Eleanor E., Theodore M. Newcomb, and Eugene L. Hartley, editors, *Readings in Social Psychology.* 3d ed. Henry Holt and Co., New York, 1958, p. 7.

9. Whitehead, Alfred N., *Modes of Thought.* Capricorn Books. G. P. Putnam's Sons, New York, 1958, p. 53. Originally published by Macmillan Co., New York, 1938.

10. Whorf, Benjamin L., *op. cit.,* p. 5.

11. Mead, Margaret, editor, *Cultural Patterns and Technical Change.* Tensions and Technology Series, United Nations Educational, Scientific, and Cultural Organization, New York, 1955. Reprinted as a Mentor Book, New American Library, New York, 1955, p. 217.

12. *Ibid.,* p. 177.

13. Wilner, Daniel M., and Rosabelle P. Walkely, "Housing Environment and Mental Health" in Pasamanick, Benjamin, editor, *Epidemiology of Mental Disorder and Mental Health.* American Association for the Advancement of Science, Publication 60, Washington, 1959, pp. 143–174.

Chapter 2

The Unity of Man

MAN'S BEHAVIOR tends to be holistic or molar rather than segmental or molecular. We may dissect him into various physiological, psychological, or social parts for purposes of analysis or description but we must not be led astray by this type of analysis. His behavior seldom, if ever, reflects clear distinctions between purposes, cognitions, emotions, and reactions.

Sensory and cognitive processes combine in a marvelous perceptual harmony to yield man a unified sense of environment. Memory traces, refined and reorganized through thought and imagination, enter into his every perception. Motives, derived through experience, are ever present and functioning to influence the selection of things to perceive, to remember, to recall, and to act upon. Expectations regarding future actions evolve out of his evaluations without any conscious awareness or effort on his part.

Inner Balances

Much has been written about the inner balances of man and about the diverse stresses that may stem from the malfunctioning of a single organ. Kidneys cannot function properly if the heart has suffered damage; imbalances in sugar metabolism may suggest a malfunctioning pancreas, infection in one part of the body may be revealed in symptoms of illness in other parts; if one part of the cortex is injured, another part may take over its functions.

As Allport has pointed out, there are many balancing agencies within the body to preserve this tendency of man to behave in a unified manner.

> . . . the homeostasis of the endocrines, the recovery or transfer of functions after injury, the remarkable adaptive properties of the sense-organs. All these *biological conditions of unity* must not be overlooked, for nature appears greatly concerned in preserving the integrity of the

individual organism. This fact is the most basic of all the guarantees of unity. Hereditary endowment in terms of *temperament* contributes to this stabilizing of the course of development, with the result that as a personality changes it seems to change consistently with itself. Nature sets limits beyond which the variation in individual development may not extend.[1]

Psychosocial Balances

Man's patterns of response to the many sociocultural systems into which his life is woven also yield evidence of this tendency of man to react as a unified being. Major social upheavals—wars, epidemics, depressions, technical or industrial revolutions—leave their impressions on both psyche and soma. Psychological and social deprivation may be as damaging to the soma as starvation, lack of sleep, cold, and exhaustion. Yet so complex are these inner-outer forces that comprise man that what appears to be the same form of deprivation may influence individuals in opposite ways: while one flounders, the other may create.

Intensive studies of abnormal or deviant behavior bring to attention many ways in which the impingements upon man's biochemical system bear relation to his psychosocial behavior and, conversely, ways in which factors affecting his psychosocial behavior leave their mark on his physiological functioning. Diagnoses in such situations are often clouded in uncertainty. Yet from such diagnoses comes a growing body of evidence of the ways in which man's biochemical and psychosocial systems are fused to make him respond in integrated fashion.

As Caudill puts it,

> The various [sociocultural] systems . . . are thought of as linked open systems rather than as closed, in that what happens in one, especially when it is under stress, can have effects in the others, and this process tends to be of a self-regulating nature (von Bertalanffy; Wiener). Stress can first become manifest in any of the systems; and it is particularly pertinent here to think of examples where the strain on a system becomes so great that it calls forth adaptive or maladaptive defenses from other systems. For example, an individual under psychological stress too great for the integrating capacity of his personality to handle may be able to shift some of the load to his family. But if his family is itself disrupted and he has no other sustaining small group to which to turn, the strain is likely to be shifted to his body and he may develop such symptoms as ulcerative colitis (Lindemann). On the other hand, if it is mainly the physiological system that is initially under great stress, and the individual cannot find added support from his psycho-

logical resources, or aid from some small group system, then death may result—as in cases of schizophrenic exhaustion or "voodoo death" (Cannon). If the initial situation is one in which the family is broken by the loss of one or more of its members, this may put a heavier load on the personality structures of the survivors, and may also bring community resources into play in such forms as social service and financial aid. Buell's concept of the "problem family" is pertinent here; he found that about 6 per cent of families in St. Paul were utilizing well over half of the combined health services. Finally, conditions of disaster such as floods and war may disrupt the community and national systems so that a greater load is placed on individual families (Wolfenstein).[2]

Studies such as those to which Caudill refers draw attention to the complex nature of causation regarding man's behavior. Multiple causation is almost invariably the rule rather than the exception. Of significance, too, are the intricate circular relationships that may exist among these various forces which impinge on man. To say that family discord has led to alcoholism and the loss of a job, or that it has been responsible for a child's emotional problems and failure in school, or that it has led to some inappropriate physiological reaction such as ulcers or asthma is to ignore the possibility that any one of these events might be *causing* the others or might be at the same time cause and effect.

Objective-Subjective Totality

This unity of man's behavior seems to involve an intimate, though often confusing, harmony between his life as he subjectively senses and perceives it and his life as others may objectively observe it to be. Subjective as well as objective factors seem to be involved in every aspect of behavior. As Gardner Murphy suggests, what results is not an "ordered and self-contained unity" but rather a life process in which objective and subjective aspects are fused.[3] "The life process is not simply a series of events within the organism, but a field of events in which inner and outer processes constitute a complex totality."[4] And one might add that this field of events is constantly in flux.

As a result, one cannot with confidence predict man's psychological state on the basis of objective evidence alone, even though this evidence may be based on extensive observations and physiological measurements. Nor can one safely estimate his physiological state on the basis of the subjective evidence obtained through interviews and psychological testing.

Pain, for example, while related to physiological damage, does not seem to reflect the degree or nature of the damage: pain may exist in the absence of any objective evidence of injury; serious injuries may occur without the person experiencing any pain at all. An individual may be frantic with hunger in the absence of physiological evidence of deprivation, or may feel satisfied when serious deficiencies are present. Physiological changes occurring during growth, development, and decay may not be perceived at all, or may be sensed in unexpected ways.

Centralizing Psychological Effort

In striving toward unity in his behavior, man tends to centralize his psychological efforts. As Allport reminds us, it does not mean that "the organism responds as a whole" nor that man's behavior from day to day is rigidly consistent. Rather, "Many concurrent activities can go along at one and the same time. A man may walk, smoke, dodge the traffic, digest his dinner, and at the same time be busy with his thoughts. The final common path means only that *one maximally integrated* activity occurs at a time. The man cannot be pursuing several different trains of thought at one and the same moment."[5]

So strong is this tendency to centralize one's psychological efforts along a common pathway that even conflicts within the individual, resulting from the interplay of conscious and subconscious factors, may be resolved without his awareness. Slips of the tongue or pen sometimes reveal inner conflicts to the outside world, yet the behavior may remain consistent from the standpoint of the acting individual.

Man has many selves. In considering this tendency toward unity in behavior, it is essential to recognize that what is appropriate and consistent for one self may be inappropriate and inconsistent for another. Self as son, self as lover, self as father, and self as employee involve different constellations of value, attitude, and action. Yet within his conscious awareness as of a single instant, man is but one of his many selves. His behavior at that instant tends to be integrated. Sherrington noted, "Even in those extremes of so-called double personality, one of their mystifying features is that the individual seems to himself at any one time wholly either this personality or that, never the two commingled."[6]

A moment of introspection will convince the doubtful that it is quite impossible to attend to many things simultaneously. Man must attend to total rather than segmental behavior in order to act. Like Einstein's centipede, he functions best when he does not consider the order in which to move his muscles. Segmental behaviors become the means whereby molar behaviors are achieved. Wright and Barker point out that a man ". . . does not sweat or salivate, nor does he often bend his knees in walking, manipulate his tongue in talking, move his eyeballs in reading, or bend his waist in sitting down. *He* walks, talks, reads, or sits down, leaving his glandular and motor apparatus to take care of the sweating, salivating, bending, manipulating and all such molecular units of behavior which, as molecular, are lost to the person in what he actually does."[7]

Public Health Illustrations

Man's behavior in sickness, as well as in health, is holistic. When he is sick in part, he is sick all over. A minor itch gains his full attention by intruding itself in spite of the best efforts to ignore it. Temporary discord in one area of behavior tends to disrupt responses in another. A toothache may be generalized to far reaches of the body. The emotional or social aspects of tuberculosis, cancer, or diabetes, for example, may be of such overriding significance for the individual that he is unable to follow a course of treatment prescribed. The interplay of cause and effect in stuttering may lead to withdrawal and social isolation or, conversely, to marked aggressive reactions.

Many of the ills of modern society stem from attempts to deal with man segmentally rather than with man as a unit. Specialization, which seems to be an inevitable outgrowth of scientific advance, results in institutions competing with one another for primary segments of a man who is seeking to maintain his integrity as a total being. How far removed we are from the medicine man, who for all his weaknesses, sought to treat the total man! He had strengths that have not been duplicated in our modern society.

One must sympathize deeply with persons responsible for the local administration of such a program as "medicare" designed to provide medical care for the aged. For how can one possibly distinguish between the physical and emotional health needs of an aged person? How can one deal successfully with his health needs without being concerned with his housing, his economic status, his means of communication, his social outlets, and his needs for achievement?

If we look at the other end of the age continuum we find evidences that the child is being pulled apart in his social and emotional development by competing institutions, each one seeking to capture a particular segment of the whole. One institution tries to teach him to share and help others; another, that private enterprise must be competitive; one appeals to social morals; and others appeal to his needs for social entertainment. Educational television competes with escapist entertainment; civics courses compete with headlines about dirty football or police brutality. Is it any wonder that children are learning a Golden Rule distorted in practice to mean, "Do unto others as they might do unto you, but do it first."

NOTES TO CHAPTER 2

1. Allport, Gordon W., *Personality: A Psychological Interpretation.* Henry Holt and Co., New York, 1937, p. 346.

2. Caudill, William, *Effects of Social and Cultural Systems in Reactions to Stress.* Social Science Research Council, New York, Pamphlet No. 14, June, 1958, pp. 26–27. In this discussion Caudill refers to the following works: von Bertalanffy, Ludwig, "The Theory of Open Systems in Physics and Biology," *Science,* vol. 111, January, 1950, pp. 23–29; Wiener, Norbert, "Problems of Organization," *Bulletin of the Menninger Clinic,* vol. 17, July, 1953, pp. 130–138; Lindemann, Erich, "Modifications in the Course of Ulcerative Colitis in Relationship to Changes in Life Situations and Reaction Patterns" in Wolff, Harold, Stewart G. Wolf, and Clarence C. Hare, editors, *Life Stress and Bodily Disease: Proceedings* of the Association for Research in Nervous and Mental Disease, Williams and Wilkins Co., Baltimore, 1950, pp. 706–723; Cannon, Walter B., " 'Voodoo' Death," *American Anthropologist,* vol. 44, April–June, 1942, pp. 169–181; Buell, Bradley, and associates, *Community Planning for Human Services,* Columbia University Press, New York, 1952; Wolfenstein, Martha, *Disaster: A Psychological Essay,* The Free Press, Glencoe, Ill., 1957.

3. Murphy, Gardner, *Personality: A Biosocial Approach to Origins and Structure.* Harper and Bros., New York, 1947, p. 10.

4. *Ibid.,* p. 37.

5. Allport, Gordon W., *op. cit.,* p. 346.

6. Sherrington, Sir Charles Scott, "Aspects of Animal Mechanism," *Mental Hygiene,* vol. 7, January, 1923, p. 16. Cited in Allport, Gordon W., *op. cit.,* p. 345.

7. Wright, Herbert F., and Roger G. Barker, *Methods in Psychological Ecology.* University of Kansas Press, Lawrence, Kans., 1950, p. 79. See also Deutsch, Morton, "Field Theory in Social Psychology" in Lindzey, Gardner, editor, *Handbook of Social Psychology,* Addison-Wesley Publishing Co., Reading, Mass., 1954, vol. 1, p. 183.

Chapter 3

Man as a Social Animal

MAN is a social animal. His slow development in a sociocultural setting enables him to learn language and technical skills that have required untold centuries to develop. Without a society to give him the products of culture, man as we know him could not exist. Other animals, particularly the higher primates, also enjoy social and family life, and share their experiences with one another through the use of some forms of symbolic language. They are even able to communicate simple motives and to express the emotions of fear, rage, desire, and pleasure. But none has developed so fully as has man the elaborate mechanisms of symbolic language, and none leans so heavily on the communications of his fellow-beings, past and present. A major part of man's life is concerned with social transactions. He is born with a greater capacity than any other animal for sharing the communications of others through the use of symbols. By using symbols to represent things, and the relations between things, he is able to transmit ideas to others whether they are present or not, and about things that may not, in fact, even exist.

Perhaps man's greatest quality is his capacity for creating and giving symbolic meanings and values to intangible and abstract things. By making use of this capacity, he is able to extend himself so that he can participate in groups far removed in time and space, and can share with others his thoughts, his beliefs, his hopes, his fears, his concerns, his expectations and intentions.

Man's Slow Development

The slow rate of human growth and maturation is of crucial significance to the role of man as a social animal who bears and transmits culture. The many years of infancy and childhood not only foster cultural learnings, but actually prevent the child from escaping during the period of his greatest susceptibility and pliability. During these

44

years of greatest dependency he learns to love and to fear, to perceive and to value, to communicate and to share. With little conscious awareness on his own part, or on the part of his informal instructors, he learns to behave in prescribed ways within a highly organized social setting. First from members of his most intimate family unit, later from members of more extended groups, he learns the many roles and functions required of man as a unit within a social system, and the formal and informal rules governing the functioning of that social system.

Independence comes late for the human child; full independence is never achieved. For by the time the child is physically, psychologically, and emotionally able to fend for himself he has become tightly enmeshed in the social and cultural trappings of his groups. The older child cannot, even if he would, discard his social heritage any more than he could discard the genes inherited from his progenitors. The extent to which this is true has led Gardner Murphy to charge that ". . . man, in becoming a culture-making animal, has often sacrificed one of his potentialities—the capacity for exploratory perceiving and thinking—to the exigencies of cultural requirements at a given time. . . ."[1]

The special features of man that help to make him the social animal that he is also make him more vulnerable than most animals to extinction should some catastrophe strike the grown members of his group. There is slight possibility indeed of an infant surviving without nurture provided by some adult. There is even less chance of his surviving as the social being we know man to be, for the infant is dependent on adults of his group for far more than physiological subsistence. Were it possible in some mysterious way for a newborn to grow and mature without some family unit to serve as a socializing agent, the resulting creature would have slight semblance to man as we know him. One can scarcely imagine what such a creature would be like without the benefits—and burdens—of culture.

Man's Group Ties

So intricately is man enmeshed in a sociocultural setting that it is meaningless to speak of man's psychological behavior apart from this setting.

For the purpose of illustration, one might think of an artichoke as representing man in, and as part of, his many social groups. Consider the core of the artichoke as representing his core personality. One need not infer that this core is completely innate, for even the single cell requires nurture; the chemical nature of this nurture and the manner in which it is presented to the cell influences the pattern and manner of cell development.

The first circle surrounding the core might represent the prenatal environment; next, peer groups environment; and in order, social and church groups, social class, ethnic groups, and finally broad religious and national groups.

Thinking of personality in this way, we may say that it is necessary

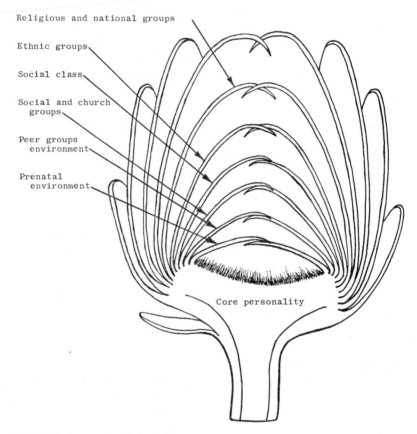

Religious and national groups

Ethnic groups

Social class

Social and church groups

Peer groups environment

Prenatal environment

Core personality

FIGURE 1. Cross-section of Artichoke: A Representative of Man in, and as Part of, His Social Groups

to peel off the concentric circles, the overlapping layers of the artichoke, in order to understand the influences more directly applied to the core. It is not easy to understand the ethnic and caste groups, for example, until the effects of the overall religious and national groups have been removed. Likewise, understanding social class requires a removal of the ethnic and caste groups, for social class exists within both and yet may be overridden by the impact of caste or ethnic group in its significance for the individual.[2]

It should not be implied for a moment, however, that these group influences are independent of one another. Man distinguishes himself from other animals in part by his ability both to absorb and to influence the milieu in which he grows. There seems to be no completely stable boundary between man and his environment at any point, physical or social.

Social Definitions of Health Status

Nationality, religion, caste, class, and the other social variables described are man-made and may be man-changed but, insofar as they exist and as long as they exist, they directly affect the health status of individuals who share them. To consider the health status of any individual or group, to consider means of influencing that health status, or even to consider the definition of health status within such groups requires an understanding of these broader sociocultural variables. Health behavior appropriate to one social setting may be disastrous in another.

The changes within himself and others that man identifies as symptomatic of illness or other abnormality; the cause, course, and cure of illness suggested by such signs or symptoms; the possibilities of treatment or control; the potentials of rehabilitation; the implications for self and others of health actions either taken or ignored—all these behaviors of public health significance are socially derived and socially governed behaviors. Sociocultural variance in response to health crises or protection against illness and differences in the availability, choice, and quality of health care by social class, caste, occupational and ethnic groups have been highlighted in research on the extent and quality of health services. Yet such studies, disturbing though they may be, barely suggest the extent and significance of man's social self to his health status and health actions.

Definitions of mental illnesses in particular tend to be greatly influenced by matters of culture. Persons having cataleptic seizures, who would be regarded as seriously ill in modern America, have been accorded great prestige by some Indian tribes in California.[3] Jahoda, in her classical review of "Current Concepts of Positive Mental Health," cites much evidence to support the view that social conventions often determine whether particular behaviors are judged normal, extraordinary, or sick.[4] An intensive study of mental disorders among the Hutterites supports the view that a favorable social and cultural climate can, to a good extent, prevent the outbreak of certain types of social maladjustment.[5]

There is growing awareness in public health of the relationships of social environment even to contagious illness, apart from the significant role of man as a bearer of disease.

> To understand what caused this patient to become sick, it is necessary to know what sort of family he has, where he lives, what kind of clothes he wears, what food he eats, what kind of employment he has, and how he reacts to these factors. These and similar facts of life make up man as a social being, and may be more provocative in the origin of his disease than the germ which has been isolated from his sputum in the bacteriology laboratory.[6]

A rise in temperature or pulsebeat, the swelling of tissues, changes in the composition of blood cells or urine, fatigue, and other medical cues to illness may not by themselves mean illness for the specific individual. The line between wellness, malingering, and illness is in good part a socially drawn line. Aches and pains that are not experienced as out of the ordinary for oneself and one's social colleagues may not be perceived as illness. Koos, in his study of *The Health of Regionville,* an upper New York community, found that less than a fourth of those in the lower socioeconomic grouping of his population recognized the need for medical attention for such symptoms as a loss of appetite, persistent backache, continual coughing, persistent joint and muscle pains, the swelling of ankles, shortness of breath, or persistent headaches.[7]

Bloom provides illustrations from many studies to support the thesis that "each illness, in theory, has a clinical unity: it is describable according to identifying signs as one illness or a cluster of illnesses. But the *meaning* of illness, from the view of the patient, is more variable. It is not capricious, but it is complex. People perceive illness in different ways. The pattern of these perceptions or definitions of illness vary according to culture and within culture."[8] Sigerist reports that among the Kuba of Sumatra even skin diseases and injuries that frequently occur in the population are not viewed as symptomatic of illness.[9] In areas of North Africa, hookworm was regarded as a normal condition according to the findings of the Rockefeller Sanitary Commission,[10] and Redlich tells us that even a person with syphilis may not be considered sick in a population where it is found within the normal range of life events.[11]

King, in his *Perceptions of Illness in Medical Practice,* has illustrated in many ways how training and experience in the health professions may influence the way health workers define and respond to health and illness, the judgments they make regarding one another's roles, responses, and practices, and the evaluations they make regarding patient symptoms and responses. For such health professionals, the hospital may become a daily workshop or laboratory. They may be quite unaware that those features of the hospital they consider normal, such as the lack of privacy, strange uniforms, equipment, and language, unusual sights, sounds, and smells, may be disturbing and even traumatic to the sick and highly anxious patient. Such features of environment may lead to an intensification of his suffering and to a delay in his recovery.[12]

We must look, therefore, at our concentric circles around the core personality of the individual as overlapping and permeable circles through which influences pass both ways. For just as the individual influences the broad cultural climate in which he lives, his physical, emotional, and psychological health is directly or indirectly influenced by that climate.

Illustrations of Social Influences on Health

Sociocultural influences on health status are many and varied. The Indian mother who insists that the newly severed umbilical cord of the infant be wrapped in cow dung, or dares not boil the sacred water of the Ganges lest some ancestral life be threatened, is led through cultural pressures, unrecognized, to threaten the very life of her infant. Yet her behavior is no less consistent with the values of her culture than that of the midwestern farmer who takes pride in the health of his children and rejects the idea of their going for regular physical examinations or x-rays, since to do so suggests weakness in the family. Such behavior is not in accord with his measure of good health as expressed by his boast, "We come from good stock; I have never been to a doctor in my life."

In our society chronological age is used as the primary measure of maturity. It is easier to count chronological age than emotional age, intellectual age, physiological age, psychological age, and so on. By reason of this we tend to use chronological age as a measurement of individual maturity and consciously as well as unconsciously associate chronological age directly with these other measurements of age. We have accepted this sort of measurement so fully that we are doing little about seeking ways of arriving at other age definitions which may have greater significance than chronological age in terms of many personal and public health–mental health issues.

The impact of this method of measurement on present society is illustrated by the difficulties arising in grade school because of the strict adherence to chronological age in placement although some children mature in physiological, physical, intellectual, or social ways much earlier than others. We find this illustrated also at the other end of life with retirement. Sixty-five as a retirement age is not only possible but compulsory for many individuals who physiologically or mentally are still comparatively young. It is quite impossible to estimate the psychological and emotional implications this choice of measurement has on individuals within our society.

One can but wonder to what extent health status is influenced by the value we in this country place on speed, on activity, on verbal abilities, on competition, on romantic love, on conformity, on personal wealth, on time–values which are by no means common to all cultures.

It is not necessary to illustrate the way in which each of these broad sociocultural variables surrounding the individual influences health status in order to recognize that all play a part in making him the unique individual he is. To understand him as an individual, one must unclothe him gradually from the social forces in which he is encased and seek to understand, as best we can by such research means available, the nature of the impact of each of these forces. Yet by the very process of attempting to remove these social forces for the purpose of analysis, we are removing parts of man himself.

Public health workers seeking new approaches to the problem of improving health status may be challenged by Gardner Murphy's observation, "The great problem is always the discovery of new dimensions, and the most universal of keys yet discovered for the unlocking of these mysteries is the study of the blind assumptions which make their existence remain unguessed."[13] One is challenged to ask, "What blindly held values and assumptions guide our health programs?"

Public health as yet lacks many of the tools necessary for isolating these ubiquitous social forces and studying their effects. Such effects are more easily viewed in sociocultural groups other than one's own where the contrast with his own behaviors and values facilitates observation. Yet, if one is to view the health notions and behaviors of others with true sensitivity and understanding, he must first seek to unclothe himself of his own cultural trappings and recognize them as artifacts of his own society.

NOTES TO CHAPTER 3

1. Murphy, Gardner, *Human Potentialities*. Basic Books, New York, 1958, p. 52.

2. Cantril, Hadley, "The Place of Personality in Social Psychology," *Journal of Psychology*, vol. 24, July, 1947, pp. 19–56.

3. Benedict, Ruth, "Anthropology and the Abnormal," *Journal of General Psychology*, vol. 10, January, 1934, pp. 59–80.

4. Jahoda, Marie, *Current Concepts of Positive Mental Health*, Joint Commission on Mental Illness and Health, Monograph No. 1. Basic Books, New York, 1958. See also Smith, M. Brewster, " 'Mental Health,' Reconsidered: A Special Case of the Problem of Values in Psychology," *American Psychologist*, vol. 16, June, 1961, pp. 299–306; and Knutson, Andie L., "New Perspectives Regarding Positive Mental Health," *American Psychologist*, vol. 18, June, 1963, pp. 300–306.

5. Eaton, Joseph W., and Robert J. Weil, "The Mental Health of the Hutterites" in Rose, Arnold M., editor, *Mental Health and Mental Disorder*. W. W. Norton Co., New York, 1955, pp. 223–237.

6. Cherkasy, Martin, "The Montefiore Hospital Home Care Program," *American Journal of Public Health*, vol. 39, February, 1949, pp. 163–166.

7. Koos, Earl L., *The Health of Regionville*. Columbia University Press, New York, 1954, p. 33.

8. Bloom, Samuel W., *The Doctor and His Patient: A Sociological Interpretation*. Russell Sage Foundation, New York, 1963, p. 98.

9. Sigerist, Henry E., "The Special Position of the Sick" in Roemer, Milton I., editor, *Henry E. Sigerist on the Sociology of Medicine*. MD Publications, New York, 1960, p. 12.

10. Stiles, Charles W., *The Rockefeller Sanitary Commission for the Eradication of Hookworm Disease*. Judd and Detweiler, Washington, 1911.

11. Redlich, Fredrick C., "The Concept of Health in Psychiatry" in Leighton, Alexander H., John A. Clausen, and Robert N. Wilson, editors, *Explorations in Social Psychiatry*. Basic Books, New York, 1957.

12. King, Stanley H., *Perceptions of Illness and Medical Practice*. Russell Sage Foundation, New York, 1962.

13. Murphy, Gardner, *op. cit.*, p. 14.

Chapter 4

The Uniqueness of Man

EACH PERSON is a unique individual. He is born into society with his own peculiar pattern of biologically determined capacities, abilities, and characteristics that make him from birth different from any other human being. As he grows and develops in his own special world, he learns through experience particular ways of thinking and acting. These serve him in applying the resources he has to take advantage of opportunities to satisfy personal needs or wants, or to cope with the problems he faces.

As the individual grows, he acquires a sense of belongingness or personal identification with many specific groups within his surroundings. From their norms and values, he knits his own norms and values; their interests and wants color his own interests and wants; he may adopt their purposes and goals as his own. Yet throughout he remains a unique individual wanting, hoping, striving for, expecting— and perhaps fearing—things different from anyone else. How he acts to apply his own pattern of capacities and talents to achieve his ends is also different in some ways from any other member of his special pattern of groups.

The lay student of individual differences is quick to note variation from one individual to another in height, weight, size, and shape. He will note differences in color or complexion, pattern and structure of the hair, strength and speed of movement, and physical endurance. If he is a critical observer he will recognize variances with respect to keenness of vision, acuity of hearing, and sense of smell and taste. He is most likely to be impressed with difference in interest and preference, variance in eagerness or willingness to participate in various kinds of activities, and difference in ability to recall specific incidents or to make critical judgments, to solve problems or to gain social acceptability; difference in attitudes, beliefs, and opinions as well as the underlying values from which they seem to derive are readily observed.

52

While he may be less aware of physiological differences, he may observe differences in speed of reaction, endurance, emotion, and temperament that reflect to some degree the differences in basal metabolism, respiratory rate, calcium, sugar, acid, and hemoglobin contents of the blood, pulse rate, concentration of acids, and so on.

One might ask, "What accounts for these individual differences? Why are they of concern to public health?"

To the extent that the causes of unhealthy conditions or characteristics can be identified, actions to influence change in these conditions can better be taken. Achievement of our goal of a more abundant and happy life, of more creative growth for everyone, hinges on a better understanding both of the conditions leading to unhealthy personal characteristics and of those related to personal characteristics to which we aspire. It is a truism to say that many of our public health efforts are futile because we lack an adequate understanding of the relationship between genetic and environmental factors and individual and group health.

The fact of individual uniqueness has been well established in biological and psychological research. The biologists Dunn and Dobzhansky, in their *Heredity, Race, and Society,* note that "The chance that any two human beings, now living or having lived, have identical sets of genes is practically zero, identical twins always excepted. The hereditary endowment which each of us has is strictly his own, not present in anybody else, unprecedented in the past, and almost certainly not repeatable in the future. A biologist must assert the absolute uniqueness of every human individual."[1]

Individuality in Other Societies

Attempts to study the individual apart from his environment become increasingly difficult as he grows older, for factors present in his sociocultural milieu are increasingly reflected in his personal behavior. This occurs to such an extent that frequently when we look at members of a group distinctly different from our own, for example, members of some foreign cultural group or members of a minority group distinguished in some particular way, we observe their similarities more quickly than we discern large individual differences. This has led the anthropologist Hallowell to observe:

> While it has been assumed from time to time that little, if any, variability in individual behavior was characteristic of the so-called primi-

tive peoples, closer observation inevitably has disclosed the fact that even in these relatively homogeneous cultures variability in personality traits, as well as in talent, thought and behavior occurs. Individuals are not completely moulded to a common pattern despite the forces at work which tend to produce this result. . . . Gross similarities must not be allowed to obscure the minutiae of genuine differences in thought and conduct. . . . Indeed, the very nature of culture allows for such variations. It is not a die which stamps out succeeding generations of individuals indistinguishable in all their habits and beliefs. It defines ends for which individuals strive and at the same time provides correlative means for accomplishing them, for gratifying human desires within traditional limits.[2]

Sources of Uniqueness

It is not proposed to summarize here the current status of the nature-nurture question or to estimate in crude fashion the relative significance of hereditary and environmental factors to individual uniqueness. It is important, however, to consider some of the factors, both hereditary and environmental, that have led to individual uniqueness insofar as such differences have significance to the planning for better individual and group health.

These are not two distinct forces influencing one another in any systematic way. Rather, there is a continuous transaction between two interdependent force constellations. Recognizing this transaction is essential if we are to understand individual differences as they appear within the life cycle of the individual. The nature of an individual's social or group norms and values, the patterns of his identifications and loyalties, and how he perceives the particular situation in which he is placed, as well as biogenetic factors are involved in understanding any unique act. As Cantril has suggested, ". . . an individual will develop in *his* particular way depending on *his* particular abilities and temperamental traits *within* the directional framework provided by his participation in a particular social context."[3]

Despite the very best efforts of our geneticists there is doubt that we can even now state with certainty the conditions necessary for, or responsible for, the acquisition of *any* single behavioral characteristic, much less the conditions necessary to duplicate this characteristic with certainty.

Fuller has suggested that "heredity is a capacity to utilize an environment in a particular way."[4] Even in the beginning of life the collection of genes which give some direction to the development of the organism must be surrounded by nutrient material of a specific type in order that the differentiation essential to growth takes place. Hence distinguishing between hereditary and environmental effects is not possible even with respect to a single cell.

The interdependence of nature-nurture factors observed in the germ cell continues throughout the life span of the individual. With growth, a continually increasing variety of environmental factors influences the organism. At the same time the genetic influences become more concealed and when they do appear, they may express themselves in unexpected ways. Change continues slowly from birth to death, and throughout its process genetic influences reveal themselves, at times in characteristics which may not appear until maturity. The length of life itself seems in some degree to be genetically determined.

The Intimate Nature of Health

To appreciate the significance to public health of the uniqueness of the individual, one must recognize that a person's health is one of the most intimate aspects of his personality. So intimate is it that he may have difficulty communicating with anyone, even himself, about it.

In dealing with the chronic illnesses, even more than in dealing with the earlier problems of public health, the active participation of an individual is required in case-finding, diagnosis, treatment, and rehabilitation. Persons working in such programs, therefore, need to be particularly sensitive to differences among individuals. One individual may have had unusual experiences that cause him to be afraid to acknowledge or report symptoms; another may have learned to distrust the methods of diagnosis used or the treatment offered; another may doubt the likelihood of successful treatment. Such persons may place greater value in their own feelings than in the x-ray or other scientific methods of diagnosis, or may have learned to distrust professional persons who use scientific method. How difficult it is for many of us to realize that slow physiological changes in our own bodies take place without our being aware of them until they are ultimately reflected in malfunction.

If the groups to which a person belongs attach shame or weakness to certain health conditions, he may not be able to acknowledge even to himself that he has such a condition. Social barriers are often more effective motivators than physical forces. Strong resistance to outside influence suggests deep personal or group motivation.

We need to remember, as Gordon Allport reminds us, that:

> Unlike plants and lower animals, man is not merely a creature of cell structure, tropism, and instinct; he does not live his life by repeating, with trivial variation, the pattern of his species. Nature's heavy investment in individuality stands forth chiefly in *homo sapiens*. While we may recognize individual differences among dogs or varying strains of temperament among rats, still their lives in all essential particulars are regulated by their membership in a species. Man alone has the capacity to vary his biological needs extensively and to add to them countless psychogenic needs reflecting in part his culture (no other creature has a culture), and in part his own style of life (no other creature worries about his life-style).[5]

Individuals acting in conformity with the demands of culture may suppress or restrain almost any biological need, and even pain, rather than violate the demands. Those who live by socially prescribed eating codes will starve before partaking of foods identified as profane. Others will suffer or die from contagious diseases before violating religious tenets by killing the insect carriers of pestilence. Many will prefer death to dishonor as defined by their social groups.

Leadership and Interpersonal Skills

Public health leaders often describe their responsibilities in terms of community programs designed to deal with community ills. Their orientation is primarily toward group needs, group planning, and group action. Such approaches and methods, to the extent that they are feasible and effective, are much preferred to individual methods under such conditions. Yet the health and well-being of individuals remains the specific concern of public health, and understanding individuals remains a key to effective action.

Even though one's primary orientation is toward group action, one must work effectively with individuals to achieve group action. This involves dealing effectively with members of groups, both leaders and followers in planning, program development, applications, and evaluation. Proportionally, a major part of the time of the successful group leader is spent in communication with individuals; his human relations skills in dealing with individuals becomes of critical importance in determining whether successful group relations develop. Furthermore, members of groups are individuals, and even within groups respond in individual and unique ways.

It has been suggested that while a major emphasis in professional education is concerned with developing technical and theoretical skills, human skills become of increased importance as the trained professional advances to leadership. The professional person, newly appointed to the job, finds technical skills of primary use, but as he succeeds and gains staff, human skills become more important. Each advancement to higher responsibilities of leadership, whether in administration, consultation, coordination, or research, places heavier demands on him for the effective use of human skills.

Cameron has proposed the diagram which is presented below as descriptive of this relationship. The relationship described seems to hold true for many professional settings.

Unique versus General Principles of Behavior

The behavioral scientist is tossed into somewhat of a dilemma when dealing with this problem of individual uniqueness. The chosen task of the behavioral scientist is concerned with developing general principles of laws regarding individual and group behavior. In carrying out this task he must choose between trying to capture the uniqueness of

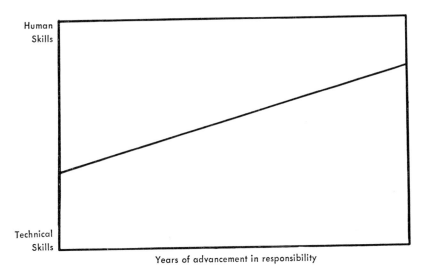

Years of advancement in responsibility

FIGURE 2. Increasing Job Demands for Human Skills Over Technical Skills During Professional Advancement

A hypothetical diagram based on a discussion with Dr. Dale Cameron any one individual or attempting to develop and test hypotheses related to group behavior. His tools and concepts seldom permit him to deal adequately in the one study with both individual uniqueness and group response. Attempts to generalize regarding more than one individual move him away from the goal of completely capturing the particular reactions of any single person.

He may choose to study the relationship of the individual to his groups and to identify factors underlying group interaction and response. Then he will be compelled by the nature of his purpose to move farther away from the intimate understanding of any particular member of his sample. This gap will increase with each step in the level of his scientific abstraction. To the extent that his description becomes one of "man in general," the unique features of any particular person will be lost in the final description.

On the other hand, the scientist may concern himself with attaining a most intimate and detailed understanding of a single person's behavior. Then his findings cannot safely be interpreted as representative of a group from which this individual comes. The description becomes one of "unique man" rather than one of "man in general."

Communicating Unique and General Findings

The behavioral scientist who seeks to communicate theory and research findings regarding individual and group behavior to members of other professions is plagued by the same dilemma that faces the research scientist. Yet he cannot as easily free himself from the responsibility of dealing to some degree with both individual and group behavior. Ignoring either may by implication lead to greater error in communication than a less adequate consideration of the relationship between the individual and the group.

This problem in communication is not one that applies to behavioral scientists alone. Warren Weaver observes that scientists in communicating their findings to the public or to one another must always recognize that whatever they communicate is to some degree in error. They must organize and select items of information in order to communicate effectively and significantly with other members of their groups. This process of selection inevitably, however, results in incompleteness and inaccuracy.

It may be helpful to suggest to such scientists that they consider the concept of "communicative accuracy." This concept rests upon the fact, not always recognized, that the effective accuracy of a written statement depends primarily upon the interpretation given to it by the reader. A statement may be said to have communicative accuracy, relative to a given audience of readers or hearers, if it fulfills two conditions. First, taking into account what the audience does and does not already know, it must take the audience closer to a correct understanding. The better an example of communicative accuracy it is, the more gain in understanding it will achieve—but the basic point is simply that it must gain ground in the right direction. Second, its inaccuracies (as judged at a more sophisticated level) must not mislead, must not be of a sort which will block subsequent and further progress toward the truth. Both of these criteria, moreover, are to be applied from the point of view of the audience, not from the more informed and properly more critical point of view of an expert.

Communicative accuracy is important to all of us all of the time. Consider the illuminating example recently offered by a newspaper reporter, of the two men coming home from work and greeting their wives. One says, "My dear, when I look into your face, time stands still." The other remarks, "My dear, your face would stop a clock."[6]

Translating General Findings

The public health official who seeks to apply behavioral science theory and findings in action programs needs to be aware of these problems in communication that face his behavioral science colleague if he is to deal effectively with the data at hand. He needs to recognize that specific meaning is often lacking in generalized reports. In fact, the most significant findings are often reported at the most abstract levels of conceptualization. For this reason they may be easily misinterpreted or ignored.

This means that information regarding the generalized needs or interests of the public must be translated back into their unique individual and group meanings if effective program approaches or appeals are to be developed. Findings about the generalized patterns of behavior of a group may have little significance for the unique individuals whose actions or responses were grouped together in arriving at the generalized description. Findings concerned with the patterns of communication within groups are likely to have action meaning only when reinterpreted with the recognition of the unique social and personal network found within the web of social life of a particular group.

In a study of adolescent behavior, for example, one might group together such activities as dating, grooming, shoe polishing, showing off in sports or dramatics, special attention to posture and manners, and a host of like actions, and refer to them as "sex-related behavior." The summary term may then be used in a report of the study suggesting that teenage children, as a group, participate in much "sex-related behavior." It would be hazardous to attempt to apply such a generalization in a public health program without translating the term, "sex-related behavior," back into the same type of specifics represented in the original coding. Yet at times such generalizations drawn from theory or research are directly incorporated into programs without seeking to discover their operational meanings.

Obvious though this may appear, many survey and other study findings go unapplied because ways have not been found to translate significant statistical or generalized findings—data developed out of research involving thousands of unique individuals—into content having meaningful, unique application for each of the individuals from whom the data were initially derived. The significance of individual uniqueness for the program planner is fully as great as for the researcher. Translating generalized findings into their particular meanings requires an analytical and creative ability much akin to that employed by the initial researcher.

NOTES TO CHAPTER 4

1. Dunn, Leslie C., and Theodosius Dobzhansky, *Heredity, Race, and Society*. Rev. ed. Mentor Books, New American Library, New York, 1952, p. 54. See also notes to Chapter 5, p. 70.

2. Hallowell, Alfred I., "Psychological Leads for Ethnological Field Workers" in Haring, Douglas G., editor, *Personal Character and Cultural Milieu*. Rev. ed. Syracuse University Press, Syracuse, N.Y., 1949, p. 329.

3. Cantril, Hadley, *The "Why" of Man's Experience*. Macmillan Co., New York, 1950, p. 36.

4. Fuller, John L., "Nature and Nurture: A Modern Synthesis," *Doubleday Papers in Psychology*. Doubleday Publishing Co., Garden City, N.Y., 1954, p. 5.

5. Allport, Gordon, *Becoming*. Yale University Press, New Haven, 1955, p. 220.

6. Weaver, Warren, "Communicative Accuracy," *Science,* vol. 127, March 7, 1958, p. 499.

Chapter 5

Patterns of Individual Variation

DURING THE PAST CENTURY the study of individual differences in behavior has attracted some of our most creative and critical researchers. Ingenious techniques have been developed for detecting differences, for determining the extent or range of variation in different population groups, for studying factors that contribute to variation, and for assessing the significance of differences for the individual and for society.

This search for patterns of individual differences, their meanings and implications, has been approached along many research fronts, ranging from laboratory studies of the experimental biologist and experimental psychologist to the participant-observation studies of the sociologist and anthropologist. Dogs, cats, rats, fish, birds, monkeys, and apes have served as subjects of experiments too traumatic or too demanding to permit the use of human subjects. Detailed observations and recordings have been made of behaviors in natural settings where even direct questionings might influence the patterns of action. Researchers under such conditions are guided by the principle, as stated by Foote and Cottrell, "Whether consciously or not, each person tells his history publicly in his behavior, and could only conceal it by withdrawing from society, an act that in itself is diagnostic and occasionally observed"[1]

The public health official who is primarily concerned with community health may question the significance of differences in individual capacities, potentialities, and responses for his program. His attention here is invited to some of the patterns of individual variation in health potential, in health-related behavior, and in response patterns that have a direct bearing on participation in health actions. Rather than attempting to evaluate here volumes of pertinent evidence,[2] suggestion will be made of a few areas of research which some health officers may find worthy of more critical examination.

Diseases and Disorders

In reviewing our present knowledge regarding heredity of health and disease, Dobzhansky emphasizes the significance of the interplay between nature and nurture in human traits. In presenting "a very incomplete list of known or suspected hereditary diseases and deviations" he reiterates the importance of recognizing the arbitrary nature of such classifications since the dichotomy between genetic and environmental factors is by no means precise. His list includes 136 conditions relating to metabolic disorders, skin, skeletal system, teeth and mouth, alimentary system, blood and vascular system, urogenital system, eyes, ears, nervous system, and musculature.[3] While such traits have long received attention from clinical and treatment points of view, less attention has been given to their significance to health communication and health action.

To such a list of primarily genetically based conditions one might add an almost limitless outline of irreversible or nearly irreversible changes that occur during growth and decay, injury and illness, social or personal traumatic experience. They, too, have relative permanence for the individual and deserve attention from the standpoint of health action.

Of major significance to health actions are deficiencies in sensory capacities and abilities. An individual's potential for effective communication depends upon both the range and quality of his sensory and perceptual capacities and abilities. To the extent that these capacities are weak, inadequate, or absent, difficulties in communication occur. Such difficulties in communication are likely to be greater if the deficiency and its communication significance is not recognized by either the person with the problem or the person with whom he is attempting to communicate.

Many deficiencies of relevance to communication *can* be detected very early in life or shortly after their occurrence if the possibility of a problem is recognized and appropriate tests applied. Unfortunately, however, major deficiencies may go unrecognized for years. This may occur with respect to vision, hearing, touch, taste, smell, and even to the response to normally painful stimuli. The use of mass screening techniques is, of course, contributing most significantly to the early detection of such deficiencies.

Vision and Hearing

Failure to detect and correct visual or hearing handicaps may retard intellectual or social development and lead to inattention or indifference based in futility, loss of self-assurance, and continued inferior performance in school and occupation. Under these circumstances, communication becomes most difficult.

The early detection of hearing deficiencies poses a more difficult problem than the early detection of visual handicaps, particularly in areas where adequate screening methods are not regularly employed. As Anastasi notes, "Contrary to popular belief, hearing deficiencies constitute a more serious handicap to intellectual development than do visual defects. Deafness in early childhood interferes more than blindness with language development and hence with normal social contacts."[4] Hard of hearing children often escape recognition. Their behavior may be interpreted as indifference, carelessness, rudeness, or dullness.

Primary attention has been given to the early detection of inadequate acuity in vision and hearing. Somewhat less effort has been made to detect other types of defects. Deficiencies in light and dark vision and color vision may continue unrecognized by the person until adulthood, or throughout life—yet a deficiency in either one of these areas may lead to accident on the part of the person who obtains, unknowingly, a job that requires proficiency in these areas. Bus and truck drivers, for example, need the best of night vision; good color vision is essential for driving and for many hazardous occupations.

There is a growing awareness in public health of the significance of individual variance in depth perception and in the differences in perception of size of the visual field such as is found in glaucoma. Some persons have difficulty perceiving distance unless the most obvious of cues are present; others may have narrower range of depth perception than is normal. Persons with either of these deficiencies will be more susceptible to accident in certain kinds of situations. The person with a narrow range of vision may have difficulty noticing the car coming in from the side road. The one with limited depth perception will not be able adequately to estimate the distance of oncoming cars while driving. Both might be considered higher than average risks in many industrial settings.

Some of these variations in individual ability may be influenced by illness, injury, or environmental conditions. It is known, for example, that diet does affect night vision acuity. Likewise, certain drugs such as benzedrine tend to narrow the field of vision so that a person under the influence of such drugs may be less able than others to maintain a breadth of vision required for certain tasks such as driving.

People differ widely also in the speed with which they are able to perceive and respond. A brief exposure may be enough for one person to make an observation, to come to a decision, and to react, whereas it may not be enough for another to make a preliminary determination of the object and movement. This individual difference may also be significantly related to various types of accidents under conditions of speed.

Highway signs and even signs on street corners in cities are often made without full recognition of the lower limits of speed of perception and reaction and of depth perception. Such highway and street signs cannot be read and comprehended at a distance early enough to make the necessary decision even for a person with 20/20 vision, good depth perception, and reaction time. The person weak in any one of these factors may have difficulty in determining in advance of a corner the type of action necessary for safety. A last minute decision and reaction in traffic tends to be more hazardous than one made calmly in advance.

Differences in vision and hearing perception resulting from an illness such as diabetes may be of particular significance for the health worker concerned with the use of educational materials. A much larger kind of type may be desired for a pamphlet directed to diabetics, who are likely to be in middle and upper age ranges and may have more difficulties in vision, than might be required for young mothers in a Child Care Clinic.

Changes in auditory and visual ability occur gradually with age. The change is so gradual in many cases that the individual undergoing the change does not recognize that it is occurring. This fact may be of considerable importance for public health. A person who does not know that his eyesight is becoming weaker or that his hearing is becoming dim will be less able to react adequately in an emergency situation. Accidents may result. For some persons, failure to recognize that these changes are going on may also have serious emotional implications. Older persons who are gradually becoming deaf sometimes think that others are whispering about them; paranoic tendencies may be enhanced by this deficiency.

Touch

Although striking variation in touch perception has been observed within groups of individuals, little attention has been given these find- ings by those responsible for training in occupations requiring a high level of ability in touch perception. Difference in touch sensitivity may be of significance, for example, to physicians who depend to a great extent on touch in making medical judgments. Accuracy in touch perception in such a situation is of great importance. While some training in this area may be possible, training probably cannot substitute for innate differences in ability.

This suggests the necessity of supporting basic research to develop more adequate measures for judging the capacity individuals have for perceiving by means of touch; to develop valid criteria for screening in occupations that require an unusual ability in this area; to determine the degree to which touch sensation and perception can be improved through training; and to develop and evaluate methods of training realistically adapted to occupational requirements. Progress in this research field may deserve greater support than it has received over the past century as more is learned about the potential significance of this area for man's health behavior.

Taste and Smell

The economic significance of taste and smell in our society has led to much research in these areas of perception. Methods of research already developed will prove of greater significance to public health practice in the years ahead as standards are required for judging the potability of waters used for human consumption. The growing demand for potable waters, together with scientific breakthroughs on processes of desalinization, places an urgency on the development of valid and reliable standards for judging water potability and for determining factors influencing public acceptance. The importance of this issue has been emphasized by Ongerth, Bruvold, and Knutson, in outlining a study now under way.

The taste of water in many arid parts of the world is affected by relatively high concentrations of the common dissolved minerals: calcium, magnesium, and sodium, in combination with chloride, sulfate, and carbonate. There are, however, no well-established limiting standards for these minerals. In the California State Department of Public Health, psychologists and engineers have joined to begin development of rational standards for these minerals in household water. This work takes on increasing importance because developing industry and increasing population in semi-arid and arid areas have led to greater consumption of high-mineral waters.[5]

Kinesthetic Senses

The need for earlier detection of chronic conditions draws special attention to the necessity of learning more than we now do about the way we perceive physiological changes through our kinesthetic senses. At present little is known in this area of perception which holds enormous potential for the early detection and control of illness. If there are ways of teaching people to recognize early changes of possible health significance, it might be possible to diagnose malignancies earlier and to initiate corrective medical actions at a point when they might have greater value in prevention.

Intelligence

Human variation in intellectual functioning is gaining greater attention from public health leaders, particularly those involved in the broad range of programs loosely grouped under the heading of mental health. Limits in intellectual abilities often underlie the problems of school dropouts, delinquency, and unemployment in our industrialized society which places a premium on the skilled technician. The widespread use of intelligence tests, often interpreted in a less than adequate manner, places a special burden on health officials responsible for decisions based on test findings. Complex interrelationships exist between intelligence, however measured, and a host of other factors such as socioeconomic class, cultural background, linguistic experience, race, religion, and social opportunity.

Since the turn of the century when Alfred Binet first demonstrated that mental ability could be tested in a practical, quantitative manner, and that this test was useful for identifying mentally subnormal children in the schools, the subject of intelligence has been intensively studied by psychologists. Many useful tests have been developed for classifying individuals along a continuum called intelligence. Painstaking efforts have been made to assure maximum validity and reliability of these tests for the specific purposes for which they have been designed.

Despite this progress, psychologists still disagree as to what is meant by intelligence and what characteristics or traits are included in the definition. Caution is therefore necessary in using any of these tests to assure that their findings are not generalized beyond their specific and intended purposes. Many excellent books are available for those interested in this specific topic.[6] Our present purpose may be satisfied by noting that intelligence as measured by most of these tests varies widely from individual to individual and varies to some degree for any one individual over the period of his lifetime. There is individual variation also in the pattern of intellectual abilities, some being more able in the manner of grasping abstract and complex ideas, some being more able in areas of verbal ability or mathematical ability. Recent research suggests that cultural background influences response more than has previously been expected, so that it is important that the test used be one adapted for the specific group under study. Although progress is being made in developing tests which minimize the influence of such factors, at present no truly culture-free test of intelligence is available. Furthermore, no way has been devised to eliminate significant effects of cultural differences between the tester and subject on the results obtained.

The wide variation on intelligence within any cultural group is of considerable significance for those who are concerned with the interpretation of test findings. Class, race, and religious comparisons, for example, may show group differences, but these differences are minimal, considering the degree of overlap between the group curves. Differences of a few points on a group mean for a large group is not very useful in predicting the ability of any member of either group. Errors most damaging to the individual may result. One must recognize also that the findings for any specific group or individual may reflect other factors than intelligence, even in addition to those previously discussed. The appropriateness of the test for the specific group or individual, the setting in which the test is given, the emotional state of the individual, the attitudes of tester and subject, and even the reference group differences between tester and subject may significantly influence findings.

Intellectual functioning, as measured by current tests, seems to be less influenced by physical injury, physiological malfunctioning, or minor illnesses than one might expect. Tyler, in her excellent review of the psychology of human differences, concludes that "no physical condition except one that acts on the central nervous system itself has a serious effect on intellectual efficiency, at least for limited periods of time, and that no developmental handicap except one that severely restricts the individual's contact with his environment and his mastery of language has a serious effect on his IQ. In a generation when so many children and adults throughout the world have been subjected to unprecedented physical deprivations and hardships, there is some small degree of comfort in these facts."[7]

Present studies suggest that one cannot expect changes in intelligence of children to result from the removal of adenoids, improvement of dental caries, or improvement of nutrition. Dull children are not likely to become brighter when these defects are corrected. On the other hand, removal of defects which impair the sensory organs such as sight or hearing, or those which result in emotional malfunctioning may be of great importance with respect to improvement in intelligence.

Constitutional and Glandular Differences

Public health leaders and other professional people who need to make quick judgments of personality are often attracted to simple methods which can be directly employed by observation. Kretschmer's and Sheldon's theories of body constitution and personality have a special appeal to such persons. Unfortunately, however, the findings from studies employing such constitutional schema have not yielded the quality of data necessary to make decisions regarding personality.[8] Independent researchers employing rigorous methods do, at times, find low positive correlations between some constitutional and some behavioral characteristics, but such correlations are far too low to permit their use in either group or individual prediction. Furthermore, to the extent that relationships do exist, they may reflect the effects of age, nutritional status, social stereotyping, or other situational factors rather than innate disposition.

Constitutional differences, both in physique and in glandular structure, activity, and balance do influence personality development. Body build both fosters and limits possibilities for certain occupational and social experiences. Social stereotypes regarding body build influence choice and promotion in some situations. Variations in glandular functioning may be reflected in emotional and temperamental behavior, sexual activity, productivity, and endurance, and under extreme conditions, even intellectual behavior. Cretinism, a condition of feeblemindedness, may result from inadequate thyroid functioning.[9]

Lurie, in a study of 1,000 problem children, found that about one-fifth showed glandular abnormality, and in about 10 per cent this seemed to be a factor related to the child's behavior. He noted, however, that a malfunctioning of any particular gland is not always reflected in the same personality variation. Different patterns of behavior may result. Poor thyroid functioning, which usually leads to sluggishness, dullness, and lack of energy, is sometimes reflected in restlessness, destructiveness, and speech disturbance. The environment, and in particular the way the individual perceives himself as related to others in that environment, appears to be a significant variable related to the pattern of action stemming from the deficiency.[10]

Constitutional differences are reflected in predispositions along emotional and temperamental lines which may be subject to environmental influences in many ways. The body is an open system which interacts with its environment chemically as well as in other ways. Variability may be influenced by diet, oxygen use, degree of exercise, and other factors of the culture that determine in part the extent to which tendencies are permitted to be expressed and to grow through use, or are repressed in some way and become less important to the individual.

A growing body of research on psychosomatic medicine raises many still unanswered questions concerned with the interaction of physiological man and psychological man. There is evidence that chronic emotional stress may be reflected in inappropriate behavioral responses which may lead to disturbed physiological functioning.[11] Here, as in other instances, one must have an understanding of the culture in which the individual exists and the pattern of the social interrelationships before attempting to explain or understand the sources of stress which lead to maladjustment.

Murphy notes,

> Within the normal range of personality in all cultures, stresses are at work which tend toward the production of hypertensions, allergies, and the rest; and the general, continuous load or strain upon the organism involved in the primary adjustment to the culture must be understood if the secondary load or strain of a specific environmental demand is to

be appraised. In the same way, the satisfactions, the positive fulfill-ments, have profound psychosomatic consequences.[12]

Conclusions

Humans vary along an almost infinite range of biological intellec-tual, physical, and social pathways. Attention here has been focused upon only a few patterns of variation of potential public health sig-nificance. Emphasis has been given to differences relating to physical and physiological factors. In succeeding chapters attention will be given to other factors of equal or even greater significance to public health action—patterns of perception, values, attitudes, interests, preferences, social roles, and social behavior.

Of great importance to the public health leader is a constant alert-ness to the range of possible variation among members of groups with which he works, even though such variance may not be immediately discernible. Of equal importance, perhaps, is an awareness that there exists no easy cookbook guideline for predicting behavior from readily observable characteristics.

NOTES TO CHAPTER 5

1. Foote, Nelson N., and Leonard S. Cottrell, Jr., *Identity and Interpersonal Competence.* University of Chicago Press, Chicago, 1955, p. 2.

2. See Anastasi, Anne, *Differential Psychology: Individual and Group Dif-ferences in Behavior,* 3d ed., Macmillan Co., New York, 1958; Birren, James E., editor, *Handbook of Aging and the Individual: Psychological and Biological Aspects,* University of Chicago Press, Chicago, 1959; Dobzhansky, Theodosius, *Mankind Evolving,* Yale University Press, New Haven, 1962; Tyler, Leona E., *The Psychology of Human Differences,* 2d ed., Appleton-Century-Crofts, Inc., New York, 1956.

3. Dobzhansky, Theodosius, *op. cit.,* pp. 100–127.

4. Anastasi, Anne, *op.* cit., p. 145.

5. Ongerth, Henry J., William H. Bruvold, and Andie L. Knutson, "The Taste of Water," *Public Health Reports,* vol. 79, April, 1964, pp. 351–354. See also Bruvold, William H., and William R. Gaffey, "The Subjective Intensity of Mineral Taste in Water," *Journal of Experimental Psychology,* vol. 69, April, 1965, pp. 369–374. This paper on the experimental study describes this taste scale in use.

6. See Anastasi, Anne, *op. cit.;* Tyler, Leona E., *op. cit.;* Hunt, Joseph McV., *Intelligence and Experience,* Ronald Press Co., New York, 1961.

7. Tyler, Leona E., *op. cit.,* pp. 428–429.

8. See Anastasi, Anne, *op. cit.,* pp. 161–188; Rees, Linford, "Constitutional Factors and Abnormal Behavior," Chapter 9 in Eysenck, Hans J., editor, *Handbook of Abnormal Behavior,* Basic Books, New York, 1961; Tyler, Leona E., *op. cit.*

9. Williams, Robert J., *Biochemical Individuality*. John Wiley and Sons, New York, 1956.

10. Lurie, Louis A., "Endocrinology and the Understanding and Treatment of the Exceptional Child," *Journal of the American Medical Association,* vol. 110, May 7, 1938, pp. 1531–1536.

11. See Selye, Hans, *The Physiology and Pathology of Exposure to Stress,* Acta, Montreal, 1950; Simmons, Leo W., and Harold G. Wolff, *Social Science in Medicine,* Russell Sage Foundation, New York, 1954; Wolff, Harold G., "What Hope Can Do for Man," *Saturday Review,* January 5, 1957, pp. 42–45.

12. Murphy, Gardner, *Personality: A Biosocial Approach to Origins and Structure.* Harper and Bros., New York, 1947, p. 79.

Chapter 6

The Behavioral Cycle

A BIOLOGIST, seeking to understand an animal's behavior, will take great pains to chart out the life cycle of his subject. He will seek to learn how this pattern of behavior develops and what factors influence its form. His attention may focus on how the cycle varies from one animal to another, and what common patterns of behaving represent the group. Then he will be particularly alert to the place and manner of interaction of this animal with other animals, either of the same species or of other species.

Such a behavioral cycle, once identified, becomes a useful conceptual tool. It may be employed to stimulate the consideration of alternative theories regarding factors that may influence the animal's behavior. It may serve a useful purpose in the design of research to test alternative hypotheses. If the biologist or epidemiologist has an interest in influencing or controlling the behavior of his subject, he may lean heavily on his knowledge of the cycle of its behavior in planning and initiating the control program.

This same approach, so useful to the biologist, is employed by the behavioral scientist in the study of man's behavior. By studying patterns of individual behavior he may gain knowledge about individual variation in capacities and potentialities and learn how differences become modified through socialization. If he is particularly alert to the social transactions of individuals, he may be able to identify the hierarchic patterns of status, power, and influence. Or he may gain insights into the nature and significance of various roles assumed by members of the group, and factors leading to changes in roles. By comparing the patterns of behavior of peoples in different societies or cultures, he may be able to chart the life experiences common to men everywhere, as distinct from those found in specific settings. Thus he may better be able to answer the question, "What is human nature?"

72

Children and Youth

Studies of the behavioral cycles of children have been given considerable attention in public health, for findings from such studies have proved practical. From the research of Gesell, Spock, Erikson, and others less well known to the public health field, it has been possible to identify phases in the growth pattern to which mother, teacher, nurse, and physician need be particularly alert.

The pinpointing of changes in behavior that occur at different growth periods, for example, has provided a key to the more effective anticipatory guidance regarding child accident hazards. Information relating to the time children start to turn over, to crawl, to climb, to stand, to run, to seek freedom out of doors, or to roam independently is most useful to the physician in the Well Baby Clinic, for such information suggests the types of accidents to which children are most likely to be exposed at different times.

The application of such information, of course, requires consideration also of knowledge regarding the psychological and emotional growth of the child. Erikson's outstanding theoretical and research contributions on this problem deserve serious attention by public health leaders.[1] In his theory, culture, development, and stress are conceived as united and inseparable forces influencing childhood. "*Culture,* in dictating different child-training methods, enters each stage of the child's *development,* and thus survives in and through the childhood of each of its individuals; while *developmental changes* as well as *changing cultural influences* are the prime causes of *stress* in childhood."[2]

The worksheet used by Erikson in presenting his point of view helps to keep psychological factors in the forefront when discussing problems of children. In developing approaches for reducing childhood accidents, for example, one must be aware concurrently of the damage that may accrue to the child if his growth of trust and independence should be unnecessarily limited. This may not mean that the child's exposure to the accident situation ought to be limited, since limiting exposure may prevent the child from having learning experiences essential to healthy growth. Rather, it may suggest ways of preparing the child and the parents to cope effectively with potential dangers as they arise.

Stressful situations may hold high positive potentials for the prepared child. The period of stress may be one of insight and rapid

TABLE 1. AN OUTLINE OF THE ORDER OF PSYCHOSOCIAL DEVELOPMENT IN CHILDREN

Lifestages	Radius of Interaction	Psychosocial Development	Related Elements of Social Order
INFANCY	Maternal Person(s)	Basic Trust: Basic Mistrust Confianza: Desconfianza Confiance fondamentale: Mefiance fondamentale	World Image
EARLY CHILDHOOD	Parental Combination	Autonomy: Shame, Doubt Autonomía: Verguenza, Duda Autonomie: Honte, Doute de soi	Law and Order
PLAY AGE	Basic Family	Initiative: Guilt Iniciativa: Culpa Initiative: Sentiment de culpabilité	Ideal Prototypes
SCHOOL AGE	Neighborhood School	Industry: Inferiority Industria: Inferioridad Application au travail: Sentiment d'infériorité	Technological Fundamentals
PUBERTY AND ADOLESCENCE	Peer Groups	Identify: Identify-Diffusion Identidad: Difusión del Rol Identité:[1] Dispersion d'identité	Ideological Perspectives
YOUNG ADULTHOOD	Partners sex Competition Cooperation	Intimacy and Solidarity: Isolation Intimidad: Aislamiento Intimite: Isolment	Patterns of Cooperation and Competition
ADULTHOOD	Divided Labor	Generativity: Self-Absorption Generatividad: Estancamiento Productivité: Egotisme	Currents of Education and Tradition
OLD AGE	My people "Mankind"	Integrity: Despair Integridad: Disgusto Desesperación Intégrité: Désespoir	Wisdom

SOURCE: Erikson, Erik H., "Childhood and Society," *Proceedings: Children of the Caribbean—Their Mental Health Needs.* Caribbean Conference on Mental Health, 1959. Dept. of Treasury, San Juan, Puerto Rico, 1961, p. 21. Reproduced with permission of the author.

growth. It need not be viewed only from the preventive or corrective point of view. As Erikson observes:

> ... I can, on the basis of my own work, only indicate that the psychosocial stages discussed in 1950 seem to open up the possibility of studying the way in which in each stage of growth the healthy child's developmental drives dispose him toward a certain set of qualities which are the necessary fundaments of a responsible character: in *infancy*, hope and drive; in *early childhood*, will and control; in the *play age*, purpose and direction; in the *school age*, skill and method; and in *adolescence*, devotion and fidelity. The development of these basic qualities in children, however, depends on the corresponding development in adults of qualities related to: in *young adulthood*, love, work, and affiliation; in *adulthood*, care, parenthood, and production; and in *old age*, "wisdom" and responsible renunciation.[3]

Anticipating Crises in Adults

Erikson,[4] Lindemann,[5] Klein and Lindemann,[6] Caplan,[7] Schwartz,[8] and many others in the field of mental health have emphasized the significance of crisis experiences for the individual, and the importance of having programs for dealing effectively with the emotional problems arising out of personal crisis.

Confirmation of the fruitfulness of this approach is coming from a growing body of research studies. Among the most insightful have been Lindemann's studies of bereavement. He has found that during periods following a deep personal loss the individual undergoes unusual emotional strain, but if he is provided with adequate opportunity to work out problems of personal concern before lasting guilt feelings develop, future emotional difficulties may be minimized or avoided.[9]

Such findings have broad implications for persons who work with patients who have lost a loved one, or who, through sickness, injury, or operation, lose part of themselves. Such patients may need, above all, an encouraging ear into which troubles may be poured. In this situation, it is of great importance that the listener be attentive, and yet patient and willing to listen without imposing judgment.

Program Planning and Research

Less attention has been given in public health to the use of the behavioral cycle of the patient or of other persons concerned as a framework for planning control programs, or for designing a research plan. Yet the approach has considerable potential value. It may be employed effectively, for example, in identifying points of weakness or potential weakness in the programs so that attention can be focused on conditions contributing to the weakness, and an adequate plan of action developed. It may be used as a means of focusing attention on the experiences and related expectations of a patient as he moves through the course of diagnosis, treatment, and rehabilitation. Or it may serve the purpose of facilitating decisions regarding the priority value of alternative research or program actions. The research of Franzen[10] and of Nyswander[11] deserve the special attention of persons interested in ways this approach has been applied in the study of school health. In short, the approach holds so many potential values for public health that some specific illustrations seem warranted.

Tuberculosis Program Research

In 1949 the National Tuberculosis Association and the Public Health Service were exploring the possibilities of continuing their long-term cooperative effort in the application of behavioral science research approaches to tuberculosis control programs. A study just completed in Mishawaka, Indiana, by Hoyt, Knutson, and Derryberry had provided good evidence of the fruitfulness of this effort.[12] Yet many questions remained unanswered: At what point would it be most profitable to begin? What aspects of the program deserved primary consideration in any long-term effort? From a behavior point of view, what were the possible relationships between various aspects of the program?

As one of the first steps toward making these decisions, a rough outline was made of the behavioral cycle of the new tuberculosis patient from the period of identification, through the program, until rehabilitated in the community. The simple outline presented (unchanged) below proved to be a valuable aid in discussing the interrelationships between various aspects of the program as they influenced the patient.

It was apparent from even this preliminary outline that educational influences, planned or not, were present at many points in the program. The reactions of the patient involved would probably be governed by the same nucleus of values, beliefs, fears, expectations, and attitudes at all of these different points unless, of course, these dynamic variables were influenced through the experiences in the program. It seemed immediately apparent, therefore, that the research to

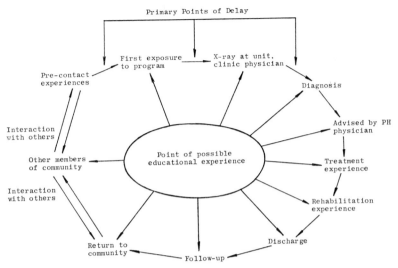

FIGURE 3. Typical Behavioral Cycle of Tuberculosis Patient Passing Through Case-Finding, Treatment, and Rehabilitation Program—Preliminary Planning Outline, 1949

be undertaken should be of a rather basic nature, to determine the nature and pattern of influence of these underlying motivational factors.

The behavioral cycle outline served as an effective stimulus in several discussions focused about these questions:

What are the points of potential loss?

Why do these losses occur?

How are they related to each other?

What are the points of greatest potential for education?

What ought the focus of this education be?

How could the educational program best be evaluated?

In the course of these discussions the outline grew as new ideas were developed. It is presented on page 78 in its original form to illustrate its usefulness as a stimulus.

This analysis drew attention to the many ways early positive or negative experiences of patients might influence their behaviors later in the program. It suggested the importance of identifying through research a potential patient's expectations regarding the course of diagnosis and treatment, outcome, rehabilitation, follow-up, and future acceptance in the community. It suggested the need for identifying factors he perceived as important in diagnosis, since he might be ex-

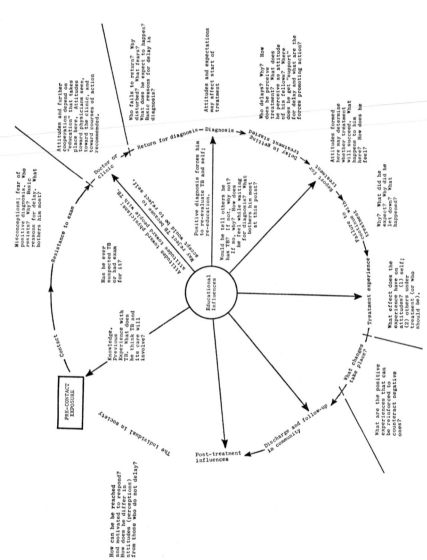

FIGURE 4. Typical Behavioral Cycle of Tuberculosis Patient Passing Through Case-Finding Treatment, and Rehabilitation Program —Outline completed with the assistance of Dr. Benjamin Shimberg.

pected to act on his own beliefs regarding the significance of symptoms in early tuberculosis.

As a result of these discussions, the decision was made to continue the cooperative research effort of the Public Health Service and the National Tuberculosis Association, focusing attention on reasons for delay in case-finding and diagnosis. Questions raised in the discussions served as a stimulus in developing the theoretical approach and hypotheses of the study which was eventually carried out by Hochbaum.[13]

Findings from this research study have helped to draw attention to significance of beliefs and expectations of patients or potential patients and their behaviors. It might be noted that a study by Hromadka,[14] conducted in California under the auspices of the California Tuberculosis and Health Association, regarding hospital leave without consent identified many factors similar to those established by the Public Health Service study as having significance for participation in the case-finding program. In other words, some of the same underlying motivations and beliefs that lead some individuals not to participate in the x-ray case-finding program seem to influence others to leave before their treatment has been completed. From this study we therefore get some empirical evidence of the intimate relationship between the dynamic factors underlying a patient's behavior at various phases of his experience in the program.

Pregnancy and Childbirth

More recently, this same method of outlining the behavioral cycle of an individual passing through a particular experience proved useful as a basis for planning a research study related to the course of pregnancy and childbirth.[15] As a step in identifying significant hypotheses of the study, an attempt was made to plot the experiences of the mother from the time she first met the father, through the period of conception, pregnancy, and childbirth. For the initial purpose, the pattern of experience of a typical middle-class American woman was used. Many deviations from this pattern occur, any one of which may be acceptable in a particular cultural group of our society. Yet one must start somewhere, and the accompanying outline served the purpose of a beginning.

Such a diagram may serve a variety of purposes in developing theory or research. An individual who is interested in the study of social, physiological, economic, or psychological experiences of the mother might find such an outline a useful framework for developing his case history, or for organizing his data for comparative purposes. If his interests were in studying psychological attitudes and their change, this frame of reference would be a useful one about which he might initiate an inquiry and about which he might identify specific, related attitude questions. If he were seeking to organize retrospective data to be obtained through interview, the outline might serve the useful purpose of giving easy orientation to the subject in responding to the interview. It follows the historical pattern through which the individual has passed while having the experience, so questions asked in this sequence flow more easily together.

On the other hand, the researcher's interest may be in a prospective study; then using the behavioral cycle as a basis for planning helps

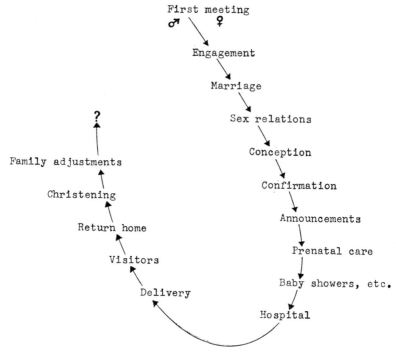

FIGURE 5. The Behavioral Cycle of a Typical Middle-Class American Mother During Marriage and First Pregnancy

him ask questions regarding the individual's expectations of future events. This permits the researcher to compare the respondent's current expectations with future realities and to identify the effect of erroneous expectations or unexpected realities. By being alert to points at which the individual in the study leaves the more generalized or common pathways, the researcher may be able to identify ways in which his subject is in conflict with cultural norms. For example, does the woman go through a pattern of formal engagement, premarital parties, announcements, formal marriage, and public identification as steps preceding pregnancy? Variance from these steps in a culture where such a pattern is normal may be significantly reflected in the prospective mother's behavior. These may be the source of negative or fearful subjective feelings, attitudes, and expectations.

Such variance, when identified, may raise many questions in the minds of the therapist or researcher: Why did this variance occur? Was it desired or not? Was it preplanned or accidental? Was it discussed with good friends or not at all? Was it reflected in strong feelings openly expressed?

Variations from an accepted pattern of behavior in an area that has deep emotional significance, such as sex behavior, is likely to have strong emotional impact upon the woman concerned. Conception resulting from illicit relations may leave its imprint in many ways. It may remove the potential mother from a whole range of social ritual and behaviors that normally accompany pregnancy—luncheons, teas, showers, discussions, expressions of pride, extra attentions, and so on. In their place she may bear feelings of shame, fear, uncertainty, anxiety, and loneliness—frantic feelings strikingly different from those of the proud, happy, secure, and excited girl who is able to take advantage of the social tributes of her group.

The generalized behavioral cycle provides a basis for inquiries regarding the expectations of events that can be predicted for most parents. How does the mother-to-be plan to handle the matter of prenatal care, of hospitalization, of medical costs? How does she expect to deal with her own parents and relatives, her peers and friends? What changes does she expect to occur in her life with the birth of the baby? In the father's life? What meanings will these changes have in terms of her interactions with other members of her own family? What changes are anticipated regarding role, responsibilities, economic and social pressures, social mobility, economic mobility, social activity, membership in groups, changes in patterns of groups, uses of space available, relations with one's own parents and husband?

By applying this sort of approach to the study of problems such as pregnancy and birth of a child, one can identify for program planning purposes areas in which anticipatory guidance may be possible in psychological, sociological, or economic areas in much the way a physician deals with problems of physiology during the same period. The physician anticipates the need for extra calcium to ensure the mother's own teeth and bone structure remaining firm. He anticipates the need for certain dietary controls and prepares the mother to take action at the appropriate time. He anticipates the need for hospitalization and medical care and alerts the family early to prepare for this eventuality. It should also be possible to anticipate necessary actions regarding areas involving psychological, social, or cultural support. Attention may need to be focused on future interpersonal adjustments that should be arranged to ensure the maximum psychological well-being of the mother and child.

By using this behavioral cycle as a basis for research planning, comparative study can be made using several interdisciplinary approaches regarding the same content. One might compare, for example, physiological changes occurring during pregnancy and childbirth as related to the psychological behavior of the mother, which may in turn reflect her acceptance or rejection by the social groups to which she belongs. Interrelationships between cultural, sociological, psychological, and physiological factors thus come to the forefront.

Conclusions

Public health leaders who have long studied the behavioral cycles of animals in epidemiological research and applied their findings in control programs have given but limited attention to the behavioral cycles of man in the planning of human research and in the development of public health programs. When this conceptual approach has been employed, it has proved to be of value in drawing attention to important relationships and in identifying potential situations of crisis. The approach is thus useful both in research planning and in program development.

NOTES TO CHAPTER 6

1. Erikson, Erik H., *Childhood and Society,* W. W. Norton and Co., New York, 1950; "Youth and the Life Cycle," *Children,* vol. 7, April, 1960, pp. 43–

49; "Childhood and Society," *Proceedings: Children of the Caribbean—Their Mental Health Needs,* Caribbean Conference on Mental Health, 1959, Dept. of Treasury, San Juan, Puerto Rico, 1961.

2. *Idem,* "Childhood and Society," *op. cit.,* p. 20.

3. *Idem,* "Youth and the Life Cycle," *op. cit.,* p. 49.

4. See works cited in note 1.

5. Lindemann, Erich, "Symptomatology and the Management of Acute Grief," *American Journal of Psychiatry,* vol. 101, September, 1944, pp. 141–148.

6. Klein, Donald C., and Erich Lindemann, "Preventive Intervention in Individual and Family Crisis Situations" in Caplan, Gerald, editor, *Prevention of Mental Disorders in Children: Initial Exploration.* Basic Books, New York, 1961, pp. 283–306.

7. Caplan, Gerald, "Patterns of Parental Response to the Crisis of Premature Birth," *Psychiatry,* vol. 23, November, 1960, pp. 365–374.

8. Schwartz, Arnold D., "Evaluation of Mental Health," *California's Health,* vol. 18, June 15, 1961.

9. Lindemann, Erich, *op. cit.*

10. Franzen, Raymond H., *Physical Defects: The Pathway to Correction.* American Child Health Association, New York, 1934.

11. Nyswander, Dorothy B., *Solving School Health Problems.* Commonwealth Fund, New York, 1942.

12. Hoyt, Cyril J., Andie L. Knutson, and C. Mayhew Derryberry, "What the People Know," *Monthly Bulletin,* Indiana State Board of Health: Part I, vol. 53, November, 1950, pp. 250 ff.; Part II, vol. 53, December, 1950, pp. 281 ff.

13. Hochbaum, Godfrey M., *Public Participation in Medical Screening Programs: A Socio-Psychological Study.* Public Health Service, U.S. Dept. of Health, Education, and Welfare, Publication 572, Government Printing Office, Washington, 1958.

14. Hromadka, Gordon V., *Reasons Behind Non-hospitalization of the Active Tuberculous.* California Tuberculosis and Health Association, San Francisco, 1956.

15. Polgar, Steven, and Robert Mielke, collaborator, "Course of Pregnancy and Childbirth." Unpublished study conducted at Behavioral Science Unit, School of Public Health, University of California, Berkeley, 1963.

Part Two

Man in His Social Environment

Part Two

Man in His Social Environment

THE TERM "SOCIAL ENVIRONMENT" is of relatively recent usage in the behavioral sciences. One may look upon it as a descriptive rubric that connotes everything related to societies, their varied cultures and subcultures, their groups and their orders, persons and their relationships, objects, ideas, and all the meanings assigned to them that together comprise the social setting in which man transacts his affairs. Thus the term may better be employed to present a generalized point of view rather than that of any specific discipline.

Volkart has used the term "social environment" to include:

> . . . the entire range of social facts which are external to individuals and which are capable of exercising constraint upon them. It is a complex environment, consisting, among other things, of:
> 1. The density and composition of various populations, conceived as communities, ethnic and racial groups, and social classes;
> 2. The organized human groups of which individuals are members, ranging from families, schools, and factories to nation-states;
> 3. The socially defined roles embedded in such groups, including for example, age and sex roles, and occupational and familial roles;
> 4. The shared symbols, values, laws, and norms which guide the behavior of individuals in groups, and which the anthropologists refer to as "culture"; and
> 5. The technologies and material apparatus available to different groups in various times and places.[1]

One might add to Volkart's outline the meanings man gives to objects or events insofar as these meanings are socially derived and have social implications for action. To do so, of course, makes the social environment of any group synonymous with their socially shared private world.

From the standpoint of an acting individual, distinguishing man's social environment from his biological, physical, or physiological environment is but a convenient fiction. The very process of giving label and meaning to any event or aspect of environment makes it social to the person concerned. To the extent that man is cognizant of any aspect of environment that exists for him, that environment has social as well as biological, physical, and physiological meaning for him.

Behavioral scientists, in approaching the scientific study of man's social environment, have found it necessary to isolate and examine particular features and phenomena of man's group life, such as society, culture, social class, ethnic groups, reference and membership groups, position, status, and role. One must recognize that these are not independent and distinct categories for describing man's transactions with man, but for any single individual are intimately bound. Their definitions are neither as independent nor as precise as a scientist might desire. Yet such features of social life that are most difficult to define are of special significance because they do involve so many aspects of man's relations to man.

Suchman distinguishes four fundamental propositions concerning the influences of social factors on health. He notes that:

> 1) Social factors are basic determinants in the distribution of many diseases. Disease is a phenomenon that varies geographically. . . . 2) Social factors play an important role in the etiology of many diseases. . . . 3) Social factors define which health conditions shall be considered public health problems and the activities that may be carried out to meet these problems. . . . 4) Social factors determine the response of society and the individual to many health problems. . . .
>
> The first proposition is firmly established in the traditional fields of medical ecology and demography. The second is rapidly achieving an accepted position with the increasing importance of the social epidemiology of the chronic diseases. The third is not as yet fully recognized as a fundamental challenge to the success of public health programs, except perhaps in underdeveloped areas where attempts at the rapid introduction of new approaches to health problems have forced a recognition of cultural factors in the acceptance and rejection of such public health activities. The fourth is growing in importance with the increased need for public cooperation in health programs and with the recognition of health behavior as social behavior.[2]

Increased attention has been given in recent years to the characteristics of man's social environment as it is related to his health actions, and a considerable body of literature prepared by behavioral scientists is now available to interested public health practitioners. Our present concern with social environment is primarily related to the manner in which it is integrated into man's personal life and thus influences his health behavior. It is hoped that the present limited discussion will entice the public health leader to examine some of the more extensive sources available.

NOTES TO INTRODUCTION TO PART TWO

1. Volkart, Edmund H., "Man, Disease, and the Social Environment." Paper read at dedication of Stanford Medical Center, Stanford, California, September 18, 1959. Processed.

2. Suchman, Edward A., *Sociology and the Field of Public Health*. Bulletin prepared for the American Sociological Association. Russell Sage Foundation, New York, 1963, pp. 47–48.

Chapter 7

Society and Culture

EACH MAN AT BIRTH becomes a member of a social group and thus becomes embedded in the culture of his society. The society in which he lives may, in some ways, be viewed as "a living cross-section of the cultural stream."[1]

Few conceptual distinctions are as difficult to make as that between society and culture. As Foster observed, "The terms are interdependent, and it is difficult to speak of one without relating it to the other. Social scientists often use the terms interchangeably, or they use the compound 'sociocultural' to indicate that the phenomena dealt with partake of both society and culture."[2]

There are, however, some advantages in trying to treat culture and the social system as separate, though interdependent, phenomena when employing them in analysis so that one does not become conceptually absorbed into the other. Geertz, in his case study of ritual and social change in a Javanese village, clearly demonstrates the value of such separate treatment of the two concepts in understanding forces influencing social change. In distinguishing culture from the social system, Geertz draws upon Parsons and Shils:

> One of the more useful ways—but far from the only one—of distinguishing between culture and social system is to see the former as an ordered system of meaning and of symbols, in terms of which social interaction takes place; and to see the latter as the pattern of social interaction itself. On the one level there is the framework of beliefs, expressive symbols, and values in terms of which individuals define their world, express their feelings, and make their judgments; on the other level there is the ongoing process of interactive behavior, whose persistent form we call social structure. Culture is the fabric of meaning in terms of which human beings interpret their experience and guide their action; social structure is the form that action takes, the actually existing network of social relations. Culture and social structure are then but different abstractions from the same phenomena. The one considers

91

social action in respect to its meaning for those who carry it out, the other considers it in terms of its contribution to the functioning of some social system.[3]

In considering some of the features of culture and the social system as they relate to health action, it is essential constantly to bear in mind that man, society, and culture are not separate and independent entities. Society and culture are as much a part of man as he is a part of them. To isolate them, even for purposes of analysis, is deceiving.

HUMAN SOCIETY

Man, as a social creature, is born into, and spends his entire life as a member of, a human society. As long as he lives, this society surrounds him and protects him while he transacts his business with other environments. By introducing him to the social heritage or culture of that society, it provides meanings, methods, and assistance in these transactions, guiding him in what to touch, taste, smell, see, hear, eat, use for clothing, energy, or transportation, and in countless other ways. When he dies, the members of that society usually perform appropriate rites and ceremonies that assure him of some kind of continued active or passive membership.

Common Features of Societies

Human societies are made up of people acting together in organized fashion to deal with the common requirements of life in a particular locale. Their common problems may include the gathering, preparation, and distribution of food, clothing, water, and other necessities of life; the protection against the hazards of climate and other natural or supernatural forces, animal, insect, and plant life, and other persons or groups that may threaten their way of life; the education and orientation of new members, and the maintenance of order and adjustment.

Linton notes that:

> Whatever the genesis of human societies may have been, all of them have certain features in common. The first and perhaps most important of these is that the society, rather than the individual, has become the significant unit in our species struggle for survival. . . . A second characteristic of societies is that they normally persist far beyond the life span of any one individual. . . . Third, societies are functional, operative units. In spite of the fact that they are made up of individuals, they work as wholes. . . . Fourth, in every society the activities neces-

sary to the survival of the whole are divided and apportioned to the various members.[4]

Inequalities in Social Placement

Each person is born into a particular social group in a particular locale. His new group may be a responsible family living in a comfortable home and enjoying an active social and cultural life in an established neighborhood. Or he may be born to a migrant laborer trying to carry on in temporary, makeshift quarters with limited social ties to other transient members of society under conditions approaching social isolation. The new group may look toward his birth as something they have sought and desired, or have tried to avoid and now fear, or may view it as a happening of chance or of fate over which they have had no influence. One's first position in life, together with the expectations and responsibilities it implies and the potentialities it offers, is not of his own choosing. Rather, it results from chance and the actions of others. Man's very existence is socially, as well as biologically, determined.

While all men may, by some definitions, be born equal, inequality of opportunity begins with birth. Mention has already been made of the varying influences of the geographic environment in which one is reared on his personal and social development. Of greater significance to one's social, emotional, and intellectual growth is his placement in a particular family, leading a particular mode of life and experiencing the special pattern of circumstances that have led to his arrival at this specific time.

Effects of Unequal Placement

In judging its members society is prone to forget, ignore, or deny responsibility for these differences in initial opportunity. Adults, and even children, may be harshly treated with the implication that they are personally responsible for inadequacies governed by the chance of birth. Physical deformities acquired in childbirth or infancy may be recognized and attended to; social, emotional, or intellectual handicaps resulting from factors present at birth or during infancy may go undetected, receive scant attention, or may actually be treated with ridicule. Social stigma is attached to the individual born out of wedlock or orphaned in infancy even though he was in no way a knowing and willing partner to the socially discredited event. The unwanted and ignored child may bear throughout life feelings of guilt, inadequacy, or loneliness fostered by society's judgment of behaviors he has acquired under conditions beyond his control.

Those who have studied the impact of environmental influences of early childhood on development call attention to many features of the infant's family group that have a bearing on the acquisition of skills necessary to cope effectively in social life as he matures. Each family has its own pattern of characteristics of significance to child development. Of importance are the number, kind, and relationships of its members; their past and current physiological, physical, and social state of affairs; the pattern of their organization and their manner of working together; the love, affection, respect they hold for one another, and the investment they have in their shared life. Of like concern are the positions they hold relative to one another and within society, the behaviors they perform of significance to one another, and the adequacy of their functioning in their varied roles. Through these behaviors are reflected the values, beliefs, and attitudes they hold and the social norms they follow, together with other features of social heritage that give meaning to their lives.

The child's initial social environment influences the limits of his activities, the resources at his command, the degree and nature of independence he can acquire, his potentiality for effective social functioning. Members of his social groups provide social models for him to observe, consider, imitate, identify with, judge, and evaluate for their usefulness to him as a person in developing his own modes of action.

Such a view of society emphasizes the bond of man to his social groups from conception into immortality. Individuals are born and live as social units with responsibilities, demands, and dependencies, positions, and roles integral to those associations. One cannot, therefore, understand and predict man's health behavior without learning the meanings he gives to these associations with other members of his society, and the way his own behaviors are integrated with those of other members of his social groups.

CULTURE AS MAN'S WAY OF LIFE

A major task of any society is the preservation and communication of a way of life, its history and significance, together with the experience gained in dealing with the problems of living together under a special pattern of circumstances. New generations acquire in this way tested and approved methods and principles for their guidance. These include ways of perceiving, valuing, thinking, believing, and striving, methods of organizing their various positions and carrying out their roles and behaviors in ways that assure effective group functioning, and ways of imparting emotional support, pain and pleasure, hope, faith, and understandings that give a sense of cohesion and purpose to their efforts.

Culture, the way of life man acquires as his social heritage, has been defined in many ways. Kluckhohn says:

> . . . Culture, like well-known concepts of the physical sciences, is a convenient abstraction. One never sees gravity. One sees bodies falling in regular ways. One never sees an electromagnetic field. Yet certain happenings that can be seen may be given a neat abstract formulation by assuming that the electromagnetic field exists. Similarly, one never sees culture as such. What is seen are regularities in the behavior or artifacts of a group that has adhered to a common tradition. The regularities in style and technique of ancient Inca tapestries or stone axes from Melanesian islands are due to the existence of mental blueprints for the group.
>
> Culture is a *way* of thinking, feeling, believing. It is the group's knowledge stored up (in memories of men; in books and objects) for future use.[5]

Culture varies in its patterns and meanings for different social units, its varying nature depending upon the history of the group in perceiving and dealing with life's issues in different settings.

Paul describes it in these words: "Broadly speaking, culture is a group's design for living, a shared set of socially transmitted assumptions about the nature of the physical and social world, the goals of life, and the appropriate means of achieving them."[6] Here and elsewhere, Paul and others have drawn attention to many ways in which cultural factors contribute to man's susceptibility and response to illness.[7] The reader is referred to these excellent sources for detailed discussion of the varying impacts of culture on man's health behavior.

Varying Influences of Culture

It should be recognized that culture is not a force that is applied in the same way to all social units and their members. Rather, it is a way of life developed through the course of a society's history by humans, with varying understandings, interpretations, and abilities, who offer their children individualized models for learning. It is imparted to unique individuals with varying capacities for recognizing, understanding, and interpreting what they experience and what they in turn pass on to others. Thus a group's cultural patterns represent modal forms of thought and action for that group, and there exists considerable variation within the group regarding what is accepted or rejected and what is consciously or subconsciously passed on to future members of the group.

Cultural processes guide, and in guiding also limit, human perspectives and human responses. A social heritage developed by societies living under stable conditions and facing similar issues, problems, and challenges from generation to generation probably served as a safe pattern of guidelines for succeeding generations. But such a social heritage has limits as well as values in a world rapidly growing smaller and more dangerous under the impact of scientific and technical development, rapid mobility, and widespread communication.

Yet cultural patterns do change, and each generation and each individual contributes to that change. Changes are required and facilitated by the rise of new problems and developments, the movement of peoples into new settings, the spread of new ideas, methods, and materials, and in many other ways. A significant force for such changes is the growth in the power of deviant members who may challenge or question accepted practices. Public health leaders might profitably consider the significance for them of Linton's observation that "new social inventions are made by those who suffer from the current conditions, not by those who profit from them."[8]

Man Internalizes Culture

Man's culture is always part of himself, for he internalizes his culture along with other experiences. Frank says: "From studies of personality and of cultures it appears that man *exists* as an organism in a common public world of animals, plants, structures, and other physical objects and processes, but each individual *lives* in his private world of meanings and feelings, derived from the impact of culture that takes place in the specific personal relations between cultural agents and the child. Different cultures tolerate varying degrees of deviation from the socially sanctioned patterns of conduct. In our culture when the individual's private world deviates too far from the official culture we speak of mental disorders; when the individual's overt conduct transgresses the culturally defined inviolabilities, or conflicts with the cultural requirements, we speak of delinquency and criminality."[9]

NOTES TO CHAPTER 7

1. Hartley, Eugene L., Personal communication, March, 1964.

2. Foster, George M., *Traditional Cultures and the Impact of Technological Change.* Harper and Row, New York, 1962, p. 11.

3. Geertz, Clifford, "Ritual and Social Change: A Javanese Example," *American Anthropologist,* vol. 59, February, 1957, p. 33. See also Parsons, Talcott, and Edward A. Shils, editors, *Toward a General Theory of Action,* Harvard University Press, Cambridge, Mass., 1951.

4. Linton, Ralph, *The Cultural Background of Personality.* Appleton-Century-Crofts, Inc., New York, 1945, pp. 15–17.

5. Kluckhohn, Clyde, *Mirror for Man.* A Premier Book, Fawcett Publications, Greenwich, Conn., 1959, p. 24.

6. Paul, Benjamin D., "Anthropological Perspectives on Medicine and Public Health" in Clausen, John A., and Robert Straus, editors, *Medicine and Society, The Annals* of the American Academy of Political and Social Science, vol. 346, March, 1963, p. 35.

7. See Caudill, William, *Effects of Social and Cultural Systems in Reactions to Stress,* Social Science Research Council, Pamphlet 14, June, 1958, pp. 26–27; Foster, George M., *Problems in Intercultural Health Programs,* Social Science Research Council, Pamphlet 12, April, 1958; Foster, George M., *Traditional Cultures . . . , op. cit.;* Paul, Benjamin D., editor, *Health, Culture, and Community: Case Studies of Public Reactions to Health Programs;* Russell Sage Foundation, New York, 1955; Saunders, Lyle, *Cultural Difference and Medical Care: The Case of the Spanish-Speaking People of the Southwest,* Russell Sage Foundation, New York, 1954; Simmons, Ozzie G., *Social Status and Public Health,* Social Science Research Council, Pamphlet 13, New York, May, 1958.

8. Linton, Ralph, *op. cit.,* p. 23.

9. Frank, Lawrence K., "Cultural Control and Physiological Autonomy," *American Journal of Orthopsychiatry,* vol. 8, 1938, pp. 622–626. Reprinted in Kluckhohn, Clyde, and Henry A. Murray, with the collaboration of David M. Schneider, editors, *Personality in Nature, Society, and Culture.* 2d ed., rev. and enl., Alfred A. Knopf, Inc., New York, 1956, p. 122.

Chapter 8

Placing Man in His Social Habitat

DEFINING MAN'S SOCIAL HABITAT requires identifying and describing the characteristics of those divisions, institutions, and groups of the society of which he is a part, including both those he is identified with and those with which he identifies himself. Such broad dimensions of society as nationality, community, demography, social class, and ethnicity tend to define the limits of his social transactions, the nature of his institutional life and social groups, and the types of relationships he may be able to develop with his fellow men. Within these broader dimensions one may define his relationships to organized institutions and groups such as his family, religious, social, and occupational ties. A person may also identify with religious, ancestral, or historical groups which, while neither visible nor tangible, are nevertheless real and meaningful for him, influencing his behavior in significant ways.

Human groups vary in many ways. They may be large or small, formal or informal, voluntary or involuntary in membership. As to purpose, they may be specific or general, of short or extended duration, constant or varying. Some confine membership to persons known and selected, whereas others are open to anyone and may include persons widely separated and unknown to one another.

It is useful to distinguish social groups from the broader dimensions of society mentioned above by following Newcomb's definition: "A group consists of two or more persons *who share norms* about certain things with one another and *whose social roles are closely interlocking.*"[1] Such a definition excludes such aggregates as the people lined up for x-rays or receiving health pamphlets, persons attending the public health clinic, or identified through an IBM sort as having similar characteristics, and so forth.

Psychological groups, whose members interact directly with one another and share common values, beliefs, and behaviors, may be distinguished from larger social organizations that include many such

98

psychological groups.[2] From this point of view, a health department staff in a small community may constitute a psychological group, but the New York City Health Department includes many such units and is better described as a social organization. The latter is true also of the American Public Health Association, which includes many different psychological groups and also individual members who may never participate in any specific psychological group of association members.

Many features of man's social habitat are determined biologically. Included here are his family, age, sex, ethnicity, nationality, social class, and place of birth. These are not all inflexible assignments for every member of society, however, since even one's sex and age identification may be changed under certain conditions, and social movement within family, nationality, ethnic, and social class categories, while limited for most people, sometimes occurs.

Man's identification with some other groups or institutions of society may also be assigned by society and thus be beyond his personal choice. He may be required to become a member of a school group or a military service, and if he violates social codes may be assigned to a labor camp or prison. Others are membership groups he may formally or informally join, such as his friendship and work groups, clubs, church, political party, union or professional groups, and neighborhood associations. Even these, under specific circumstances, may be compulsory rather than voluntary. He may need to join a union to obtain a job or his employer may require that he join a particular professional association. In Nazi Germany even membership in the neighborhood association was required.

SOCIAL CLASS

A public health nurse may be requested to make a home visit to a family she has not previously met. She may receive from the referring agency a card on which is given the following information concerning the mother she is to see:

Age: 40
Nationality and ethnicity: second generation (?)
Color: white (?)
Marital status: married (?); husband frequently away
Husband's occupation: laborer when employed
Mother's occupation: housework when employed
Children: 5 or 6 (?)
Family income: less than $2,000 (?)

Residence: temporarily housed in old apartment building "across the
  tracks"
Religion: highly emotional, participating type of church

This ambiguous description is not unlike many others seen by public health workers. It yields only a minimum outline of the characteristics of an unknown individual and suggests that the subject lacks
status and acceptance to the person who made out the referral card.
The question marks suggest both uncertainty and prejudice on the
part of the reporter: When does one become "American" rather than
"second generation"? What constitutes "white" as distinct from
"white (?)"? Why should one question marital status in this situation?
The last two items are descriptive rather than specific, since specific
addresses and churches would have little meaning to the reader who
does not know the city concerned.

Each item of information in this brief list tells the public health
nurse something significant about the mother's social habitat, and
about the nature of her participation in the culture of her society.[3] Together, these items describe a middle-aged woman with a large family
left in her care by a frequently absent husband and responsible for
feeding, clothing, and housing them. The nurse's earlier experiences
will permit her to make a fairly good guess about the kind of person
she will visit, and about the family's way of life.

From the description of social habitat provided above, the public
health nurse is likely to judge this woman to be the mother of a "problem family," and may make many educated guesses regarding the
health status, problems, and behaviors of its members. They are probably getting along with inadequate means, are disheartened, and have
a sense of apathy regarding the future. A history of poverty, hardship,
and dependency may have contributed to a passive attitude toward
outside advice and guidance, and an apparent indifference to ideas of
improvement or achievement.

Children of such a family are likely to be undernourished, poorly
clothed, unkempt as judged by the nurse's standards. They are probably inadequately supervised, and if in school, are having difficulty
with their studies and are identified as "problem children" by their
teachers. They "get into trouble" with children from more "respect-
able" neighborhoods. They may respond in an aggressive or withdrawn fashion to the taunts and ridicule of other children, experiences
which probably leave them with feelings of inadequacy and of not be-

ing accepted. An apparent lack of interest and attention and demonstrated poor achievement in school mark them as prospects for early dropout. The risk of their becoming ill, injured, or delinquent in one way or another is considerably above average.

The public health nurse is likely to feel uncomfortable working with such a family, but at the same time feel that it is the kind of family that urgently needs the services she can offer. The manifest indifference on the part of its members to simple codes of cleanliness, grooming, and social relations, and the seeming lack of any desire to get ahead or "improve," or to plan and work for a better future may be frustrating to her. It is difficult for her to "tie in with" their manner of thinking and behaving, to find ways of building a communication bridge to their private worlds so that she can help them to cope with the problems that are so evident and to "take care of themselves."

How differently the public health nurse might respond to her task if the description of the mother's placement in society were as follows:

Age: 40
Nationality and ethnicity: American
Color: white
Marital status: married
Husband's occupation: professional
Mother's occupation: housewife, formerly school teacher
Children: 3
Family income: $8,000
Residence: own home in stable neighborhood
Religion: member of stable, traditional church

Such a description suggests a way of life and a pattern of values, beliefs, attitudes, and strivings that may not be so hard for the nurse to understand, because they are probably in keeping with those acquired in the course of her own upbringing. She may even wonder why it is important to make a home visit to a family that has the markings of being fairly self-sufficient and having a range of resources at its command.

If a woman were needed to serve on the board of a new hospital in the community to help it gain community acceptance, status, and support, the person sought might be described in this way, using the same descriptive items:

Age: 40
Nationality and ethnicity: old American family
Color: white

Marital status: married
Husband's occupation: member of various boards and committees
Mother's occupation: housewife (with adequate aid)
Children: 3
Family income: independently wealthy (?)
Residence: home in exclusive neighborhood
Religion: formal, impersonal church of standing

This person is likely to come from an old established family in the community, so that a card with such items of information would be neither necessary nor appropriate. One would expect her to hold social position, power, and wealth, and to have ready access to many resources, should assistance be needed. She is likely to be accustomed to gracious living, to feel at ease and to command respect in the better social circles.

The public health nurse might hesitate to approach a woman of such status without careful preparation and planning in order to present an effective request. She may ask someone else of high status for help in enlisting the woman's cooperation.

The Use of Class Terms

The public health nurse is not likely to question that these three fairly distinct ways of life, with many variations intervening, are present in our society. But she may feel uncomfortable referring to the first as a "lower class family," to the second as a "middle class family," and to the third as an "upper class family." Public health practitioners do not readily accept these terms used by behavioral scientists to describe American class structure. They prefer terms like "the hard core group," "the poorly educated," "migrant workers," or "people on welfare" in referring to those whom social scientists call "lower social class."

Like most Americans, public health leaders seem to accept the *idea* of class structure and employ it in placing people according to their social habitats and in making judgments about their behavior. But to label people as "lower class," "middle class," or "upper class" conflicts with American democratic values. It seems to smack of prejudice to stereotype people in this way.[4] Centers found that, when given a choice, most people preferred to call themselves members of the "working class" or "middle class"; only one per cent identified themselves as "lower class." One per cent rejected the idea of class.

Implications of Social Class for the Practitioner

It is difficult for the public health practitioner who has a particular place in American society to recognize the broad implications of social class in interpreting his own behavior as well as the behavior of others. He may tend, without being aware of it, to use his own standards in judging the behavior of others as right or wrong, appropriate or inappropriate, healthy or unhealthy. One of his greatest difficulties may be in distinguishing the "problems" truly disruptive to lower class life from those that would be disruptive to his own way of life.

To the extent that lower social class ways of behaving are rooted in cultural tradition and are functional for the individual in that particular setting, they are appropriate and adaptive for his society. They may serve him well in maintaining personal security and stability within his social habitat. To urge on him middle-class values of cleanliness, self-improvement, achievement, and creative growth may be personally disruptive to him in that social setting.

A true conflict exists in the value behavior of those who would work for the betterment of society without disrupting the lives of its members. This is seldom better seen than in working within a class structure for the improvement of the lives of those less fortunately placed in that structure. For, as Davis and Havighurst have noted, while the lower social class culture offers its members effective methods of adaptation, it prepares new members inadequately for growth and development beyond the limits of that class.

> The social-class system maintains cultural, economic, and social barriers which prevent intimate social intermixture between the slums, the Gold Coast, and the middle-class. We know that human beings can learn their culture only *from other human beings,* who already know and exhibit that culture. Therefore, by setting up barriers to social participation, the American social-class system actually prevents the vast majority of children of the working classes, or the slums, from learning any culture but that of their own groups. *Thus the pivotal meaning of social class* to students of human development is that it defines and systematizes different learning environments for children of different classes.[5]

Measuring Social Class

Public health practitioners and researchers have need for simple measures of social class for studying the cause and course of illness, the patterns of its distribution and effects, its varying impact on different populations. Such data are needed for program planning and development and for evaluating the varying effects of program efforts.

Mention has already been made of many of the variables associated with social class: occupation, income, education, place of residence, prestige, power, social interaction, and self-placement. The reader is urged to consult other sources for information regarding the development and use of indices of social class within the health field.

Sociologists have been in the forefront of the behavioral science disciplines in developing measures for stratifying society in terms of social class, and in the use of these methods for studying health status. Their research has already yielded significant data regarding the significance of class position on the distribution of illness and the use of health services. One must agree with Clausen's observation:

> . . . Since the first studies of differences in mortality between the prosperous and the poor, no other single index of social characteristics has been so potent a predictor of health status as position in the social hierarchy.
>
> Although social scientists have often disagreed with each other in their theories of social stratification and although the connotations of class are many and varied, there would be little disagreement that, in modern industrial societies, class is linked most closely with occupational status. In all industrial societies, one finds a broad range of variation in job prestige, power, security, and income, which results in a hierarchical ranking of the population in social status and level of living. At the lower end of the scale, one frequently finds poverty and deprivation. And associated with poverty have been high incidences of most infectious and many chronic diseases.[6]

The Use of Indices of Social Class

Some of the indices currently employed by behavioral scientists to place man in terms of his position in the social hierarchy are the product of years of diligent research effort. Although these indices may employ few variables, such as residence, occupation, and education, and appear disarmingly simple, they have been validated under varying conditions against a range of other measures and observations to assure that they adequately differentiate members of urban populations along lines reflective of social class behaviors.[7] Hollingshead's two-factor index based on occupation and the amount of formal schooling appears to be an adequate measure for general comparison.[8]

Accordingly, when such indices are employed in health studies or programs, it is essential to bear in mind that they yield evidence regarding a constellation of behaviors of the populations studies. Failure to recognize this may lead to narrow and superficial interpretation. Clausen points out that:

> . . . The differences in health experience associated with social class are not merely reflections of poverty and deprivation. They reflect a wide variety of differences in life style, in diet, in physical activity, in the daily rhythm of work, sleep, and other pursuits, in family patterns, and in attitudes toward self and others. Some of these are clearly linked with health, as in the case of hazardous occupational pursuits—for example, the high incidence of respiratory diseases among certain types of miners. Other aspects of class may be equally associated with patterns of disease, but the linkages are often not clear.[9]

Public health officers are accustomed to employing many indices in their daily work. Among these, infant and maternal death rates are often used to obtain crude estimates regarding the adequacy of medical care. When population groups or institutions are compared in terms of these measures and significant differences noted, the health officer makes an educated guess that the variation observed may reflect such factors as the availability of trained medical personnel, the adequacy of diagnostic and treatment facilities and services, the awareness and use of appropriate preventive measures, the availability and proper use of disinfectants and medicines, and so on. The purpose of using the indices in this way is not only to determine relative death rates, but to make some quick estimates regarding a cluster of potentially related conditions. The health officer who failed to consider the potential implication of his findings obtained by use of the index would be negligent indeed.

As more health officers learn to interpret and apply the findings obtained by using indices of social class, they will find them valuable for making estimates concerning behavior descriptive of life patterns. When these indices reveal significant differences in population groups regarding the patterns of illness or responses to health services, the differences will be recognized as reflecting behavior of broader significance than economic status alone.

Distinguishing Caste and Class

The term "caste" is used to designate groupings within society whose positions in society are fixed by the chance of birth, and who are not permitted to move out of that caste designation. The term most particularly applies to a hereditary structure of society such as traditional India, where members were born into a particular occupational and social status and remained there throughout life. Caste differs from class, in that members of a social class may achieve membership in a higher, or lower, class during their lifetimes.

Intricate codes of social conduct may exist to maintain a caste structure. A member of a minority caste cannot engage in intimate transactions on an equal basis with members of a higher caste. Social transactions such as social club membership and intermarriage with other castes are not possible.

Historically, the relationship between whites and Negroes in America has been in some ways similar to such a caste pattern, although significant progress is now being made toward the removal of barriers to social movement. Restrictions to the free movement of Negroes in our society has led to their being systematically deprived of opportunities for education, occupation, and political and social position.

This distinction between caste and class is an important one to consider in applying measures of social class, for classes vary within castes. Accordingly, separation by caste should precede separation by class in comparative studies. In such areas as caste treatment accorded Negroes, a middle or upper-class Negro may be deprived of some types of social transactions accorded even lower-class whites. Furthermore, he may feel the deprivation deeply, for it represents a social injustice from which he has no recourse.

Although caste barriers, as compared with class barriers, are relatively impermeable, "passings" across caste barriers do occur. Persons identified as "Negro" in one area of the country may be accepted as "white" in another, and some persons cross the caste line each year. Under experimental conditions, whites have also passed as Negro in areas where caste distinctions are rigidly held. While the barriers of class are relatively easier to cross than the barriers of caste, movement from one class to another is seldom easy for persons involved. A person reared in one cultural setting cannot easily discard the ways of life and social ties of childhood and youth without experiencing many personal concerns and inner conflicts, and possibly even social difficulties.

OTHER REFERENCE AND MEMBERSHIP GROUPS

The term "reference group" is a particularly useful one for understanding social influences on behavior. One's reference groups include any groups he identifies or compares himself with in judging his own standards, attitudes, and actions. They serve him as anchorages or points of reference in shaping his own values, beliefs, attitudes, and actions. He looks to these groups for guidance in making judgments or decisions. Such a group may, but need not, be one of which he is a member. It may, in fact, be a group which he is not even permitted to join. It has been reported that prisoners in internment camps sometimes identified with their guards and used them as reference groups for some behaviors; army privates often identify with their officers.

A reference group, in providing values and standards against which to measure and judge one's own behavior, at once provides direction for the individual and helps him to coordinate his beliefs, attitudes, and actions. In some ways it may protect and support him by relieving him of personal responsibility for decisions or actions taken. He may assume credit for successful action and project on the reference group responsibility for ill chosen action. If he has faith in his reference group, he may accept its decisions without question. His reference group identification may thus simplify his life by making personal judgments and decisions unnecessary.

At times one may even use as a reference group a society, club, organization, or social class from which one is personally excluded. As Centers has shown, persons in one social class may identify with those in another and use them as a reference group.[10] Professional people who identify themselves as members of the working class tend to hold more liberal economic attitudes than those who identify with groups of higher social status. Small businessmen often identify with big business on matters of political and economic interest. Members of minority groups may identify with majority groups in making evaluations, even with regard to decisions detrimental to their own group's position. Persons engaged in public health who have never joined the American Public Health Association nevertheless may employ Association standards or use positions it has taken as guides in their professional conduct.

Ethnic Groups

The term "ethnic group" generally refers to any continuing group or division of mankind, such as a religious, nationality, racial, or language grouping which has retained a common biological or cultural identity. If the referral card received by the public health nurse, mentioned above, had identified the person she was to visit as a member of some minority ethnic group, her expectations regarding the person and the visit might be significantly influenced. Willingly or not, each of us holds stereotypes of members of other groups and tends to make certain assumptions in terms of these stereotypes. Our expectations concerning our relations with minority members and their behaviors thus influence our own approaches and may stand in the way of objective appraisal and valid judgments.

The stereotypes we hold of Negroes, for example, often lead us to think of all Negroes as belonging to a lower social class, and as having the values, attitudes, and aspirations of that class. We may overlook an important distinction between ethnic group and social class in making such judgments.

Public health practitioners who frequently work with minority group members recognize that they may also hold stereotypes that interfere with effective communication and services. If members of a minority group expect to be rejected, to be given inferior treatment, or to be regarded as socially inferior, they are not likely to seek or to accept services that are offered. As in the case of majority group stereotypes, these expectations may have no basis in fact regarding the particular situation or services. Like other attitudes, they may be acquired through contact with other members of their groups, or may be generalized from experiences that have little relationship to the situation at hand.

Religious groups differ in their orientations with regard to many health issues. Public health practitioners have learned to expect Protestants, Catholics, Orthodox Jews, Christian Scientists, and Jehovah's Witnesses to take specific positions on such matters as family planning, nutrition education, the use of medical services, and scientific experimentation with animals. Sociologists and epidemiologists are also finding that patterns of behavior associated with certain religious subcultures lead to different patterns of chronic illness.[11] Since members of religious faiths differ in their adherence to beliefs and practices, one should expect marked variation with respect both to attitudes and to the incidence of particular illnesses.

National groups bring with them distinctive cultural traditions, customs, beliefs, and practices. A designation of an individual's nationality, therefore, should suggest to the health worker the importance of considering cultural factors in working with the individual concerned. The acceptance of other American ways does not lead to a disregard of long-held cultural traditions which may concern matters of modesty, taste, attitudes toward medicine, family structure, social and sexual behavior, or even the manner of use of alcohol and ways of expressing pain.

Professional Membership and Reference Groups

Through his primary groups man may receive opportunities to satisfy many of his basic requirements for food, shelter, protection, comfort, affection, love, affiliation, acceptance and belongingness, status and achievement. As he matures and his requirements increase, these primary groups may also help him extend his memberships and identifications to larger groups in accord with his special interests. From birth, however, he has been identified as a member of large as well as small groups which at once serve particular purposes and provide restricting influence on certain behaviors. Yet the personal meaning of these large group identifications for him may not be acquired until he goes to school, or in other ways moves beyond his primary groups and is able to compare his identifications with those of others.

We tend to acquire a growing number of large group or institutional identifications as we mature. Some groups we join because our parents or other adults we consider important are members, and we may join these groups without fully considering alternatives. Others may have an attraction for us because some of our friends are members and membership is a way of binding or extending existing friendships. Additional personal interests may lead us to membership, and we may not ourselves recognize the individualized concerns or motives that attend our joining. Thus the stated philosophy or purpose of an association may at times have little directly to do with personal and individualized purposes or interests that attract members to its fold. In judging the significance of association membership, therefore, it is necessary to know what purpose the large group satisfies for the individual members, and to what degree members identify with association goals.

Of particular interest to those concerned with the protection and improvement of the public's health is the role of professional groups as reference groups for their members and for others who look to them for guidance. Professional and voluntary associations provide the social mechanism whereby leaders of common interest can join forces to develop and promote a common social philosophy or ideology and means of translating it into effective action.

In performing this leadership role, professional and voluntary groups may promote progress through eliciting community support for new developments and by serving as effective pressure groups on legislative and executive bodies. In democratic societies such groups often assume a major responsibility for developing standards and recommending procedures for their members and others who look to them for guidance. They may, of course, also retard progress at times, for sanctioned goals, standards, and procedures which become widely established may not readily be subject to change as new knowledge is developed.

The APHA as a Membership-Reference Group

The American Public Health Association, since it serves as a common reference group for many public health leaders, provides a useful frame of reference for considering the varied personal as well as group purposes such associations serve. The philosophy and goals of this Association are well known to interested members and have been amply described elsewhere. Attention here will focus on membership and identification from the individual's point of view.[12]

The large group or association may offer the individual the satisfaction of belonging to something greater than himself, knowing that others who feel as he does also belong. By identifying with the purposes, action, and leadership of the larger association he may derive a sense of ego extension and ego satisfaction from being a part of greatness. Past achievements of the Association yield a sense of security in the hope for further great achievements. One may thus derive a sense of faith in the future regarding the field in which he works.

Such a general desire to identify with something larger, more powerful, more influential than oneself, may be differentially reflected in the ego wants of members. Some may find through this means a way to satisfy personal wants for power and influence, for identification with power makes oneself also powerful. Others may find that identification with the powerful association satisfies personal wants for dependence upon authority.

Members having a crusading spirit who tend to identify with the underdog, or who strongly desire to aid the ill, undernourished, underprivileged, or handicapped, or just to "help mankind" in general ways, may see the association as a means of extending their efforts in serving such personal concerns and ideals. If they view the association philosophy and goals as being in harmony with their own, such members are likely to be active supporters of new group ventures. They are likely to feel deeply the significance of positions taken or actions planned and may push strongly for resolutions and commitments in areas of concern. Such persons may not hestitate to contribute time, money, or effort to achieve those association goals they identify as being in harmony with personal ideals.

The gregarious needs of others may lead them to join. They may see national and local group meetings as opportunities to acquire new friends, develop a sense of comradeship with others holding similar interests, and possibly to develop contacts with members of the opposite sex. Scientific meetings and papers, by themselves, may not attract them, but may be seen as settings within which members can get together with other persons having like values, attitudes, and concerns, and thus foster personal wants for social affiliation, acceptance, and belongingness. Persons who feel isolated from others having similar views may find that membership in the association offers a sense of acceptance, identification, and belongingness.

Desires for prestige, status, and power, and the possibility of achieving leadership make professional, business, occupational, and similar large groups attractive for some persons. The very acceptance to membership or fellowship carries with it prestige and status among associates and may contribute to personal progress within a person's own agency. Additional honors conferred through the association may further advancement in his job. Association activities may offer many opportunities to participate and to demonstrate his abilities.

The American Public Health Association offers its members many opportunities to participate in committees and task forces, to present papers or contribute to symposiums, to participate in significant research and action programs. The recognition they receive from papers presented and published writings, from being identified as committee members and for their contributions to significant research programs may be amply rewarding. Those with status and power needs may view election to section or association office as primary gains of membership and may make outstanding contributions in order to gain such rewards.

Significant personal gratification may result from the publication in one's local papers of acceptance to membership or fellowship in a community organization, appointments to committees, election to offices, or other noteworthy achievements. Such local recognition, particularly if not self-initiated, may exceed national association announcements in its worth to the member whose colleagues, friends, and neighbors may be unaware of, or unimpressed by, the national announcements.

Most professional associations maintain special services to assist their members in achieving professional growth. Members who hold jobs that are unsatisfying, unchallenging, or that offer limited opportunity for advancement may be less concerned with status within the association than with opportunities to learn about more satisfactory positions. For them the employment service and position listings may hold special value. The opportunities offered for informal association with significant people who might be of assistance, or to identify prospective employers at local and national meetings may be a primary reason for membership. For those seeking occupational advancement, opportunities to participate in committees or programs that permit them to demonstrate abilities are particularly attractive. Participation in other kinds of activities may hold less appeal.

Some may join the association as a means of extending their opportunities for education, to obtain access to a common fund of knowledge presented in its journal, newsletters, and exhibits, and to gain opportunities to learn and practice new skills through participation in program activities. Persons to whom this is a primary interest may seek out scientific exhibits, workshops, symposiums and lectures, and may volunteer readily as participants in new projects. The association may fully satisfy their image of purpose if these opportunities for creative growth are served.

Thus people join large associations for many diverse and conflicting reasons. Once having joined, they may be drawn into activities they had not anticipated, and through participating may acquire new friends, new interests, broader and more active roles, and, perhaps, closer identification with the association and its purposes. Such identification tends to be fostered by the special communication system that develops within any group of people who have worked together for a long time with a common purpose.

Large groups tend to provide a special language and channel of communication exclusively available to those accepted into memberships. Patterns of expression and symbolism employed may be simple, as in the Boy Scout handshake, the association flag, Ghandi's weaving and fasting, or an association's insignia. In other cases, however, the symbolism may require years of study, as in the case of certain church prayers and rituals, or the codes of service groups such as the Masons or Odd Fellows. While some media employed in communication may be available to nonmembers, such as the *American Journal of Public Health,* others, such as newsletters, section and committee communications, or discussions regarding decisions, are limited in circulation to members or to specific members.

Most groups develop a common fund of knowledge and language over time which they may not individually recognize as unique or exclusive, but which excludes the newcomer from full participation. This is even true of such professional associations as the American Public Health Association. The outsider is recognized by the way he participates, or fails to participate, in meetings. He may question tacit agreements of purpose or method. He may fail to recognize cryptic references to other meetings, sections, or committees, or may fail to note the significance of alternatives being discussed.

He may demonstrate his newness to the group also by lacking an awareness of the relative status of members present, the hidden powers of informal leaders, the roles of persons in positions of significance together with the rights and responsibilities that attend such roles. He is likely at first to be uncertain regarding the meaning of his own membership, the meaning of his position in the group, what to expect of others, and what others in the group expect of him. Such features of group life must be acquired by the new member through active participation, for it involves a give and take in communication and action in some ways unique to the specific situation.

While individuals differ widely in their reasons for participation in associations, they also vary in degree and nature of their memberships and identifications. There are persons who participate as members who lack strong identification with an association; others may never formally join but may identify strongly with association positions and use them as guidelines in their work.

The choices man makes in selecting some membership groups rather than others, or in choosing some groups as reference groups rather than others, are choices that reflect his personal and social values. A person's identification with the American Public Health Association, for example, tends to reflect a certain attitude and value orientation regarding health, acceptance of the possibility of influencing health behavior, recognition of the possibility of influencing environment to improve man's well-being and welfare. One who identifies with the

Association is expected to conform to certain values, standards, and practices supported by the Association and also to others that are in tune with its general philosophy and goals. A certain manner of conformity is assumed and encouraged. The pressures for conformity to group standards and values is strong, and one who opposes such pressures may find himself alone in the midst of colleagues.

Thus values that accrue to him through professional membership and identification may at times be offset by certain limiting influences of such identifications. While the individual may be aware of the significance of his association identifications in many decisions, there may be times when the effects go unrecognized, so that decisions may be made without adequate consideration of alternatives.

Reference groups tend to influence what a person sees or hears, what types of persons he interacts with, how relevant information and actions are interpreted, and what significance they have for his own behavior. When the reference group identification is strongly held—when it is important for the individual—it may lead one to respond without personally evaluating the quality of recommendations made or the validity of standards held. Judgments regarding new legislation, for example, may tend to be in terms of how he sees significant members of his association responding. When he is uncertain as to what actions to take on some local health issues, he may seek examples from among his association colleagues or peruse policy statements for guidance. He would be less likely to interact with those opposed to these values or to hear and see evidences contrary to what his association supports. Contrary views or evidence may be given less significance or validity. Witnesses having contrary views may be heard with the expectation that they are in error. Opportunities for unique or creative actions or developments may be unseen.

At times, strong identification with a reference group, whether or not an individual is a member of the group, may force him into conflict with other individuals or groups. Membership in an "ingroup" implies that an "outgroup" is present and the possibility of disagreement or conflict. Thus one who identifies with the American Public Health Association as the reference group may soon find himself in conflict with such groups as those supporting anti-fluoridation, anti-vivisection, or food faddism of one sort or another. If he were not using the American Public Health Association as a reference group, these issues might not have been important to him, and he might not have entered into the conflict involved.

Since each of us identifies with many groups concurrently, conflicts between groups at times lead to conflicts within ourselves. We may have difficulty acting when our groups disagree in their positions or policies. A health officer who identifies equally strongly with the American Public Health Association and the American Medical Association may find himself almost immobilized on certain issues. A health educator who strongly identifies with both the Health Education Section of the American Public Health Association and the Society of Public Health Educators is likely to find himself involved in conflict when making decisions concerning policies, areas of responsibility, program choices, committee responsibilities, and so on. The behavioral scientist may find himself forced to choose between participating actively in American Public Health Association affairs or in the activities of his scientific professional groups. Since most American Public Health Association members hold more than one professional identification, such decisions are of common occurrence.

NOTES TO CHAPTER 8

1. Newcomb, Theodore M., *Social Psychology*. The Dryden Press, New York, 1950, p. 492.

2. Krech, David, Richard S. Crutchfield, and Egerton L. Ballachey, *Individual in Society*. McGraw-Hill Book Co., New York, 1962, p. 383.

3. *Ibid.*, p. 337.

4. See Centers, Richard, *The Psychology of Social Classes,* Princeton University Press, Princeton, N.J., 1949; Miller, Walter B., "Implications of Urban Lower-Class Culture for Social Work," *Social Service Review*, vol. 33, September, 1959, pp. 219–236.

5. Davis, Allison, and Robert J. Havighurst, "Social Class and Colour Differences in Child-Rearing," *American Sociological Review*, vol. 11, 1946, pp. 698–710. Also quoted in Krech, David, Richard S. Crutchfield, and Egerton L. Ballachey, *op. cit.*, p. 316.

6. Clausen, John A., "Social Factors in Disease" in Clausen, John A., and Robert Straus, editors, *Medicine and Society, The Annals* of the American Academy of Political and Social Science, vol. 346, March, 1963, p. 142.

7. Hollingshead, August B., and Fredrick C. Redlich, *Social Class and Mental Illness*. John Wiley and Sons, New York, 1958.

8. Hollingshead, August B., *Two Factor Index of Social Position*. Published by August B. Hollingshead, 1965 Yale Station, New Haven, Conn., 1957.

9. Clausen, John A., *op. cit.*, p. 142.

10. Centers, Richard, *op. cit.*

11. Graham, Stanley R., "Social Factors in Relation to Chronic Illness" in Freeman, Howard E., Sol Levine, and Leo G. Reeder, editors, *Handbook of Medical Sociology*. Prentice-Hall, Inc., Englewood Cliffs, N.J., 1963, pp. 65–98.

12. Galiher, Claudia B., Ruth Grout, Andie Knutson, Benjamin Shimberg, and Mary Lou Skinner, "Interview Study," *Adult Leadership,* vol. 5, November,

1956. This paper summarizes some of the findings of an intensive interview study of members of the Health Education Section of the American Public Health Association. Many of the illustrations for the discussion of the APHA as a professional reference group were gained in the process of conducting this study.

Chapter 9

Position, Status, and Role

THE NAIVE VISITOR to a local public health clinic is likely to be unable to understand what is going on and what the people in charge are trying to do until he learns through observation or inquiry how the members of the group relate to one another, why they respond to one another's requests, commands, or actions in particular ways, how they are able to anticipate one another's behaviors, and what leads them to indicate satisfaction, displeasure, or uncertainty regarding the activities observed. Perhaps without even thinking of the terms involved, the visitor will try to define the various positions in the group, the relative status of these positions, the roles expected of persons in these positions, and how these roles should be, and are, performed. In seeking understanding, the visitor will therefore be applying his own role theory in making an analysis of their transactions.

Position and Status

The structure or organization of any society and of any group within that society may be described in terms of a pattern of interrelated positions. The health department staff, for example, has many different but related positions such as that of health officer, supervising nurse, visiting nurse, health educator, sanitarian, laboratory technician, statistician, secretary, clerk, receptionist, and janitor. At a particular time each of these positions is occupied by a specific person although the same person may not always occupy the same position. A health officer may resign and someone else replace him in the same position; in the absence of the chief nurse, the ranking visiting nurse may serve in her place and, of course, some established position may remain vacant for lack of funds, with the functions carried by others or dropped. In describing a social group in this way, positions are considered to be locations within the society and their interrelationships may be discussed without considering the persons occupying the positions.

As Linton has noted, most societies provide at least five different kinds of positions for their members as related to age and sex, occupation, family or kinship, membership in association or interest groups, and in prestige or status groups. Many of these positions are assigned on the basis of factors over which the individual has no control and in this sense one may say they are ascribed positions. Others may be acquired or achieved; still others may be the result of preference or choice. Sex and age, for example, are ascribed to an individual since one cannot choose these. In some societies, positions of prestige are also ascribed, and to the extent that status is related to factors over which the individual has no choice, it, too, may be ascribed. On the other hand, most occupational or leadership positions in our society tend to be achieved positions and the status that accompanies these positions is achieved status.[1]

The distinction between ascribed and achieved positions and statuses is by no means precise. Even achieved positions and the status they carry are commonly validated by some social recognition or acknowledgment. To that extent they, too, may be seen as ascribed. A person who achieves the prescribed training and preparation to become a physician does not receive recognition and acceptance as a physician unless these are ascribed to him by members of his professional and social groups.

Romano, in his study of donship in a Mexican-American community, nicely outlines the various ways in which this position of status may be conferred or achieved by males in the community, and the "halo effects" which accrue to the person so honored.

> With regard to the aspects of Mexican-American male life which donship highlights, the traditional and achieved classes involve those which are considered most important. For example, the patrón represents a source of steady employment and security. The Mexican consul represents a formal connection with Mexico as well as a rallying point for patriotic fervor. And certain wealthy men are considered important as individuals who can provide assistance in times of need. The political don constitutes a tangible connection with government, a person of influence who can assist another who may be at odds with the law. The curandero, or folk-healer, provides control over illness. And very old men represent a long life. Finally, the achieved don represents successful masculinity. In short, employment security, Mexican patriotism, assistance from a "strong man" when needed financially or in legal difficulties, health, a long life, and masculinity are the aspects of Frontera existence which are considered of supreme importance by the male

immigrant population. And the prestige system of donship involves all of them.[2]

An understanding of the ways in which such status and respect is ascribed or achieved within a group thus provides some insights into the dynamics of community life. One can learn from an analysis of the manner in which donship serves as a mechanism for ascribing or achieving status what members of the community regard as important contributions to their interdependent group life.

One should distinguish clearly between position and status. The term "position" refers to a location within a social group; the term "status" refers to a rank within a hierarchy of positions, or may be assigned to individuals in terms of some prestige ranking. A health officer, for example, holds higher status within the organization than the chief nurse who works for him. The nurse, however, may have higher status than the health officer in some of the social groups to which both belong. To some extent, of course, status becomes attached to the individual and accompanies him from one position to another; a certain "halo effect" may be observed as a person of status moves from one position to another. The individual's total status in the society may be defined as the sum of his various statuses.[3]

Roles as "Sets of Expectancies"

The roles of an individual in any position are dependent upon the roles of other individuals in that setting. There are certain things a person in a position is expected to do, other things he may do but is not expected to do, and still other things he is expected not to do or may be forbidden to do. Social roles may be described, therefore, as "sets of expectancies" regarding positions.

Hartley and Hartley clearly distinguish social roles from role performances or behavior. They define a social role as

. . . an organized pattern of expectancies that relate to the tasks, demeanors, attitudes, values, and reciprocal relationships to be maintained by persons occupying specific membership positions and fulfilling definable functions in any group. The emphasis here is on expectancies rather than on behavior because the role is defined by what others expect of the person filling it. Behavior refers to actual performance—how a person fills his role.

Social roles furnish a basis for communication between people. They help the individual group member to know what to expect of other members, how to approach them, and how to communicate with them. Social roles provide guides to behavior and eliminate the necessity of constant experimentation.[4]

How a member of a health department staff performs the roles expected of him in any situation depends, in good part, on how he interprets these expectancies, his own expectations regarding other members of the group, and how he defines other features of the situation at hand. Understanding his behavior involves knowing the rights and obligations or demands the group has placed upon him as well as his personal desires or concerns. It also requires knowing how these are related to the possibilities he perceives for action and the areas of freedom or permission, limitation or restriction, competition or support of which he is aware.

Each position in a social organization, whether it be a family, a school, a church, club, or health department carries with it certain role demands on the person who occupies that position. While these requirements or expectations may be generally understood by parties concerned, they are neither completely nor precisely defined, and members of the group do not always agree upon them. Nor are they consistent over time; different occupants of a position, as well as other members of the group, may have varying ideas regarding the philosophy of the organization, policies, goals, and relationships, and changes in conditions may require variation from possible written descriptions; thus they vary depending upon individual choice and experience not only of the occupant, but also of other members of the group and the expectations these other members have of the occupant together with his need for adapting to their expectations.

Arnold, in a study of a sample of physicians, public health nurses, and health educators in 23 local health departments of California found marked variation in the way these members of health departments described their own responsibilities and the responsibilities of other members of the public health team. Her study suggested need for clearer definition and agreement regarding the role requirements of the different positions in the health department, especially with regard to activities concerned with the internal functioning of the organization.[5]

Line and Staff Positions and Roles

In many public health agencies, particularly larger health organizations, a distinction may be noted between the administrative, or line, positions and the professional, or staff, positions. This separation into line and staff positions is similar to that of certain industrial and military groups. Where these two types of positions exist in organizations, clarity and understanding regarding the role expectations or demands of each position is of particular importance.

Sources of difficulty may arise regarding the relative status or rank of parallel line and staff positions and the relative rights, responsibilities, and privileges which accompany these positions. In a study of the National Institutes of Health, for example, it was found that the area of greatest strain reported by members of the organization occurred between administrative officers or their assistants and the professional research officers.[6] While we do not have information regarding the relationship between line and staff members in other public health organizations, it seems likely that many health departments and other health agencies face the problem of dealing with these two types of positions since the staff person may exceed the line person in education or specialized training, but must nevertheless be responsible to the line administrator with regard to some decisions which concern his work. A potential source of conflict exists.

In an insightful study of the staff organization which has responsibility for research and advice and the line organization which has exclusive authority for production of three industrial plants, Dalton has identified a number of the factors leading to conflict in such a setting. He notes that staff professional persons are relative newcomers in many organizations. Included here are specialists of many kinds: scientists, statisticians, public and industrial relations officers, personnel officers, accountants, and engineers who apply their specialized knowledge in problem areas and advise or consult with officers who make up the line organization and have authority over production. The staff officers thus have no formal authority over production and influence decisions through suggestions or other means of providing guidance.[7]

In these industrial plants conflict between the line and staff groups hindered the attainment of organizational goals. Some of the line executives expressed the hope of achieving greater control over the staff groups, possibly by training line officers for staff positions; whereas staff members wanted more recognition and a greater voice in the control of plans to ensure that their suggestions or findings were used. Among the reasons for conflict between the groups were their differences in responsibility and function; their differences in age, formal education, and status, with staff officers being younger and having more education but lower occupational status; the need for staff officers to justify their existence; the fear of line officers that the staff groups would undermine line authority; and the fact that staff members could only gain promotion through approval of line executives. While one cannot directly generalize from Dalton's study to public health agencies, it seems likely that some of the kinds of problems Dalton described do exist in public health agencies and may, at times, be an undefined source of difficulty. A critical analysis along the lines described by Dalton might contribute to significant improvement in agency functioning.

Role Dilemmas

While we tend to look at the demands and requirements of positions in terms of structure and from the administrative point of view, it is important also to view these demands from the standpoint of the person involved, the meaning the position has for him, the feelings it invokes, and the ways in which it creates stress or security and support for him.[8] Role dilemmas may arise when an individual experiences conflicting pressures regarding the demands of his position. The administrator must often face choices between the needs or desires of an individual and those of the group. The chief public health nurse may find herself in the cross pressures between the demands for efficiency and economy and the demands of staff for freedom from schedules so that the emotional as well as the physical health needs of mothers may be attended. The sanitarian, whose responsibilities may be defined as both educational and enforcement, is faced with a serious role dilemma, for one course of action may block the other.

Role dilemmas such as these may arise from either pressures within the organization or pressures within the individual himself, but however they arise they lead to difficult problems for the person who must make decisions.

Role Definition

How an individual defines his role and carries it out within a group is likely to differ greatly from the way it is defined by the administrator or by other members of his group. Each person coming into a new group may have a defined position to fill and may be told what his rights and responsibilities are, together with how he is expected to perform them. In reality, however, these definitions cannot be complete and precise, with the result that each person must go through a period of adjustment or adaptation to his new role. In the process of this adaptation, the definition of the role and the manner of its performance is likely to change somewhat from the initial definition.

How an individual adapts to a new position or a position new for him, though old in the organization, will therefore depend not only on how the position is defined by significant others but also how he himself defines the situation together with his own unique capacities, abilities, experiences, and style or manner of coping with problems in performing his duties and carrying out his responsibilities. Understanding the personal role definition therefore involves understanding both how the role is conceived and how the role is performed.

The state health department, for example, may decide to set up a position for a behavioral scientist, and the health officer and his staff may go to great lengths in defining this position to meet the requirements of civil service and budget committees. In this definition some consideration may also be given to the relationships which this behavioral scientist will have to other members of the staff, the manner of his functioning, and his position in the chain of command. The health officer and members of his staff will develop certain expectations regarding what he will do when employed, and may have in mind some criteria by which they will judge the effectiveness of his efforts.

Since this is a new position in the health department, the health officer and members of his staff are not likely to have had wide experience with members of the behavioral science group. They may not really know whether they need an anthropologist, a sociologist, or a psychologist for the specific job they have in mind. They may not realize that the theoretical orientation of the person or the kind of research training he has had may be even more important for certain aspects of the job than the specific discipline from which he comes. They are likely to have little idea regarding the range of variance among the different social scientists in their areas of interest and competence, in their approaches to research, in their ideas regarding what constitutes significant knowledge regarding health action, and in their ideas regarding the relationships of the research person to other members of the staff, particularly those responsible for the program. Unless members of the department staff have an opportunity to discuss these issues with someone able to develop with them a bridge to the type of person they desire and need, they may have difficulty even finding someone who fits the pattern of requirements they have set up for the particular position.

Once a behavioral scientist has been selected and placed in the position, a period of adjustment will occur during which he will seek orientation to their expectations; members of the staff, in turn, will have an opportunity to judge his potentialities for satisfying their expectations. He and they are likely to find, after a period of time, that there is a considerable difference between their definition of his role and his own conception of his role. Many factors, unstated in either the job description or application, will have significant bearing on how the final position is mutually defined. Some of these unstated influences include one's philosophy regarding public health and science; differences in value orientation; differences in ideas about the organizational structure within which one works, the hierarchy of command and channels of communication; variations in what one interprets consultation, advice, guidance, and assistance to be; differences in the meaning of responsibilities and rights regarding such matters as the definition of the problem, potential sources of information, access to useful resources, freedom of design, conduct of research, publication, and so on. How adequately the new behavioral scientist performs his role in the situation will depend in good part on how he defines it and how his definition relates to the expectations of others. When disagreements exist, his criteria of success in performance will then be different from the criteria used by his superiors or by other members of the staff.

In a new situation, such as the one described, where neither the employer nor the employee has had a range of experience in the particular setting, the problems of adapting the individual's conception of his role to the role demands of the organization and, conversely, reorienting leadership so that the demands better fit the realism of the situation is a slow, arduous task. To the extent that agreements are ultimately reached, both employer and employee will be satisfied with performance, provided, of course, the performance is adequate relative to the common definition. To the extent that agreement in role conception is not reached, there will be varying criteria used in determining successful performance of role in that particular position. Thus what one member may view as success, another may define as failure in performance.

A somewhat different set of conditions exists when a new employee is chosen to fill an existing position with which the agency already has had experience. The behavioral scientist may be selected to fill the position previously held by another behavioral scientist who had performed with success as defined by the administration and staff. In this instance the administration and staff may be somewhat more positive in their role demands and be less flexible regarding the role definition and performance of the new employee. They may have unrealistic expectations regarding his adaptation to their demands, for they may fail to recognize the extent to which the previous employee's success depended upon this period of common give-and-take in reaching mutual agreements and upon the unique pattern of characteristics, both personal and professional, of that employee. The new behavioral scientist may arrive with different orientations to theory and method and with different ideas regarding the manner of work. Were he able to experience the same give-and-take adaptation of his predecessor, he might be even better in the situation. But if the expectations regarding his predecessor are applied to him—that is, if the same role demands are made of him as of the previous behavioral scientist—he may have greater difficulty in successful adaptation and role performance, for these earlier demands do not take into consideration his unique qualifications and potentialities and his specific ways of coping with new issues.

One needs to recognize that neither the role demands of an administrator nor role demands of members of a staff are stable things. Role demands and role conceptions are constantly changing, for no social group remains stable. New requirements may be identified, new situations will arise and require different patterns of role definition and role performance. People grow on the job and it is essential that the job grow with them. Likewise, organizations change their orientations and policies and change in their definitions of purpose and immediate goal.

Each of these group or individual changes requires adaptation on the part of management, staff, and the specific individual concerned. The successful functioning of an organization and the satisfaction derived by the members of that organization depend in good part, therefore, upon a frequent review, evaluation, and change regarding the patterns of responsibility and rights assigned to a position and expected from the incumbent, and those conceived by the incumbent as significant for him and as giving him directions for action.

Role Sets

The role demands, role conceptions, and role performances of the different members of the social group are interdependent things, for the positions involved in a social setting are interrelated positions. How an individual functions in any setting depends, therefore, not only on his own unique characteristics and experiences, but also on the way his role conceptions and performances relate to other members of the group and how well he is able to identify and interpret these interrelationships. Each person occupying a particular social position may be said to acquire a "role set" appropriate to that position. This role set includes a cluster of roles demanded by that position and conceived by him as being appropriate; it includes the appropriate roles for each type of significant other person with whom he interacts in that position.[9] Thus roles do not exist in isolation; rather, the role set an individual has in a particular position is related to the roles of others in that particular group or society.

Role-Taking

Social behaviors are cooperative undertakings. As has been mentioned, no role exists independently of other roles, but is firmly tied to someone else's role. To perform his role effectively, the acting individual must "read" or "take the role" of the other person. Such a process, known as "role-taking," is a most significant aspect of all social activities.

When two persons work or live together over a period of time, they learn to anticipate each other's behavior in various situations and respond in ways the other person expects. Were they to act in a contrary manner, a disruption of communication and transaction would occur. To the extent that their role performances are in harmony with one another, effective cooperation results.

For an established situation such as a medical examination, the physician and nurse learn to anticipate one another's expectations and to respond accordingly. Repeated experience with patients may help them also to "take" the patient's role, anticipating her expectations and adapting to her needs even before requests are made or concern is expressed. A patient with characteristics different from those usually attended becomes a difficult one to work with, for neither physician nor nurse may be able validly to "take her role." A new patient faces even a simple examination with much concern and uncertainty, in part because she does not know what to expect from the physician and nurse. She is unable to "take their roles" adequately and to adapt her behavior to their expectations.

Similar situations arise each time a new employee joins the public health staff. He must learn to take the roles of many persons with whom his own actions are interlocked, and until he acquires the necessary understanding of the roles of significant others his own behavior is likely to appear awkward and uncertain. His own role conceptions and the role demands required in his particular "role set" depend upon his ability to interpret accurately the behaviors of others concerned. His success depends, in part, on his ability to enter into the private subjective worlds of those about him to see how they view the situation, and to interpret their own and his relationships within it.

Effective role-taking thus requires understanding of why others respond as they do, what they expect of one, what they expect one to do in response to their actions. It also requires effective communication of one's own role, one's own definition of the situation, and expectations regarding the significant others. It tells the other person, "I expect that of you and you may expect this of me," and further asks, "have I read you correctly?"

Projecting one's feelings, interpretations, and intentions, and at the same time "reading" the other person's feelings, interpretations, and intentions becomes a continuous aspect of social transaction. Roles and role expectations are in constant flux, so that reorientation to others in one's role set is a continuous process.

After people have lived or worked together for some time, much of the communication that takes place in their social transactions becomes nonverbal communication. Groups develop intricate and effective nonverbal means of communicating feelings, expectations, and intentions. A newcomer within such a group is at a serious disadvantage, for he neither recognizes nor understands the nonverbal symbols such as gestures, expressions, pauses, glances, and movements used. Nor are those using such nonverbal symbols always aware of the extent to which they communicate in this way. Thus the new member of the group is deprived of information essential for effective role-taking and for defining his role set, but neither he nor others may realize the extent to which communication with him is inadequate.

Role Conflicts

While major attention has been given in this discussion to the significance of role theory for understanding roles and relationships in the public health staff, it should be recognized that what has been discussed applies generally to other social groups; each member of any social group holds a position in that group, and the members of that group place certain role demands upon the person in that position. He, in turn, develops his own role conception and performs his role in terms of his conception of it and how he defines the situation in which he is performing. As in the public health department, role conflicts may occur when roles of different members of the group overlap or, as sometimes happens, when a person finds himself filling more than one position and therefore performing more than one role at the same time. The demands of the two roles may be in conflict with each other or the conceptions of how they should be performed may be in conflict.

Each person is in many social groups, thus holds many positions, and responds to varying role demands which he defines in different ways.

A health officer, for example, in addition to holding his official position in the health department, may hold a position of father, son, brother, uncle, husband, private physician, member of the medical society, member of the P.T.A., chairman of a welfare committee, member of a school board, member of a political party, member of a social club, deacon of a church, and, in fact, an almost infinite number of positions which at first glance may seem to have little relationship. When he occupies these positions, each of them places certain role demands upon him which are defined, in part, by tradition, the administration of the particular organization, the members of the group whatever it may be, law or common law, and many other types of social pressures. For each of the positions he has his own concept of the role he should perform, and for each will vary in his effectiveness in role performance. This will depend both on his ability to deal with the unique situation demanded by the position and on the degree with which there is harmony between the role demands of others on him and his own conception of the roles.

Conflicts between these roles frequently occur. Often they are of minor nature, but at times they may be most significant. As director of the health department, he may see new health problems which demand greater budget and staff. As a member of a political party, he may be opposed to the increase of funds for public services. As a member of the school board, he may see school demands as exceeding those of the health department. As the father of several children in school, he may feel that a priority should be given to education; yet as a son of aged parents needing medical care and assistance, he may see the need for greater public assistance for the aged and public medical services. This may be in conflict with the policies of the medical society of which he is an active member. One would need to identify his various positions, determine the role demands placed upon him, and determine his own conception of his roles in these positions in order to understand his behavior as he seeks to cope with these conflicting demands and requirements.

Since both role conceptions and the role demands are frequently changing, any description of the individual's behavior in a particular situation has only limited predictive value with regard to other situations. Inconsistencies may be frequently observed by those who judge other people's behavior; yet in some strange way each of us, through various means previously discussed, makes personal adaptations and reinterpretations of a situation in which he finds himself and maintains an internal consistency regarding his own acts.

Transactional Ties with the Community

Major attention in this discussion of role has been given to public health staff roles, since an examination of role behavior in terms of a particular setting may help to highlight the transactional nature of all social behavior. The same process of analysis may be applied to the role relationships of public health persons in other agencies, in their professional associations, and in their social lives.

Of particular significance to public health are the transactional ties between health personnel and members of the community. One tends to speak of the public in general terms as "it" or "they," or to view members of the community primarily as recipients of services. However, members of the community hold many different positions of public health significance. In each of these positions they hold different role conceptions, role demands, role sets, and are faced with role dilemmas and conflicts. Effective work with members of the community requires a recognition and understanding of the specific position of concern at the time, and the role implications of that position.

Each of the following positions which may be held by a member of the community has different meanings for public health and requires a different course of action on the part of the public health worker who would influence the behavior of the individual holding the position:

Patient with chronic condition
Patient with contagious illness
Patient receiving emergency care
Recipient of specific services
Member of family or other cohesive group receiving service
Participant in some preventive program or case-finding program
Carrier of behaviors that foster mental or emotional illness
Carrier of superstition, fear, uncertainty, false information which provides the basis for "cultural lag" in public health, or conversely, carriers of new knowledge and understanding
Source of social pressure for colleagues or others regarding public health action
Resource in case-finding or rehabilitation
Resource in communicating with "hard to reach" groups
Leader in community action programs
Consultant or adviser to activities
Volunteer worker
Taxpayer
Voter
Member of political group
Friend or associate

Members of the public health team will recognize these positions as implying different roles of significance to health action. Persons in these positions have role conceptions and role demands reciprocal to those held by members of the public health team. The effectiveness of transactions involved will depend upon the degree to which these reciprocal relationships are recognized and mutually defined.[10]

NOTES TO CHAPTER 9

1. Linton, Ralph, *The Cultural Background of Personality*. Appleton-Century-Crofts, Inc., New York, 1945.

2. Romano V., Octavio I., "Donship in a Mexican-American Community in Texas," *American Anthropologist*, vol. 62, December, 1960, p. 975. For a brilliant discussion of the folk-healer as a significant innovating force in Mexican-American life, see "Charismatic Medicine, Folk-Healing and Folk-Sainthood" by the same author in the *American Anthropologist* for Fall, 1965.

3. Linton, Ralph, *The Study of Man.* Appleton-Century-Crofts, Inc., New York, 1936, pp. 113–131.

4. Hartley, Eugene L., and Ruth E. Hartley, *Fundamentals of Social Psychology.* Alfred A. Knopf, Inc., New York, 1952, p. 486.

5. Arnold, Mary F., "Perception of Professional Role Activities in the Local Health Department," *Public Health Reports,* vol. 77, no. 1, 1962, pp. 80–88.

6. Institute for Social Research, *Human Relations in a Research Organization: A Study of the National Institutes of Health.* University of Michigan, Ann Arbor, 1953, vol. 1.

7. Dalton, Melville, "Conflicts Between Staff and Line Managerial Officers," *American Sociological Review,* vol. 15, June, 1950, pp. 342–351.

8. Levinson, Daniel J., "Role, Personality, and Social Structure in the Organizational Setting," *Journal of Abnormal and Social Psychology,* vol. 58, March, 1959, pp. 170–180. Levinson's brilliant discussion, together with that of Hartley and Hartley, *op. cit.* (see Chapters 16 and 17), has been most helpful in developing the framework of this discussion. For more extended discussions of role theory, see also Rose, Arnold M., editor, *Human Behavior and Social Processes: An Interactionist Approach,* Houghton-Mifflin Co., Boston, 1962; Sarbin, Theodore R., "Role Theory" in Lindzey, Gardner, editor, *Handbook of Social Psychology,* Addison-Wesley Publishing Co., Reading, Mass., 1954, vol. 1, pp. 223–258; Shibutani, Tamotsu, *Society and Personality.* Part I. Prentice-Hall, Inc., Englewood Cliffs, N.J., 1961, pp. 31–78; Goffman, Erving, *The Presentation of Self in Everyday Life,* Doubleday Anchor Books, Doubleday and Co., Garden City, N.Y., 1959.

9. Merton, Robert K., "Role-Set: Problems in Sociological Theory," *British Journal of Sociology,* vol. 8, June, 1957, pp. 106–120.

10. King, Stanley H., *Perceptions of Illness and Medical Practice.* Russell Sage Foundation, New York, 1962. King's analysis of the rights and duties, demands, and role expectations of the physician, nurse, social worker, and patient will be of great interest to public health personnel concerned with patient care. See also Mechanic, David, and Edmund H. Volkart, "Stress, Illness, Behavior and the Sick Role," *American Sociological Review,* vol. 26, February, 1961, pp. 21–58; Parsons, Talcott, *The Social System,* The Free Press, Glencoe, Ill., 1951 (see Chapter 10, Social Structure and Dynamic Process: The Case of Modern Medical Practice); Parsons, Talcott, and Renée Fox, "Illness, Therapy, and the Modern Urban American Family," *Journal of Social Issues,* vol. 8, no. 4, 1952, pp. 2–3, 31–44 (reprinted in Jaco, E. Gartley, editor, *Patients, Physicians, and Illness: Sourcebook in Behavioral Science and Medicine,* The Free Press, Glencoe, Ill., 1958, pp. 234–245).

Chapter 10

The Meaning of Food*

WHEN DISCUSSING MAN'S HEALTH BEHAVIOR, it is in many ways meaningless to make distinctions between his social environment and other aspects of environment. Man's biological, physiological, and physical environments are socially labeled and defined. Thus they largely exist for man through socially derived interpretations and meanings, and in this way become part of his social environment.

The meaning of food has been chosen as a topic here in order to illustrate the range of meanings man may give to any aspect of environment, and to examine some of the implications of these meanings for his behavior. In discussing food, one can see how social meanings stand between man and environment, at once guiding and limiting his transactions with the physiological, biological, and physical worlds.

What constitutes food for any human society may have little direct bearing on what is physiologically consumable or on what could provide adequate sustenance. Each society sets its own limits on what is edible for its members, and how the food should be prepared, cooked, and served. In our society, such newly developed foods as fish flour and sludge-grown algae, in spite of their high nutrient values, are not likely to gain rapid acceptance. One might say we are all squeamish about what we eat, and many of us would starve in the presence of plenty—of dogs, cats, rats and mice, snakes, snails, slugs, ants, worms, roaches, locusts, and lizards. These are biological items of environment which could be eaten but which our society has not found fit to label as "human food."

Social definitions of food thus have much to do with the kind, amount, and accessibility of food available to any society. They de-

* Many of the ideas in this chapter were pretested in seminars in Public Health Nutrition conducted by Ruth L. Huenemann, Mary M. Murai, and Leona R. Shapiro.

termine also the amount and nature of the work required to make it acceptable for consumption.

Some Definitions of Food

Food has an astonishing range of meanings. These meanings may vary by sociocultural group, by social class, caste, or ethnic groups, by religion, occupation, sex, age, marital status, and many other factors. Even within each professional field, food may vary in its meanings in accord with the level of conceptualization involved and the nature of the specific issue or purpose at hand.

Food, to a nutritionist, may at different times mean nutrients, calories, intake, preferences, flavors, fads, services, habits, practices, and objects of praise or complaint. The sanitarian may regard food in terms of the services of restaurants, hotels, diners, grocery stores, or warehouses; the problems of safe delivery, storage, and disposal; of samples to collect and test to assure protection against contamination; or as problems involving customer complaints, political pressures, and conflicts of interest. The epidemiologist, on the other hand, may view food as a medium for carrying disease, a source of infection, or as the base for a bacterial culture.

Under the circumstances, Webster's definition seems wholly inadequate for imparting the meaning of food:

> Material consisting of carbohydrates, fats, proteins, and supplementary substances (as minerals, vitamins) that is taken or absorbed into the body of an organism in order to sustain growth, repair, and all vital processes and to furnish energy for all activity of the organism < any population is limited by the available supply of ~>; ESP: parts of the bodies of animals and plants consumed by animals: PROVENDER, PROVISIONS, VIANDS <acres devoted to growing ~> <longing for the ~s of her homeland>—compare METABOLISM, NUTRITION.[1]

A much better sense of the diverse and rich meanings that food may have is imparted by Roget's Thesaurus. Note how the implications for meaning change in accord with the cultural and social setting involved, the nature of the groups and their patterns of eating, the time, place, and purpose of the occasion, and even the temperamental and health status of the persons involved:

> . . . nourishment, nutriment, sustenance, pabulum (esp. food for the mind), support, keep, nurture, subsistence; provender, corn, feed, feedstuff, fodder; provision, ration, board, dietary; regimen; staff of life,

bread, . . . viands, comestibles, foodstuffs, edibles, grub (slang), eats (colloq.), flesh, roast, meat, dainties, delicacies; creature comforts, ambrosia, manna; good cheer, good living, high living, the fleshpots . . . cracker, pretzel, rusk, cracknel; hard-tack, sea biscuit, ship bread, ship biscuit . . . eating, consumption, deglutition, devouring, devourment, mastication, rumination; epicurism, gastronomy; carnivorousness, gluttony; vegetarianism . . . draught, libation, carousal, drunkenness . . . cuisine, bill of fare, menu, table d'hote (F.), a la carte (F.) . . . repast, feed (colloq.), spread (colloq.); mess; course, dish, plat (F.), plate; refreshment, entertainment; refection, collation, picnic, feast, banquet, junket; potluck; chota hazri (Anglo-Indian), breakfast, dejeuner (F.), lunch, luncheon, tiffin (Anglo-Indian); tea, afternoon tea; dinner, supper.[2]

Food is the primary focus of, or intimately tied to, most of the significant personal and group experiences of man. It is not surprising, then, that food has so many meanings and values to the varying societies of man, and also to each individual.

Food and the Life Cycle

Food contributes in some meaningful social or religious way to most of the critical events in man's life cycle. His birth may be celebrated with food or food offerings. It is a negligent father in some social groups who does not mark the occasion with offerings of cigars or candies to his friends. Birthdays are also marked by special foods and feasting. Proper celebration of each of the many graduations that mark his steps in progress in educational, occupational, religious, or social life requires food and feasting or, in some societies, fasting. Well wishers who come to cheer him and his successes may bear food as symbolic of praise and joy and, furthermore, may join together with others in appropriate festivity.

Special foods with special meanings contribute to the intensity of the experiences of confirmation, communion, engagement, wedding, and pregnancy. Each of these significant social steps involves movement into new social settings and the assumption of new roles and identities. Food serves as a vehicle for drawing together those intimately concerned and providing them with a setting within which to express their feelings of joy, surprise, or relief in accord with rules of conduct which govern the order and form of such events.

The unhappy or sad occasions of failure, injury, rejection, illness, or death find food serving quite different social purposes. Food may then be given as an expression of sympathy, condolence, sorrow, or support. The meaning of food on such occasions may vary widely from group to group. One group may share a funeral supper in deep mourning. Another may mark the same occasion as a time to stop mourning and to express their joy at the passing of the departed into a new and better world; for a third the focus of the occasion may be providing food for the bourne of the departed to feed his ghost while it travels over the rugged passage into a new land.

On these many occasions the preparation, serving, and eating of food may provide the central focus for reaffirming rules of etiquette concerning the manners and order of behavior. Social customs are in this way reenforced through practice. Such occasions also serve to remind one of his relative statuses in the social group, a matter that is usually highlighted by such behaviors as the time of arrival and departure, the manner of greeting and introduction, the order of seating and serving. It is an appropriate setting in which to alert all present to the new status accorded the individual honored, his new roles and functions. It alerts all members of the group as to what new behaviors they may expect of him, and he may now expect of them.

Food and Religion

When we think of the relationship of food to religion we may think first of the Lord's Prayer, "Give us this day our daily bread," to the saying of grace at mealtime, or to the offering of thanks at the time of harvest. However, the ties of food to religion and of religion to food in any culture extend far beyond the serving of food alone.

From earliest time onward man has implored the gods to give help in all phases of food-gathering and preparation. Many religions have special forms of prayers, songs, or rituals for use at the time of planting, caring for, harvesting, or hunting food. One begs his Maker for assistance in obtaining food and offers praise and thanks when it arrives. The rain dance, the harvest feast, and the offer of sacrifice are closely bound in meanings.

Special taboos regarding particular foods or their manner of serving have been carried into modern society from ancient times through custom and religious verse. In some cultures the blessing of foods to give them special powers has been extended to include the selection and judgment of quality of the food in order to assure the approval of the gods. The inspection and certification of kosher foods long preceded modern restaurant inspection. Food taboos often seem to reflect a most commendable folk wisdom regarding the possibility of contamination and spread of disease. The rituals of both sacrament and sacrifice are symbolically bound to the use of foods—a testimony to the significant awareness past religious leaders have had of the dynamic bind between man and his food.

Religious beliefs have much to do not only with what is eaten, but when it is eaten, and how it is eaten. Prasad's report on beliefs and customs of a rural Indian community brings this sharply into focus:

> Certain members of the orthodox Hindu castes take a bath before taking meals, take their meals without a shirt on the body; take their meals only within the precincts of the home kitchen: meals cooked only by members of their own caste or of their families. *"Kachcha"* food is not taken from the bazaar but *"Pucca"* food can be taken by some castes. The intake of fried or "Pucca" food in the evenings is a custom with some castes, especially the Vaishyas and is perhaps a factor in the higher incidence of obesity and diabetes.
>
> Jains take their meals before the sun sets, in order to ensure the purity of food against insect pollution. Orthodox Jains do not take root vegetables, as they are considered to carry on their skin ground organisms which will get killed in the cooking. Even honey may not be taken for the same reason. The intake of wine and meat is prevalent among the *Kayasthas* and the lower castes, especially on ceremonial occasions. A community feast may not be considered complete without these. Nonvegetarian Hindus do not take beef; Mohammedans do not take pork; some Harijans do not scruple to eat the flesh of dead cattle; certain lower castes (*Lonia*) eat rodents, and some Muslims eat locusts.[3]

Food, Work, and Social Organization

Food means work for much of the world's population. The kind and amount of food available together with the problems of obtaining, distributing, preparing, and serving it, therefore, have much to do both with the broad social and industrial organization of a society and with the nature and manner of functioning of family units.

The way a society becomes organized to deal with its food problems has a significant bearing on the pattern of its industries and business establishments, the kinds of work people are called upon to do, and the kinds of lives they lead. An agricultural or fishing village with an immediately available food supply differs sharply in way of life from that of an industrial village that imports all its foodstuffs. Both differ in patterns of occupation and manner of living from the small community whose primary source of income is derived from the distribution of foods and other goods prepared elsewhere. These ways of life are strikingly different from that of the metropolitan industrial worker who eats in a cafeteria or purchases already prepared T.V. dinners and disposes of leftovers and waste in a garbage disposal unit or other modern plumbing facilities.

Within any society, members become identified by the roles they enact in relation to food problems. Each society has its food growers, hunters or food seekers, its food movers and distributors, its food preparers, food servers, waste removers, and so on. They may wear special clothing or insignia designed to draw attention to their roles, and may develop societies or unions to deal with one another and other groups in society on matters of common interest. Status may be conferred in terms of the type of food work performed and, as in India, even caste designations may be associated with particular food tasks, making it difficult, if not impossible, for young members of the family to move into occupations significantly different from those traditionally held by the family.[4]

As Prasad has observed:

> Customs in regard to eating are observed, to ensure and maintain community, caste and family brotherhoods, which in turn provide social and psychological satisfaction. Among the Mohammedans drinking from and eating out of a common utensil is a sign of community-brotherhood. Among orthodox Hindus *"Kachcha"* food is taken with the caste members only. Eating together from the same utensil is common among relatives in Hindus (again a sign of brotherhood). Hindu ladies are enjoined by custom and religion to eat from the plate containing food left over by the husbands; they do not take food until the husbands have eaten.[5]

The kind and type of food available, its ready accessibility, and abundance also have much to do with the order of smaller social groups such as the family. The size and member distribution of family units and, in fact, the form of marriage that binds families together may vary according to the nature of the food supply. It ought not be surprising that nomadic tribes that must roam far to maintain their herds in sparse areas of Asia support a polyandrous type of marriage and a family with a major male proportion. In such a family less value is placed on daughters. Infanticide has in the past been the means of controlling both family size and sex distribution. Among the Eskimos, on the other hand, where travel is rugged and requires that male and female depend more heavily on one another for mutual support, the sharing of wives by traveling husbands gains greater favor. The succulent islands of the South Seas provide an abundance of fish and food with little effort. Children may then become less a personal responsibility than a group responsibility and may roam freely from home to home, possibly without even knowledge of their true parents.

Food and Personality Development

The relation of food to personality development is an area of theory and research which has scarcely been touched, yet offers great potentiality for the personality theorist. One should expect significant differences in patterns of behavior among children reared during their formative years in strikingly different settings influenced by the nature of the available food supply.

The infant carried in a confining basket on the back of his mother in a rice paddy while she wades in the water to plant or gather rice is having a strikingly different pattern of experience in childhood from the infant who waddles after bees, butterflies, or other insects while his parents are gathering the new hay. And how different still must be the life of the Navajo child whose parents herd their sheep and goats on semi-arid hills.

The child reared in a fishing village may see a constant stream of new and interesting faces, hear a variety of spoken languages, and view a constantly changing social and physical environment. This pattern of his early perceptual and coping experiences is in striking contrast to that of the Eskimo child who spends so many months in darkness and confinement with little opportunity to experience such a wide range of verbal and social stimuli while his father may be absent from home for long periods in search of food.

Changing Food Practices

One who is interested in changing food habits, either his own or someone else's, should be aware that any food holds different meanings for the varied members of society who affect its movement from field to mouth. Lewin, in his brilliant paper, "Psychological Ecology," notes that "neither group 'habits' nor individual 'habits' can be understood sufficiently by a theory which limits its consideration to the processes themselves and conceives of the 'habit' as a kind of frozen linkage, an 'association' between these processes. Instead, habits will have to be conceived of as a result of forces in the organism *and* its life space, in the group *and* its setting."[6]

Foods have different meanings for the wholesaler, the grocer, the shopper, the bearer, the storer, the preparer, the server, and the diner. It has different meanings also for the hunter, the planter, the caretaker, the reaper, and the seller.

Why we eat what we eat is a matter that involves many cultural and social as well as psychological factors. Any one of a long series of what Lewin refers to as "gatekeepers" of the food channels can influence the kind, amount, quality, and availability of food. The meaning foods have for them, their definitions of role, and the expectations others have of them are matters of significance for the nutritionist who would seek to improve food habits of community groups. Anyone who has tried to reduce his own food intake knows that these gatekeepers, in making food attractive, tasty, available, and socially desirable make difficult his efforts to change, and, particularly, to maintain changes over time.

Food as Incentive for Social Change

In recent years we have heard much more talk about changing food habits than of food changing habits. Yet we must remember that many major changes in society have stemmed from the need or desire for specific foods, food shortages, or the development of new foods or new food processes.

Food famines of various types, such as the potato famine in Ireland and the rice famines of Burma and India, have been responsible for major population movements. Desire for exotic foods or different types of foods fostered significant steps in progress. A search for new spices provided both purpose and support for Marco Polo's and Columbus' discoveries.

One can scarcely imagine the extent of the influence of discoveries of new foods and the development of new food processes on society. During the past several decades the discovery of new foods, the improvement of other types of foods, and the development of more efficient methods of growing, harvesting, preserving, packing, and marketing have revolutionized farming, changing completely the patterns of life of a major part of our population. Mechanization on the farm and of the canning and freezing industries has resulted in important changes in the compositions and distributions of population and at times has led to the growth of factories in previously barren areas. Consider, also, the employment resulting from, and the many jobs related to, the distribution of these new food products, and the unemployment effects on those unable to adapt or incapable of performing the technical tasks now required.

Because of its dynamic meaning for the individual, food has frequently been used as a symbol in fostering major change. The Boston Tea Party was less concerned with tea than with taxation. Marie Antoinette's "Let them eat cake" was at once a taunt and threat to the revolutionists. The breadline and apple hawkers have been used to symbolize the Great Depression. Ghandi's fasts imparted deep symbolic meaning to his Hindu followers, uniting them in their struggle for independence.

Symbolic Uses of Food

Through the use of food, one may express good or evil, morality or guilt, status or punishment. The good mother is viewed as a good provider of food. She supplies plenty of milk for her infant and sets a good table for her husband and children. This causes a less adequate mother to have serious guilt feelings even though, as Harlow's research suggests, the warmth, comforting, and attention provided the child yield him far greater satisfaction than the provision of milk alone.[7]

Many of us have acquired special feelings regarding the use of food. We may feel guilty at throwing any away, having a sense of responsibility to eat every crumb. Yet at the same time we may follow a social practice of leaving a bit on the plate to tell the hostess we have been exceedingly well fed.

Discipline may be expressed by withholding food. The child may be sent to bed without any dessert, or even without his dinner as punishment for disobedience. The term "bread and water" has come to symbolize the punishment of a restricted prison diet. Special service or good performance may be rewarded by candy, a party dish, or "going out for dinner." One may express thanks or beg forgiveness for his errors also in such ways.

The relationships of food and status are many and immediately evident. Status is related to the kind and quality of food served, the difficulties involved in obtaining it, the place and time it is eaten, the manner of preparation and service, and even the form of dress and décor suitable to the occasion. Entertaining a distinguished guest may require considerable planning and preparation. On such an occasion one may "splurge" to obtain exotic foreign dishes served in an exclu-

sive setting with silver and crystal settings on linen cloths, with candle-
light and select music, with appetizers and wines served by costumed
waiters. Yet the food of the evening may be no more tasty than the
potluck served to one's friends.

Thus status demands status foods and status servings. But status
foods also confer status, and one may draw heavily on his income in
order to confer status on others or even on himself through what
Veblen has referred to as "conspicuous consumption."

What constitutes a status food depends not only on what it is, where
it comes from, and how and where it is prepared and served, but also
on when it is served. A food loses status when served a second time,
and may in fact even lose its identification as human food after the
first serving: "Thus the borderline between what is a leftover, to be
eaten at a less important meal, and what is waste—something to be
given to those who are considered members of a lower order, serv-
ants, members of another race, pets, domestic animals, farm animals,
or to be discarded altogether and buried, burned, or carried away by
the garbage man—is a shifting line. . . ."[8]

Other Social and Emotional Meanings

Foods serve many other social and emotional purposes in addition
to those mentioned. Certain coffee houses, restaurants, cafeterias, or
bars may be better known for their sociability than for their food.
They may serve as places to meet one's friends or make new friends or
to relax contentedly in the presence of much social activity. Lunch
hours and coffee breaks may provide opportunity for social inter-
change, shopping, or rest, with food itself being of secondary importance. At teas, coffees, and cocktail parties, liquids and party foods
are served as social stimulants rather than for their nutritive values.

Many tensions and value satisfactions may be involved in the preparation and serving of foods for special occasions, whether formal or
informal in tone. Such experiences may yield a high sense of creative
achievement, for the perfect serving, whether by chef, cook, or housewife, wins acclaim as a work of art and beauty from those sensitive
to quality standards of form, color, odor, taste, and consistency. Rare
indeed is the cook who is not sensitive to the response of his audience.

Eating may help one avoid boredom or loneliness or to escape from
the pressures of daily life. Through eating, one may subconsciously
seek to release tensions by substituting food for some unattainable

goal. He may eat to reward himself for achievement, or to console himself for failure and feelings of inadequacy. He may even satisfy needs for social attention by eating particular foods in a special way, by eating to excess or by abstaining from foods others about him enjoy. Under such circumstances, the meaning of food may be only remotely associated with matters of sustenance.

Implications

Food has so wide a range of personal and social meanings that one may have daily dealings with food and food matters with scarcely any awareness of its role as part of physical, biological, and physiological environment. Yet what has been said regarding the meanings of food might be applied likewise to other aspects of environment, to land, to air, to water, and the like.

It seems reasonable that in the planning of actions to initiate change, primary attention should be given to the definition of the dependent variable—what specific behavioral change is intended. Once the dependent variable is specifically defined, one is better able to make the value judgment regarding the necessity for change. Then, should change be desirable, attention can be given to independent variables—actions that may be expected to have a significant influence— and to other necessary and sufficient conditions that must be satisfied in order to affect the desired change.

The various meanings given to foods pose serious difficulties for those who would influence man's food practices. In planning for change in food behavior, one must first know what meanings the specific foods involved have for the person and society, what purposes they serve, with what customs, beliefs, and statuses they are associated, and to what behaviors they are bound.[9]

When food meanings are emotionally bound to social custom and religious practice, or when they are in other ways embedded in social structure, it may be particularly difficult to effect changes in food behavior through public education without involving key "gatekeepers" within the social order. Such gatekeepers, through their influence on factors that change or interpret meanings, can have great influence. They may revolutionize food practices by changing the form of preparation or packaging, as in the case of powdered milk, powdered eggs, dehydrated vegetables, or prepared food mixes containing milk, eggs, and vitamins. Since food form and meaning may be emotionally related, such changes in the form of food may influence meaning, and thus acceptability. Religious leaders, through adapting their interpretations of scripture to meet the needs of a growing society, have sanctioned many changes in social behavior. In this way, through time, the symbolic uses of food, as in the sacrament, have come to replace other forms of sacrifice. A more liberal interpretation of fasting requirements has resulted in less hardship for travelers, and for persons who are required, for health reasons, to eat special foods.

Clarity in planning any program of action or research requires a precise answer to the question: What is the dependent variable? Such a question cannot adequately be answered in nutrition education without first knowing what meaning food has in the particular situation of concern.

NOTES TO CHAPTER 10

1. *Webster's New International Dictionary of the English Language.* 3d ed. G. and C. Merriam, Springfield, Mass., 1961.

2. Mawson, C.O.S., editor, *Roget's Thesaurus of the English Language in Dictionary Form.* Rev. ed. Garden City Publishing Co., New York, 1939.

3. Prasad, B.G., "Some Common Beliefs and Customs in Relation to Health and Disease in Uttar Pradesh," *The Antiseptic,* vol. 58, May, 1961, pp. 229–230. Published in Madras, India.

4. Hasan, Khwaja Arif, "Social and Cultural Factors Affecting Health in a Rural Community." Unpublished doctoral dissertation, Department of Anthropology, Lucknow University, India, 1961.

5. Prasad, B.G., *op. cit.,* p. 230.

6. Lewin, Kurt, *Field Theory in Social Science: Selected Theoretical Papers.* Edited by Dorwin Cartwright. Harper and Bros., New York, 1951, p. 173. See especially Chapter 8, Psychological Ecology (initially published in 1943), and Chapter 9, Frontiers in Group Dynamics (first published in 1947). In these two papers Lewin describes some of the most creative ideas concerned with changing food habits. These papers are combined and reproduced with modification as: Lewin, Kurt, "Group Decision and Social Change" in Maccoby, Eleanor E., Theodore M. Newcomb, and Eugene L. Hartley, *Readings in Social Psychology,* 3d ed., Henry Holt and Co., New York, 1958, pp. 197–211.

7. Harlow, Harry F., "The Nature of Love," *American Psychologist,* vol. 13, December, 1958, pp. 673–685.

8. National Research Council, *Manual for the Study of Food Habits: Report of the Committee on Food Habits.* National Academy of Sciences, Bulletin 111, Washington, January, 1945, p. 36.

9. Cassel, John, "Social and Cultural Implications of Food and Food Habits" in Jaco, E. Gartly, editor, *Patients, Physicians, and Illness.* The Free Press, Glencoe, Ill., 1958, pp. 134–143.

Part Three

Perceiving the World

Perceiving the World

UNDERSTANDING MAN'S BEHAVIOR requires an understanding of the means whereby he acquires the knowledge necessary to act effectively in his physical and social environment. This process of acquiring and maintaining awareness of self and environment is called perception. It is the process whereby an individual acquires meaning of the things about him. It is a means he has for predicting effective actions to take in order to satisfy his growing needs and purposes or to avoid discomforts or danger.

How have we as adults gained our awareness of the world in which we live? Where have we obtained the awareness of the feelings we call pleasure and pain, the sense of safety and danger, of hope and fear which lead us to take actions of significance to our health? Where do we receive the ability to recognize early symptoms of illness, or to identify possible sources of assistance for ourselves and others?

Perception is one of the most remarkable of all life processes. It involves the harmonious functioning of emotional and motivational, sensory, and cognitive effort. A network of emotional and motivational forces provides the impetus to perceive, and lends guidance and direction to the process; contact with the internal or external world is provided by means of sensory receptors that gather the raw sensory data from which perceptions are formed; other cognitive functions such as reflection, imagination, memory, recall, and expectation are intimately concerned with the organization and meaning of the sensory data obtained.

Through this remarkable process of perception, each man develops for himself his own way of defining the world in which he lives. Each creates through experience a private world, a world of personal meanings which guide him in his choice of actions. How he responds on any health related matter will depend upon the meaning the specific situation has for him, and on the relative significance he assigns to alternatives perceived.

Chapter 11

Man's Knowledge Comes From Experience

ALL LIVING THINGS seem to have the capacity to maintain some awareness of their environments and to respond selectively to changes in environment. Even one-celled animals, like the amoeba, possess a sense of irritability that guides them in moving from irritating acids or "danger" toward food or "comfort."

How the newborn human infant acquires a knowledge of his physical and social environments, of the things to love, to hate, to want, or to fear, is one of the most fascinating yet elusive problems of all science. He is born with an elaborate and efficient sensory apparatus for obtaining sense data, although the physiological maturation of this sensory apparatus is not complete until some time after birth. These sense organs alone cannot, of course, provide awareness and understanding. Also necessary is an adequate nervous system that communicates the stimuli received from environment, and interprets and evaluates their significance. The nature of this process of perception will be discussed more fully in the following chapter.

Of immediate concern is the question: Where does knowledge come from? Philosophers, from Plato and Aristotle through the years to Whitehead and Dewey, have struggled for a rational answer to this question. Any effort at obtaining a unified and meaningful conception of the universe hinges on the quality of information available to man himself. The quality of the information from which philosophies and sciences are built can be no better than the source of the information available to the observer.

THE NATURE—NURTURE QUESTION

A primary question that has concerned philosophers and scientists alike may be stated as follows: Is man born with certain "innate ideas" implanted there through heredity or must each man through experience acquire his own knowledge of the external world? E. G. Boring, in his monumental treatise on *Sensation and Perception in the History of Experimental Psychology* notes that the controversy between these two points of view is centuries old. In the fifth century B.C., Heraclitus argued that sensations come to man "through the door of the senses," and after him a minority group of Sophists preceded Locke by 2,000 years in using the idea of a *tabula rasa* or blank wax-tablet to describe the mind on which experience becomes impressed.[1]

The question was brought sharply into focus by the seventeenth and eighteenth century philosophers Descartes, Hobbes, Locke, Berkeley, and Hume. Much of the research of modern experimental psychology is still being carried on within the general philosophical framework of this period of history. Many findings since that time tend in a general way to support the position taken by John Locke in his "Essay Concerning Human Understanding," published in 1690, that the mind is a *tabula rasa* on which experience is written, even though findings also suggest that the infant inherits certain tendencies for organizing sensory data. Locke's position was that the simple ideas such as whiteness or motion come through experience. The mind has a capacity for reflection, and through reflection these simple ideas may be combined in association to form more complex ideas such as the ideas of specific things—dogs, cats, elephants, and the like, or specific social concepts such as love, hate, or gratitude.

The question as to whether knowledge is innate or is acquired is one of great significance for public health. If it were true that health beliefs, knowledge, attitudes, and feelings were inherited, attempts to change these ideas through education would probably be futile. Current evidence tends to support a contrary view that such beliefs, attitudes, and feelings are acquired through experience, and since they are acquired through experience, are subject to change through experience.

It cannot be questioned that there are some innate or inborn factors in perception. Perceiving is only possible to the extent that our sense organs are adequate for perception and lack inherited defects. We cannot see colors if our eyes are so constructed that we are color blind. It may be physiologically impossible for us to hear certain specific ranges of tone. We may differ from one another significantly in our capacities for discriminating touch, and taste, and smell.

The psychologist E. R. Hilgard reminds us that some sensory preferences are present at birth although the question as to whether these preferences are truly inherited or result from prenatal influence remains debatable. "Studies of the sensory discriminations of newborn infants show, for example, a preference for the taste of sugar over quinine, a preference for moderate ranges of milk temperature over extremes of hot or cold. Avoidance responses are made to noxious stimuli by the fetal animal prior to birth. The preference for one kind of stimulation over another places a motivational or affective component at the very beginning of perceptual discrimination."[2]

Hilgard further suggests that it is possible that some patterns of stimuli are innately preferred over others. That is, it is possible that a hen raised in isolation might, under appropriate conditions, see an egg as something to be sat on. He cites the interesting study by Tinbergen, who prepared a silhouette of a bird which looked like a hawk when moved to the right and a harmless long-necked bird like a goose when moved to the left. When this figure was presented as a stimulus to birds in captivity, it created fright when moved in a hawk-like direction, but was not reacted to in the same way when moved in a gooselike direction.

While there is disagreement among psychologists working in this area, there is considerable acceptance of the idea that man is born with an innate tendency to organize his perceptions, but how he organizes them, what priority or value he places on one pattern of perception over another, and what meanings he gives to them seems to be acquired, rather than innate, behavior.

LEARNING TO PERCEIVE

Considerable attention has been given to the importance of adequate physical maturation of the sensory equipment of the individual as necessary before perception can occur. The sense organs are not available in fully matured form during infancy. Some sense organs are developed while the infant is in the fetal stage, but sight, on the other hand, develops after birth. It has long been recognized that perception cannot occur by means of a particular sense modality until the physical sense organ has matured sufficiently to respond to stimulation. Likewise, adequate responses cannot be made until sufficient physiological development occurs.

Less attention has been given, however, to the equally important matter of learning to perceive. The process of learning to perceive appears to be just as significant a factor in perception as maturation of the sense organs and response mechanisms. The sensory and neural apparatuses are useless to the individual for interpreting his environment and for predicting the specific types of actions to take until he has learned the meanings of the things about him.

It is difficult to look at the fairly integrated, purposefully moving, sensitive, and perceiving year-old child who seems to know what he wants and how to get it, and to realize that at birth he lacked the specific awarenesses and purposes. Yet, as Murphy has observed:

> There are a number of reasons for believing that perceptual responses in the newborn are relatively diffuse; sensory projection areas being poorly developed, sense impressions are massive, blurred, incompletely differentiated. There is a rough quantitative difference between a big impression and a little impression, but there are probably no clear distinctions between colors or tones, or even, apparently, between color as such and tone as such. The mind as a whole is a blur; there are no sharp outlines within it. A loud sound and a bright light combined may produce an effect something like that produced by a much brighter light or a much louder sound acting alone. The qualities of sensation which do not belong to any *one* sensory field, the "intersensory" effects are well marked in infancy. Though the sense organs are for the most part active in the newborn and are constantly funneling energy to the central nervous system, the latter is not differentiated enough to register them independently. But differentiation and learning go on rapidly.[3]

Research Difficulties

Scientists have long sought to determine whether the process of perception is one that is subject to maturation alone or whether learning through experience as well as maturation is required. Studies of chicks and of rats have suggested that both maturation and learning are involved. While maturation seems of great importance, the lack of use during the period of maturation seems to retard learning in chicks. The period of maturation for chicks is short, however, as is also the period required for learning. Controlled studies are very difficult to carry out under such circumstances. The attempt to differentiate maturation from learning during the brief period is filled with hazards.[4]

The interlocking relationship between maturation and learning places serious limitations on studies of the influence of experience on perception in infants, for experiments with infants that could possibly have negative effects cannot be tolerated in our society. It is not possible to keep a human infant blindfolded during infancy in order to study this process of maturation with regard to vision, nor can we readily substitute some other sense modality for the experimental studies. Hearing and touch perception, for example, seem to be fairly well developed in the fetus.

Insights from Observation

Attempts have been made to gain some insight regarding this problem by studying persons who have been blind or nearly blind when they first regain the capacity to see. Reports from such patients differ widely, for while they cannot see, they have varying degrees of sensitivity to light and dark. Then, too, they have been exploring with their other sense modalities during the period of blindness and verbal descriptions from others regarding the outside world have been available to them.

Some interesting information is nevertheless available from studies of persons who have restored vision. Senden reports that the man once blind may distinguish between a ball and a block as visual objects but does not know which is the ball and which is the block until he has handled them. He has to learn to relate his visual cues to the touch cues he has already been using.[5]

How much effective perception involves learning to ignore as well as learning to respond to the masses of stimuli coming from our environment is highlighted by the reaction of the man who recovered vision after three decades of blindness. "When I could see again, objects literally hurled themselves at me. One of the things a normal person knows from long habit is what *not* to look at. Things that don't matter, or that confuse, are simply shut out of their seeing minds. I had forgotten this, and tried to see everything at once; consequently I saw almost nothing."[6]

The evidence from patients who have recovered from blindness or near blindness is primarily clinical or introspective in nature without adequate controls to permit critical judgment of validity. Yet some interesting hypotheses evolve from the review of such reports. Riesen tells us that patients operated on at advanced ages for congenital cataracts "invariably report an immediate awareness of a change after a successful operation. They begin at once to distinguish differences in the parts of the visual field, although they cannot identify an object or describe its shape. After a few days practice they can name colors. From this point on progress is slow, often highly discouraging, and some patients never get beyond the ability to distinguish brightness and color. Others, over a period of months and even years, develop the ability to identify simple geometric figures, read letters and num-

bers and, in rare cases, to identify complex patterns such as words, outline drawings and faces."[7]

Studies of Chimpanzees

In 1942 Riesen began a series of experiments at the Yerkes Laboratories of Primate Biology in Orange Park, Florida, to see whether
he could, under control conditions, obtain more valid evidence on the
relationship between experience, practice, and vision. After three years
of preliminary explorations, a crucial experiment was under way.

> In 1945 the experimenters tried again. This time two newborn chim-
> panzee infants, a male and a female respectively named Snark and Al-
> falfa, were housed in a completely darkened room. During the first 16
> months the only light these infants experienced was an electric lamp
> turned on for intervals of 45 seconds several times daily for their rou-
> tine care and feeding. When they were first tested for visual perception
> at the age of 16 months, both chimpanzees showed extreme incompe-
> tence. Their reflex responses indicated that their eyes were sensitive to
> light—the pupils constricted; sudden changes of illumination startled
> the animals; they responded to a slowly waving flashlight with jerky
> pursuit movements of the eyes and side to side following motions of the
> head. But both chimpanzees failed to show any visual responses to
> complex patterns of light until after they had spent many hours in il-
> luminated surroundings. They did not respond to play objects or their
> feeding bottles unless these touched some part of the body. They did
> not blink at a threatening motion toward the face. When an object was
> advanced slowly toward the face, there was no reaction until the object
> actually touched the face, and then the animal gave a startled jump.[8]

The failure of these animals to perceive in an orderly way other
than light and dark before they had had many hours of experience is a
finding of great significance. Further study with other newborn chimpanzees under control conditions have supported these findings. A
control animal which was given one and one-half hours of patterned
daylight each day, having the opportunity to view the edges of his
crib and movements of his own body and persons moving about the
room, acquired normal vision ability. Considerable individual differences were found among other experimental animals:

> Kora did not develop the blink response to a moving object until 6
> days after her removal from darkness, and Debi not until 15 days. It
> took Kora 13 days and Debi 30 days to acquire the ability to pursue a
> moving person with the eyes, and they did this by a series of refixations
> instead of following smoothly as normal animals of comparable age do;
> it took Kora 20 days and Debi 16 days to pursue visually a moving

feeding bottle; Kora 13 days and Debi 30 days to fixate the image of a stationary person.[9]

In yet another experiment reported by Riesen, a chimpanzee, Faik, was raised in normal light in the laboratory nursery until the age of seven months and had achieved an excellent use of vision, but was then kept until the age of twenty-four months in the dark room. When returned to daylight he had lost all ability to use vision in his interplay with the environment; he no longer recognized the bottle, and failed to look at objects or persons, stationary or moving—his recovery of vision was slow and only partial.

These chimpanzee studies have established several fundamental points. They show that newborn animals, and older infants that have been kept in darkness for a time, exhibit visual reflexes when they are first subjected to light. Some responses that bear a close resemblance to reflex behavior, such as blinking at something rapidly approaching the face, become automatic only after considerable practice. Visual pursuit of moving objects, the coordination of the two eyes and convergent fixation, and the first recognition of objects come only after many hours or weeks of experience in use of the eyes. It takes the chimpanzee hundreds of hours of active utilization of the eyes to develop its vision to the stage where it can adequately guide locomotion and complex manipulations. The findings in the cases of two subjects that were kept in darkness for long periods indicate that the postponement of light exposure for too long can result in making the development of normal visual mechanisms extremely difficult if not impossible.[10]

Studies like these could not be carried out on human beings without great risk of serious damage to the individual. Chimpanzees were chosen for the experiments because, like man, their behavior is dominated by vision to a good extent and because their maturation is somewhat like man's. They are intelligent and tractable animals and resemble humans in much of their social as well as their intellectual behavior.

In the absence of contrary evidence, the findings of these experiments suggest that man, too, learns to perceive and that learning to perceive is part of the initial socialization process through which man grows. Perception seems to involve more than having adequate neurosensory mechanisms. It involves also more than the physiological maturation of these mechanisms. A psychological and sociological maturation in the sense of learning external relationships, and giving them meaning, seems to be a part of the process of learning to perceive.

POSSIBLE IMPLICATIONS

The implications for public health of findings which tend to support the conclusion that man's knowledge is derived from experience have scarcely been explored. To the extent that facts, ideas, beliefs, and attitudes have an experiential basis, we may view them as potentially subject to change by new or different experience. Meanwhile, all deserve the same critical examination and evaluation that we give to other conclusions derived from experience. This applies to our own facts, ideas, beliefs, and attitudes as well as to those of other groups of people whom we think we ought to change.

Paul suggests that "an inner layer of culture . . . mediates between man and world about him . . . and begins to shape his perceptions long before he stops to question whether his is the only way of viewing things."[11] The case studies in his book describe public reactions to health programs carried out in communities in Canada, Brazil, Peru, Chile, Guatemala, Mexico, Puerto Rico, South Africa (with the Zulus), rural Rajasthan and also Kishan Garhi in India, Thailand, China, the Pacific island of Yap, as well as in Boston, Colorado, and Alabama. The social scientists who prepared these research studies report many illustrations of how meanings prescribed by culture have influenced public health actions.

A critical look at some of these health-related meanings in our own and other cultures may suggest the need for significant modifications in some public health programs and approaches. From such analysis we may learn how and why groups differ in their definitions of food and waste, cleanliness and filth, preventive health action and contamination.

Perception of Pain and Physiological Changes

Individual and group differences in pain perception have long been of interest to psychologists. There is evidence that people do differ in their perceptions and judgments regarding pain and also in their responses to pain. Furthermore, the same individual may react to pain differently, depending on the physical or social circumstances in which the pain experience is encountered. Edwards, in summarizing research on this topic, calls attention to the difficulties of establishing definitions of pain adequate for purposes of comparative research due to the subjective nature of this experience.[12]

In studying cultural factors in response to pain, Zborowski found significant differences between Jewish and Italian respondents in their attitudes toward pain. He noted that Italian patients tended to place greater emphasis on the pain experience itself, whereas Jewish patients were more concerned with the meaning of the pain and its significance for health, welfare, and family. Whether these are true Italian-Jewish differences or social class differences might be questioned. The findings do suggest, however, that persons with different sociocultural backgrounds differ in responses to pain and in the meanings ascribed to it.[13]

Cantril and Livingston, drawing on experimental studies of animals and from human observation, note that past experiences tend to condition sensory input so that we learn to attend to inputs of significance and to ignore those of lesser significance. They suggest that such blocking may occur before the impulse patterns reach perceptual levels.[14] Does this occur with regard to bodily states on pain? Do we learn in childhood to ignore certain kinesthetic sensations that might help to warn us of potentially malignant changes? If so, how can perceptual alertness be reawakened?

There is experimental evidence that individuals differ considerably in the relative attention they give to stimuli arising within their own bodies as compared with stimuli arising in the surrounding environment.[15] Such a finding could have significance for early case-finding of bodily changes that may be potentially dangerous for the individual.

By reason of early life experience, some persons may become aware of, and learn to discriminate between, stimuli others may not have encountered. They may also learn to discriminate in more precise ways than others, or to place different meanings upon similar stimuli. Such experientially based differences in perception could have high health significance. Are some persons more sensitive than others to certain types of physical or physiological change? Can some detect chronic malignancies earlier than others? Does this contribute to differences in feelings of illness or well being?

Can Perceptual Abilities Be Changed?

People vary greatly in their abilities to communicate with others in the exchange of knowledge, ideas, feelings, and emotions. Some demonstrate unusual abilities in verbal or other formal means of communication; others are unusually sensitive to the feelings and emotions communicated through nonverbal cues. These different abilities are highly valued in many health pursuits. To what extent do they reflect differences in early experience? To what degree are they teachable?

Human differences in early access to knowledge and in the opportunities to develop fully the faculties of perception and discrimination essential for acquiring, assessing, and employing knowledge seem to a striking extent to be culturally based. But to say they are culturally based is to say they are humanly based. As Lynd reminds us, "We watch culture change and say that 'it changes.' But culture does not 'work,' 'move,' 'change,' but is worked, is moved, is changed. It is *people* who do things, and when their habits and impulses cease to carry an institutional folkway, that bit of culture disappears."[16]

NOTES TO CHAPTER 11

1. Boring, Edwin G., *Sensation and Perception in the History of Experimental Psychology*. Appleton-Century-Crofts, Inc., New York, 1942, p. 4.

2. Hilgard, Ernest R., "The Role of Learning in Perception" in Blake, Robert R., and Glenn V. Ramsey, editors, *Perception: An Approach to Personality*. Ronald Press Co., New York, 1951, p. 96.

3. Murphy, Gardner, *Personality: A Biosocial Approach to Origins and Structure*. Harper and Bros., New York, 1947, pp. 333–334.

4. Solley, Charles M., and Gardner Murphy, *Development of the Perceptual World*. Basic Books, New York, 1960, pp. 14–35, 125–146.

5. Senden, M. von, as reported by Hilgard, Ernest R., "The Role of Learning in Perception" in Blake, Robert R., and Glenn V. Ramsey, editors, *op. cit.*, p. 107.

6. Muenzinger, Karl F., *Psychology: The Science of Behavior*. The World Press, Denver, 1939, pp. 55–56.

7. Riesen, Austin H., "Arrested Vision," *Scientific American,* vol. 183, July, 1950, pp. 16–17.

8. *Ibid.,* p. 17.

9. *Ibid.,* p. 18.

10. *Ibid.,* p. 19.

11. Paul, Benjamin D., editor, *Health, Culture, and Community: Case Studies of Public Reactions to Health Programs*. Russell Sage Foundation, New York, 1955, p. 467.

12. Edwards, Ward, "Recent Research on Pain Perception," *Psychological Bulletin,* vol. 47, November, 1950, pp. 449–474.

13. Zborowski, Mark, "Cultural Components in Response to Pain," *Journal of Social Issues,* vol. 8, no. 4, 1952, p. 4.

14. Cantril, Hadley, and William K. Livingston, "The Concept of Transaction in Psychology and Neurology," *Journal of Individual Psychology,* vol. 19, no. 1, 1963, pp. 3–16.

15. Rudin, Stanley A., and Ross Stagner, "Figure-Ground Phenomena in the Perception of Physical and Social Stimuli," *Journal of Psychology,* vol. 45, 1958, pp. 213–225.

16. Lynd, Robert S., *Knowledge for What?* Princeton University Press, Princeton, N.J., 1946, p. 38.

Chapter 12

The Function and Process of Perception

MAN'S PERCEPTUAL MECHANISMS are his sole means for maintaining an awareness of himself, other people, and other things. They serve him in filtering out of environment things that appear to be of immediate or potential significance to him, organizing them in meaningful ways, and bringing them into attention so that they may be used in guiding future actions.

The significance of the relationship of perception to future action has been a focus of research in psychological laboratories for more than a century. For a quarter-century it has also challenged those who have extended their laboratories into the human community. Volumes of their exciting discoveries may be found in libraries; yet so intricate is the process of perception that even today many fundamental questions remain unanswered.[1]

This process of perception cannot be directly observed. Rather, it is one of the many life processes that are inferred from observation. It is assumed to take place if the individual responds when a stimulus is presented to a sense organ—an eye, ear, taste bud, hair follicle, and so on—and fails to respond when the stimulus is not presented. The process of perception may in this way be distinguished from related "knowing" processes of memory, reflection, imagination, thinking, or dreaming. The need for a stimulus to be present distinguishes perception also from hallucination.

PERCEPTIONS GUIDE ACTIONS

Man tends to act in terms of what he knows, expects, or hopes that action to yield; how man behaves with respect to any situation tends to be in accord with how he perceives or defines that situation. What he does not perceive does not exist for him insofar as he personally

159

is concerned. It makes no difference how the situation may be defined by other—even more competent—observers. This applies whether the situation involves man's physical environment, his biological environment, his social environment, or his physiological, psychological, and social self. Persons concerned with influencing man's health behavior, with eliciting his support and participation in community action, or with gaining an understanding of his problems, concerns, fears, hopes, or expectations therefore need, above all else, to understand how man perceives the world about him.

While an individual's perceptions are meldings of past experiences with present sensations, they are oriented toward the future, for man's perceptions serve the purpose of providing him "with best estimates" regarding future happenings. Man tends to act on his expectations of what *will be* rather than what *has been* or what *seems to be* at present. In hitting a baseball, for example, he reaches out where he expects the ball to be when his bat is in motion, not where he sees the ball when he starts to swing; in passing a football, he passes to the position he expects the runner to reach while the ball is in transit.[2]

In this process of maintaining an awareness of what is significant in the world about him, man draws heavily upon what is familiar. Expectations grow out of experience. Since people vary so widely in the personal and group experiences that guide expectations, it is not surprising that the meanings they give to health-related events also vary in many seemingly unpredictable ways.

Failure in public health efforts may, at times, rest upon differences in the meanings given to health events by professional and lay persons. Public and professional definitions of health status and of illness differ considerably, particularly with respect to conditions which can first be detected by means of x-rays, blood tests, urinalyses, and other technical methods. Persons identified as sick on the basis of evidence obtained by such technical means may perceive themselves as being in good health. Such persons cannot be expected to seek or accept treatment until their self-perceptions have undergone change. Even a person with a chronic pain may not perceive himself as needing treatment if he has learned to accept his condition as "normal" for himself, or if others in his group have a condition similar to his own. Severe visual or auditory deficiencies may go unnoticed for years when they occur slowly, so that an individual does not perceive any change in his physical condition.

One can readily identify many ways in which a person's expectations regarding the course of health events perceived—their future implications—may influence health actions. One should not expect a person to seek immunization, whatever disease is being highlighted by the health program, if he perceives himself as healthy and already immune to the infection. Nor should one expect him to recognize the need for some nutritional supplement that works on the body in ways he does not understand or appreciate, and shows no immediate overt evidence of effect. A woman with a small lump on the breast may not seek consultation or medical aid if she perceives this as an unchanging part of her anatomy. Should she perceive growth or change in the symptom, this may influence her estimate regarding the future significance of the lump, and lead her to seek attention quickly.[3] What is important to action here seems to be perceived change; growths that are not perceived will be ignored. On the other hand, a woman who examines her breasts for the first time and observes "lumps" may interpret these as new and sufficiently threatening to be alerted to action even though what is present may be part of the normal breast structure.[4] In order to judge change, it is necessary first that she have some valid basis for judging what is normal.

PERCEPTION AS A DYNAMIC SELECTIVE PROCESS

Current evidence suggests that perception is a learned, active, motivated process. What is perceived tends to be governed by personal interests, wants, concerns, anxieties, fears, hopes, and expectations—motivating forces that are acquired through experience. As Cantril has expressed this principle, "what we are aware of is not determined entirely by the nature of what is out there or by our sensory processes . . . the assumptions we bring from past experience, because they have generally proved reliable, are involved in every perception we have."[5]

Thus while individuals are guided in their actions by their perceptions, they do not directly, fully, and accurately perceive the world about them with its meanings, but perceive selectively and purposefully, giving individual and group meanings to things in terms of their individual and group significances. The perceptual mechanisms of each person are not only purposeful for him, but function for him in a unique, individualized way.

Any number of factors may lead the perceiving individual to give this or that specific meaning to a given perceptual event. Of all these factors, however, the "psychological set" he brings with him to the situation deserves primary consideration. We may all see more social factors influencing the communication process in a public health clinic if we are alert. The patient who is set to expect positive effects from treatment may report progress even if given a placebo. The staff member who is set to expect criticism may perceive such criticism even in the friendly inquiry of his health officer.

That even the most highly skilled health professional may be misguided by his assumptions is well illustrated by an experience reported by Johnson in the interesting paper, "Seeing's Believing."

> A child with a persistent cough had its throat x-rayed for diagnosis. The radiologist reported that there was nothing in the radiograph to show why the child was coughing. The cough persisted, and the child returned to have another radiograph taken. This time the shadow of a button was seen in the throat region; the button was removed and the child stopped coughing. When the first radiograph was re-examined the shadow of the button was seen there too, but it had been explained away by the radiologist, who had supposed that the child had been x-rayed with its vest on. The radiologist had failed to see the significance of the button for the problem in hand—diagnosis of the cause of the cough—because another explanation for its presence seemed more probable. After all most people wear their buttons outside and not inside their throats.[6]

Perceptions are so intimately knit to the assumptions we have built out of personal experience that it is most difficult to remove oneself from one's own setting sufficiently to view this relationship with objectivity. In this instance it takes greater wisdom and detachment to learn from one's own experience than from the experience of others. When we view the behaviors of persons who have grown up in environments far removed from our own, the relationship of experience, assumption, and perception comes more sharply into focus.

PERCEIVING CONSTANCY AND STABILITY

It is this transactional bond between experiences, assumptions, and perceptions that yields man his sense of constancy regarding his own identity and that of the world about him. In some strange, but marvelous way, intricate processes relate each perception to memory traces of past experience to provide a sense of continuity in the experiencing of time, space, movement, and action. Past events merge with those of the present to yield expectations regarding the future. Thus are born the only cues man has for drawing inferences about the potential values or dangers resting in any actions he may consider.

It is through his perceptions that man is able to maintain a sense of dynamic stability in an ever-changing physical and social world. Through cues reaching him by many channels he gains a sense of assurance that the things he has just seen and felt remain to be seen or felt again by someone else, if not by himself. To him they are more than fleeting shadows which pass out of the world the second they are no longer observed. He becomes certain the landscape is continuous even though he is never able to perceive all of it at once. He becomes confident that there was a yesterday and that there will be a tomorrow even though he can experience time directly only second by second.

Constancy in Perceiving Things

Perceiving is a continuous function of the organism. The eye, like a movie camera, provides a series of glimpses of a changing world. In a general way, one must agree with Murphy that:

> Most stimulus objects deliver their energies to the organism in patterns which change from moment to moment. The size, shape, and color of a mahogany table and the inflection and timbre of the mother's distant voice are not fixed entities; in such a multiple stimulus the phases constantly change, so that their organization is perpetually on the march. For all that, the child learns to know the table and his mother's voice. This is a problem of "constancy." One finds constancy in the thing, or the person, or the law, though nothing ever recurs in quite the same form.[7]

Rather than many worlds of many types and forms appearing and disappearing in haphazard fashion, each person tends to perceive one world with himself as center. So much is this so that he may tend to sense himself as different and apart from all else—the core about which things of varying significance move and interact. He speaks of "me and my environment" rather than "me as part of my environment."

Life is perceived as ever in flux. The sense of constancy or stability man perceives in the world about him is a product of the capacity he has for maintaining a sense of identity regarding things that are ever changing and sending different patterns of stimuli to his sense receptors. The individual learns through experience that a particular group of light waves organized in a particular way is identified as a "chair" in his culture. He must learn, too, that a wide range of other groups of stimuli also connote "chair," for the pattern of light waves reaching his retina changes as he moves nearby or further away, as he looks from the top, the bottom, or the side; as the "chair" is moved from light into shadow, tilted or raised, turned or inverted, and so on.

What applies to the perception of physical objects applies to words also, for they too are organized groups of light waves or sound waves to which the perceiver gives meaning. Whether written or spoken, any particular word presents a somewhat different pattern of light or sound waves each time it is received by the sense organs. Man must learn to impart common meanings whether a word is spoken softly and scarcely heard, or expressed in a shout; whether the sound arrives at the ears from right or left side, above or below, from front or back, thus presenting different patterns of sound waves to each ear.

Constancy in Perceiving Persons

By means of his perceptions, man gains a sense of stability or constancy with respect to other persons and things as well as to time and space. He learns to identify a friend whether he is nearby and creates a large image on the retina, or so far away that the size of the image is minute. He recognizes him in bright light or in shadow, from front or side, standing or sitting, moving or sprawled. He knows him by the sound of his voice, or by the presence of some familiar mannerism such as a cough or a sniffle. In some miraculous way he resolves gross discrepancies from among different images received and perceives his friend as he assumes or expects him to be, yet is never conscious of the intricate processes involved.

Nor need one see all of his friend in order to perceive his total presence. As the friend sits behind a desk one may only see his upper torso, yet perceive him as a whole. The torso is not cut off by the desk. His hand, with a familiar ring, may be all that is necessary to identify him as he stands beyond the corner. Yet when the hand is perceived it is not detached from the body. While seeing only one side of him one infers three dimensions without effort or hesitation. Though the perceptions are received as single repeated images, one perceives him as a living, moving being.

Ignoring Constant Stimulation

The perceptual processes serve man as a selective filter through which what is changing or of potential significance in the world about him is brought into meaningful focus and what is stable, unchanging, or dependable is omitted from conscious awareness. This permits him to be more sensitive and aware of that which has greater potential for effective action.

He wears clothing without being sensitive to the pressures unless he becomes uncomfortable and change is indicated. He sits in the lecture without being aware of the pressures of sitting until he feels weary. He walks about the room without either consciously observing or touching tables, chairs, or other things as long as they remain in their expected positions. As he moves over familiar ground he does not measure his steps; he may bend to avoid bumping a familiar branch or corner, yet may stumble on an obvious article that is out of place. When he eats, he holds the knife, fork, and glass without being aware of the pressure or the weight, yet becomes immediately alert if anything begins to slip or spill. He becomes attuned to familiar sounds or noises, yet responds to a whisper that might have significance for him. A tired young mother will sleep through the din of a neighboring radio but respond at once to an unfamiliar movement in the crib.

GIVING MEANING TO ENVIRONMENT

Man's search for meaning in his environment involves, then, in good part, giving meaning to this environment; and this process of giving meanings tends to be directed by the significance that specific events have for him. Anything that has no personal significance may not be attended at all; anything that has a constant significance and little immediate urgency may be seen but ignored; anything that has primary urgency in terms of personal purpose or meaning tends to stand out as the central theme or figure against the background of the individual's reality world.

The individual has many sensory mechanisms at his disposal for evaluating and maintaining awareness of the constantly changing pattern of this reality world. While sight and hearing are often considered to be his most efficient sensory mechanisms, he also obtains information by means of tasting, smelling, touching, feeling temperatures and pressures, and various kinesthetic sensations. Each of these means has the potential for providing many types of information. By means of sight alone, for example, man may learn to perceive depth, distance, breadth, width, height, form, illumination, color, shadow, texture qualities, solidity, location, movement, and many other things.[8]

The receptors located in man's sense organs cannot reach out and *directly* sense and identify the objects to which they are exposed. They cannot provide man with *direct* information regarding the universe. Rather, they are dependent on information brought to them by a wide array of light wave particles, pressures, heat and cold waves, and chemical atoms—minute stimuli—which continually bombard the various sense receptors. Man's sense organs, like marvelous radar systems, select from these masses of indirect data those that may have potential significance and organize them into meaningful wholes that help him predict the significance of alternative action possibilities.

During any specific moment of life, man's sense organs are bombarded by a wide array of these stimulus particles carried by light and sound waves, heat waves, cold waves, pressures, and chemical atoms. It would be physically and mentally impossible for anyone to be consciously aware of each and every one of the minute stimuli reaching the sense organs, much less pay attention to them and react accordingly. Fortunately, this is not necessary. Man learns through experience to organize these masses of stimuli into meaningful wholes that make sense to him and have meaning for him—wholes that help him decide how to act.

What determines how these masses of particles carried by light waves, sound waves, heat waves, and other stimuli are organized into meaningful wholes? What is the underlying process that results in some of these groups of stimuli being given prominent position in perception while others remain in the background or are ignored? What determines "the figure" and what determines "the ground" in any perception?

Cantril has suggested:

> What makes up our environment is as meaningless as the cryptograms of an undeciphered language until we can make sense out of it. The impingements with which our sense organs are constantly bombarding us take on the meaning and significance they do only in terms of our own purposive behavior. A happening becomes an event for us only when *we* assign it some importance or consequence: we do not merely react in mechanical fashion to objects, people, or the goings-on in the world because they have some fixed characteristics in their own right.[9]

THE PERCEPTUAL PROCESS

The process of perception is a most complex and rapid one. Even though understanding of this process has received high priority in the

TABLE 2. THE INDIRECT NATURE OF THE PERCEPTUAL PROCESS

The perceiving individual from his special vantage point influenced by:	Receives sensory data from environment by means of:	Sensory data reach his sense organs by means of:	Which may be given off concurrently by many sources:
Genetically based tendencies to organize sensations	Seeing	Sight wave particles	Cat
	Hearing	Sound wave particles	Fire
The quality of his sensory equipment	Tasting	Chemical particles	Speaker
	Smelling	Chemical particles	Sizzling steak
Neural traces of experience	Touching	Pressures	
Values	Feeling	Pressures, Tensions, Vibrations	
Wants	Heat		
Concerns	Cold		
Fears	Pain		
Hopes	Tension		
Assumptions	Movement		
Expectations			

history of science and philosophy, the gaps in understanding remain great. So many intimately interlocked events occur within a split second of time that no one has as yet been able to establish empirically the exact steps in the process, nor the order in which these steps occur. Science and logic together provide only a general description of the many happenings during that split second.

It is apparent that the perceiving individual must first scan the environment to make a preliminary determination of what there is "out there" to perceive, what there is to see, to hear, to feel, or to sense. Yet how this scanning takes place puzzles philosophers and scientists alike. The scanning itself involves identification of things, hence perception. Many decisions are made during this scanning process, but these are not conscious decisions. A person is not aware of the choices he makes. Rather, in seeing he selects and gains awareness of things. But how does the individual know which of many competing masses of stimuli he should be aware of? How does he know which of his many sense modalities deserves primary attention? How does he know which of many alternative interpretations will have the greatest significance for him?

This preliminary scanning of the environment involves all the sensory receptors available to the organism, for the perceiver must make choices between masses of stimuli presenting themselves to the eyes, ears, nose, mouth, or any part of the body bearing sense organs, and in some way determine what meanings to attach to them, which to give primary attention, and which to ignore. While maintaining an awareness of change in the external environment he must also maintain sensitivity to competing stimuli coming from within himself and impinging on one or another of the various sense organs of his body.

In some mysterious way memory traces bring value and purpose into this transaction. Expectation regarding future events helps to give meaning to the immediate event. Yet this entire transaction takes place in so brief a time it has never been adequately measured nor precisely described. So elusive a transaction is it, that no one has been able to isolate it within an experimental situation or to bring it into conscious awareness so that it may better be understood.

Components of the Perceptual Process

Solley and Murphy, in their *Development of the Perceptual World,* employ the following diagram to show the relationship between the major components in this complex process. They advise that "the arrows indicate the major transitions between expectancy, attending, reception, trial-and-check, autonomic and proprioceptive arousal, and the final structured percept. Admittedly, the perceptual process, the process of structuring stimulation, does not consist of way stations that are rigidly separated from one another. There is overlapping and articulation between the subprocesses, and many more arrows could be drawn. Indeed, we find it convenient to define perception as the structuring of stimulation, and percepts vary considerably in structuredness."[10]

It must be recognized, of course, that a multitude of such linear units, involving different sense organs and receptors, are going on simultaneously within the perceiving individual. Motivational, experiential, and other factors may influence the nature and quality of perception at any point along the pathway.

Steps in Acquiring Meaning

Accordingly, we derive by logical analysis some of the primary phases or steps involved in this effort of an individual after meaning. These are steps of which he may be completely unaware, yet they are steps which must be completed before the individual has acquired meaning regarding his environment:

Scanning the environment,

Searching for meaning,

Organizing the sense data indirectly received by the sense receptors into figure and ground and into form and shape,

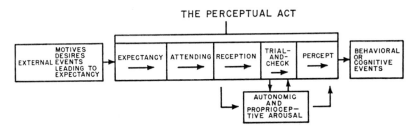

FIGURE 6. Diagrammatic Schematization of the Perceptual Act

SOURCE: Solley, Charles M., and Gardner Murphy, *Development of the Perceptual World*. Basic Books, New York, 1960, p. 25. Reproduced with permission of the publisher.

Determining what to attend to and what to ignore,

Determining degrees of significance between alternative possible meanings,

Deciding to which of many sense modalities to give primary attention,

Integrating with memory traces of past experience,

Orienting in terms of expectations,

Predicting the action that offers the highest probability of success for the individual.

It should be emphasized that the steps described are not distinct, clearly discernible, and ordered as outlined. Rather than clearly discernible steps, there seems to be a flow process in which all steps are included just as there is a flow in the content perceived rather than a series of distinctly different pictures, sounds, or chemical stimuli.

The perceiving individual himself tends to be unaware of the complexities of the process required in order to obtain meaning from environment. For him, the process of perceiving is effortless and continuous. The steps concerned tend to be unconsciously taken without any awareness on his part, other than an awareness of the final result of the process, of the meanings attached to events.

THE EFFICIENCY OF THE SENSE ORGANS

Even though complex in their manner of functioning, the sensory and perceptual mechanisms available to man are remarkably efficient; so efficient, in fact, that it is most difficult to appreciate that the information man gains through them is not obtained by means of direct experience. One can but marvel that the precision with which the eye can discriminate objects in the environment, whether massive as a forest or delicate as the pollen of a rose, is not the result of direct contact between these objects and the sensory organs in the eye. Neither the sounds created by a distant thunder nor the words whispered at the elbow directly reach the sense organs that report sound, for the only data directly available to the sense organs are minute waves: light waves, sound waves, pressures, chemicals, hot and cold waves, and so forth. It is within the sensory organs that the data drawn from these light waves, sound waves, pressures, and chemicals are transferred into biological energy within the nervous system, and it is within the minds of men that these biological energies are grouped, organized, and given symbolic meaning.

In discussing the precision and selectivity of perception, Allport emphasizes that both are essential for effective functioning.

The fact that we perceive the world around us fairly accurately is due to the evolution of sensory and brain processes well tuned to outer reality. Eyes perceive color, line and shape with exquisite fineness; ears register accurately a wide range of air vibrations. The skin, less perfect in sensitiveness, still mediates evidence of shape and the finer gradations of temperature. The reason for this mirroring ability is undoubtedly its "functional usefulness." The organism has a better chance of survival if the sensory equipment is finally accurate. In a recent book, Woodworth rightly maintains that the first and foremost motive in life is man's pervasive need to handle his world competently. For Woodworth the process of perception is the fundamental dynamism serving man's fundamental motive.

Yet by following the same line of reasoning we can say the perceptual process must likewise depart from true mirroring in order to be of maximum use to us. Not every tree in the forest comes into perceptual focus, but only the one we are chopping. Not every object on the dinner table is perceived with clarity, but only the bite we are about to put into our mouths. If you hear a babble of vague conversation how quickly *your* name stands out if it is mentioned. Selective perception is as much a functional necessity as is veridical perception.[11]

FACTORS CONTRIBUTING TO ERROR

The broad implications for public health practice of the purposeful and selective nature of perception will receive frequent attention in the pages following. At this point, it may be well to consider other special characteristics of the perceiving individual that may contribute to errors of public health significance.

Sensory Factors

As already mentioned in Part One of this book, the sensory organs necessary for perception must be present and adequate for the particular setting if adequate perception is to occur. To speak softly to one who is deaf, or to show written instructions to those unable to make critical visual discriminations, fosters not only frustration but also distortion and confusion. Errors resulting from partial hearing or seeing may exceed in significance no communication at all if either subject fails to realize that distortions are occurring.

A host of factors other than native inadequacy may contribute to error in the functioning of sensory mechanisms. Illness or injury, the use of drugs or alcohol, stress resulting from fear, anxiety, excitement, or other factors deserve mention. The body chemistry, which may be influenced by diet, as in the case of vitamin A deficiency, or occupational conditions such as may lead to oxygen imbalance, for example, may seriously impair sensory reception. Often overlooked is the time required for sense modalities to adapt to new situations before efficient perception can take place. Dark adaptation normally requires more than twenty minutes. During this period of adaptation errors in perception may result in confusion and accident.[12]

Constant stimulation of a sense modality over a long period of time often results in a decrease in alertness. The long-distance driver in a steady stream of traffic tends to become adapted to the conditions of fast driving. Should he relax his attention momentarily, he may be unprepared to deal with sudden changes in the conditions of traffic. The use of "rumble strips," constructed by using alternate sections of coarse and rough cement on the freeway at the approaches to hazardous intersections or curves, has been found to be an effective way of jarring the complacent driver into alertness. Where such techniques have been employed, they have led to a decrease in accidents.[13]

Influence of Ego-Defense Mechanisms

While error in perception and response may be fostered by conditions of fatigue, illness, distraction, or excitement, these factors, Freud reminds us, do not account for the type or kind of distortions made. Freud draws our attention to the purposeful nature of psychological errors of all types, noting that they contribute in many ways to ego satisfaction or ego defense.[14]

Freud and his followers have also drawn attention to a number of psychological mechanisms that individuals employ, possibly in subconscious ways, to deal with threats to the ego. These may serve the individual by helping him to cope, often in unrealistic ways, with information of a threatening or unsatisfying type.

These defense mechanisms have received much attention elsewhere, and are but mentioned here to alert the reader to some of the dynamic ways in which perceptions can be distorted even without the conscious awareness of the perceiver. Responses of individuals on health matters, particularly when personal concern may be high, need to be interpreted with great caution. A person may subconsciously repress by

RUMBLE STRIP EXPERIMENTS
SOUTH OF RODEO, CALIFORNIA

FIGURE 7. Rumble Strip Experiments—South of Rodeo, California

Six accidents occurred at this hazardous intersection within four months after this road was opened. The stop sign was obscured by the embankment of the curve. Not a single accident caused by nonobservance of the stop sign took place during the year following installation of the rumble strips. Reproduced with permission of the California Research Corporation, Richmond, California

forgetting or, through the mechanism of denial, even fail to perceive information of high personal threat. He may deceive himself as well as others by the rationalization of evidence suggesting weakness, failure, or possibly symptoms of illness. He may employ the mechanism of projection to blame other persons or things for weakness, error, or unsocial behavior for which he himself is justly responsible. When his behavior is blocked or frustrated, he may, by the displacement mechanism, transfer his feelings of aggression or hostility to innocent or defenseless persons or things. Thus the frustrated husband may suppress his feelings of hostility toward superiors and colleagues and subconsciously vent his pentup emotion in aggressive response to minor family annoyances.[15]

It is not always possible to recognize the presence of defense mechanisms that influence perceptual behavior. Yet a wealth of clinical and some research evidence suggests they are frequently employed, particularly when communications involve areas of insecurity. When significant decisions hinge on reported evidence, validation of information by other means may be warranted.

Personality Factors

Factors relating to personality style also influence the perceptual process. Allport, in summarizing current research evidence, notes:

> A person who is insecure, self-distrustful, who feels threatened by life or otherwise inadequate, tends to have a congruent cognitive style which is rigid, field-bound, concrete, acquiescent. By contrast, the more active, able, secure, relaxed individual is able to perceive and think in channels that are flexible and on the whole better adapted to the objective demands of the situation he finds himself in.[16]

Health leaders will find the insecure, dependent person Allport first describes more responsive to the communications of authority, willing to listen, and anxious to please. The secure, independent person, on the other hand, will tend to be more selective in what he attends, more critically evaluative of the perceptual field, and possibly even reject authoritative pressures while making his own decisions. While health officials might feel more comfortable communicating with the dependent-receptive individual, the long-range success of their programs may rest upon the decisions of those independent and secure. There is ever a danger that dependency becomes chronic. Lasting effects may depend on the initiative of others in developing the program.

Yerushalmy, in his classical studies on observer error in the reading of x-rays used in screening programs for tuberculosis, draws attention both to the seriousness of such errors and to the individual differences among observers in making such errors.[17] He notes: "On the average, a competent and experienced physician misses in a single reading as many as 32.2 per cent of the 'positive' films and provides 'false positive' diagnoses on 1.7 per cent of the negative films."[18] By increasing readers this error may be reduced. However, the problems of value judgments and their significance for the well being of the individual and society still play an important role in this mass procedure. Failure to recall a subject for more intensive diagnosis may leave a person with active tuberculosis undetected in the population. Dual reading nearly doubles the number of false positive diagnoses.[19] To draw these persons in for clinical follow-up may subject many persons "to trouble, expense and psychological trauma associated with false diagnosis."[20]

It is of interest that the errors in reading that Yerushalmy describes are of both random and systematic types. Physicians and other readers differ systematically in recognizing specific types of deficiencies, in failure to recognize others present, and in the types of "false positives" they identify.

DEALING WITH COGNITIVE STRAIN

Man's perceptual process is at once a remarkably efficient one and a highly selective one. Since the individual cannot perceive everything at once nor perceive everything in equal emphasis, the role of selectivity in perception is of great importance. What, then, influences the nature of selectivity? What determines what an individual shall or shall not perceive among the many things to which he is potentially exposed? What determines the order in which things are perceived, the intensity with which they are attended, the manner in which they are related to other experiences?

We are all being continually exposed to a far wider range of stimuli than we could possibly perceive or respond to at any one time. Each of us has a limited span of awareness, of attention, of memory, or recall. Each is limited in his capacity for identifying, grasping, holding, interpreting, and recalling things. If we were not selective, the cognitive and emotional strain would be overbearing; we must be selective to survive.

Narrowing Range of Observation

Bruner has suggested three ways in which we act in order to minimize the cost of cognitive strain. First we "narrow the selectivity of attention more or less to those things that are somehow essential to the enterprises in which we are engaged."[21] Whether in social situations or in professional situations, we tend to limit our attention or focus our attention on those aspects of the situation in which we are primarily concerned.

The pediatrician in the Child Health Clinic, for example, may give greater attention to parent-child relationships and their implications for the healthy emotional and mental growth of the child than he would to the intellectual or artistic interests of the mother he is interviewing. Even though art may be an area of major personal interest to him, his professional interest and responsibility serve as a guide in his selective process. Likewise, the social worker, in a home visit to the same family, may be professionally oriented toward being aware of socioeconomic problems or intrafamily relationships. The type of professional training he has received has helped to establish in his mind specific orientations for observing the situations in which he works. In some ways these are unstated hypotheses which he tests in each interview or situation observed. His orientation to a similar but nonprofessional situation may be in the direction of interests far removed from these.

Grouping and Stereotyping

Bruner next suggests that we "recode into simpler form the diversity of events that we encounter so that our limited attention and memory span can be protected."[22] We learn to use formulas, technical jargon, stereotypes for grouping and classifying the events observed. Just as we see dots in groups when flashed before us on the board, we tend to see situations as "wholes" or "gestalts" which are in part formed or influenced by our expectations. We have stereotypes regarding the attitudes and actions of minority groups—Negroes, Jews, Mexican-Americans, the poor, and so on—which help us group masses of observations into simpler form; yet in the process we often leave out some of the most significant aspects of a situation which we do not see, or we may add to the observations that we do make in terms of the context that we bring to the situation.

Long ago Walter Lippmann called attention to the importance of stereotypes in influencing the way we see and react to the world. He called them "pictures in our heads"—pictures that keep us from being wholly objective about anything.[23] They help us simplify our observations so that we can see more or hear more in limited time or in a limited situation. Yet while serving us in this way they distort what we see or what we hear into patterns along the line of our expectations.

Bruner's principle implies a somewhat greater degree of awareness, intention, and volition on the part of the perceiver than is usually the case. The process of developing expectations regarding a stimulus pattern and of responding to specific cues, rather than attending the entire perceptual field, tends to be a subconscious process. While we are at times aware of the stereotypes we hold and react to, our stereotyped behaviors tend more often to be automatic, uncritical, and less susceptible to change than we might prefer.

Recording Observations

Finally, as Bruner suggests, "We deal with the overload of information provided by the environment, the overload relative to our limited capacities for noticing and registering and remembering, by the use of technical aids, aids that are designed to lengthen the noticing process."[24]

For this purpose we may use cameras or recordings to keep an accurate record of the situation for future observation, forgetting when we later make our analyses that even these refined recording tools leave out much that may be significant. They may even highlight areas of observation in ways much different from the natural setting. We may use pencil and paper, schedules and interviews, observation schedules, or various other tools for summarizing quickly what appears to be of maximum significance in that which concerns us. In the end, however, the public health worker returning from the laboratory or from the field with his records and detailed observations must be selective and make choices regarding the items to report and the items to ignore. His manner of grouping becomes germane in making these final selections. He has, in one sense, postponed decisions he might otherwise have made in the field. In postponing these decisions he hopes to make them better.

Epectations Guide Efforts to Reduce Strain

All three of these approaches for dealing with the excess knowledge to which we are exposed are directed by the frame of reference we bring to the situation. We approach each situation, new or old, with certain psychological sets or expectations which determine the frame of reference within which we are aware, observe, recall, and evaluate. Despite our best efforts to be scientific, to be objective, to be honest, the frames of reference we bring to the situation tend to trap us into perceiving, recording, and recalling things in particular ways, ways influenced largely by our previous experiences.

This is not to say that all people notice, record, and recall only those things in tune with their expectations. Rather, priority tends to be given to certain things and the pattern of this priority is strongly influenced by the frame of reference of the individual concerned. Great individual differences between persons exist in their patterns of observation and recall. In this, as in so many other things involving individual behavior, there are many shades of gray as well as black and white.

NOTES TO CHAPTER 12

1. See Boring, Edwin G., *Sensation and Perception in the History of Experimental Psychology,* Appleton-Century-Crofts, Inc., New York, 1942; Ittelson, William H., and Hadley Cantril, *Perception: A Transactional Approach,* Doubleday Papers in Psychology, no. 7, Doubleday and Co., Garden City, N.Y., June, 1954; Kilpatrick, Franklin P., editor, *Explorations in Transactional Psychology,* New York University Press, New York, 1961, cf. pp. 1–57, 148–153; Solley, Charles M., and Gardner Murphy, *Development of the Perceptual World,* Basic Books, New York, 1960; Blake, Robert R., and Glenn V. Ramsey, editors, *Perception: An Approach to Personality,* Ronald Press Co., New York, 1951. For an analysis of alternative theories, see Allport, Floyd H., *Theories of Perception and the Concept of Structure,* John Wiley and Sons, New York, 1955.

2. See Ames, Adelbert, Jr., *An Interpretive Manual,* Princeton University Press, Princeton, N.J., 1955; Cantril, Hadley, *The "Why" of Man's Experience,* Macmillan Co., New York, 1950; Cantril, Hadley, editor, *The Morning Notes of Adelbert Ames, Jr.,* Rutgers University Press, New Brunswick, N.J., 1960; Hastorf, Albert H., and Andie L. Knutson, "Motivation, Perception, and Attitude Change," *Psychological Review,* vol. 56, March, 1949, pp. 88–94; Ittelson, William H., and Hadley Cantril, *op. cit.;* Kilpatrick, Franklin P., *op. cit.*

3. Roberts, Beryl J., "A Study of Selected Factors and Their Association with Action for Medical Care." Unpublished doctoral dissertation, Harvard University, 1956.

4. Bond, Betty, *Group Discussion-Decision: An Apprisal of Its Use in Health Education.* Minnesota Department of Health, Minneapolis, 1956.

5. Cantril, Hadley, *The "Why" of Man's Experience, op. cit.,* p. 67.

6. Johnson, M. L., "Seeing's Believing," *New Biology,* no. 15. Penguin Books, London, 1953, p. 69.

7. Murphy, Gardner, *Personality: A Biosocial Approach to Origins and Structure.* Harper and Bros., New York, 1947, pp. 336–337.

8. Gibson, James J., *Perception of the Visual World.* Houghton Mifflin Co., Boston, 1950.

9. Cantril, Hadley, *The Politics of Despair.* Basic Books, New York, p. 11.

10. Solley, Charles M., and Gardner Murphy, *op. cit.,* pp. 25–26.

11. Allport, Gordon W., "Perception and Public Health," *Health Education Monograph,* no. 2, 1958, p. 3.

12. Granger, G. W., "Abnormalities of Sensory Perception" in Eysenck, Hans J., editor, *Handbook of Abnormal Psychology.* Basic Books, New York, 1961, pp. 108–166.

13. Kermit, Mark L., and Ted Hein, Personal communication, July, 1961.

14. Freud, Sigmund, *General Introduction to Psychoanalysis.* Garden City Publishing Co., Garden City, N.Y., 1920, pp. 1–71.

15. Hall, Calvin S., "Psychoanalytic Theory and Its Applications in the Social Sciences" in Lindzey, Gardner, editor, *Handbook of Social Psychology.* Addison-Wesley Publishing Co., Reading, Mass., 1954, vol. 1, pp. 143–180.

16. Allport, Gordon W., *Pattern and Growth of Personality.* Holt, Rinehart and Winston, New York, 1961, p. 270.

17. Yerushalmy, Jacob, and associates, "The Role of Dual Reading in Mass Radiography," *American Review of Tuberculosis,* vol. 61, April, 1950; *Idem,* "The Importance of Observer Error in the Interpretation of Photofluorograms and the Value of Multiple Readings," *Bulletin of the International Union Against Tuberculosis,* vol. 26, January–April, 1956, pp. 110–124.

18. Yerushalmy, Jacob, "The Importance of Observer Error in the Interpretation of Photofluorograms and the Value of Multiple Readings," *op. cit.,* p. 112.

19. *Ibid.,* p. 121.

20. *Ibid.,* p. 123.

21. Bruner, Jerome S., "Social Psychology and Perception" in Maccoby, Eleanor, Theodore Newcomb, and Eugene L. Hartley, editors, *Readings in Social Psychology.* 3d ed. Holt, Rinehart and Winston, 1958, New York, p. 86.

22. *Ibid.*

23. Lippmann, Walter, *Public Opinion.* Macmillan Co., New York, 1922.

24. Bruner, Jerome S., *op. cit.,* p. 86.

Chapter 13

Man's Private World

EACH MAN is the center of his own universe. Rather than perceiving many worlds of different kinds, appearing and disappearing second by second in haphazard fashion, each person learns to perceive but one world with himself as center—a private world in which all his experiences are fused.

Cantril notes that:

> The more the psychologist studies human beings, the more he is struck by the unique nature of any individual's personal awareness or focus of reality: not only reality in the sense of the various objects that constitute his physical environment, but the "reality" of ideas, loyalties, and values which are just as operationally real for him as chairs, mountains, or automobiles. What is "real" is whatever an individual experiences as real, whatever affects his behavior, not something existing with invariable characteristics in its own right outside of man himself, which he can probe and manipulate without in turn affecting the very nature of the reality he is himself experiencing.
>
> The reality world of any individual is highly personal: it is *his* and his alone. It is the only world he knows. It is the center from which all his behavior stems. It guides all his purposeful action. It is his psychological matrix with the term "matrix" used in its dictionary sense as "a place or enveloping element within which something originates, takes form, or develops."[1]

Each man's individual world or private world may be a happy one or a sad one, easy or difficult, challenging or frightening. It is a world each man creates for himself out of the transactions of growing and developing in a sociocultural-physical setting uniquely his own. However happy or sad, broad or narrow it may be, therefore, it is in good part so because he has learned through the experiences of living to make it so.

A man may share parts of his private world with other persons who have had experiences similar to his own, or who hold beliefs, concerns, hopes, or expectations related in some way to those he himself holds. This may apply, at times, to even the most intimate of his personal experiences. Yet no man can completely share his world with anyone else. He can communicate to others regarding only those parts of his private world in which his own experiences overlap in some way the experiences of others.

This private world or reality world of each individual is not a world of fantasy or imagination, nor is it a lovely retreat from reality. Rather, it is for each person an essential map or chart whereby he can evaluate possible future activities against past experience and obtain guide lines for future action.

Man's private world has been the focus of much psychological research during the past quarter century. Many terms have been used to describe it—"life space" or "psychological field,"[2] "assumptive world" or "reality world,"[3] "private world,"[4] "phenomenological method,"[5] and "phenomenal field."[6]

Brilliant theorists and researchers who have guided explorations in this area still disagree in many ways regarding the nature and boundaries of man's private world, how it develops, what causes it to change, in what specific ways it is related to motives, emotions, and actions. From their efforts to find answers to such questions have come some of the most creative studies of our times—studies that have influenced the course of both government and industry. The success of theoretical research regarding man's private world in these other areas of society suggests far-reaching possibilities for public health research and practice.

THE APPROACH OF FIELD THEORY

Perhaps Kurt Lewin, more than any other psychologist, has given leadership in the research regarding man as part of his environment. In the process of trying to bring laboratory theory and methods to the solution of practical community and industrial problems, he found it essential to develop new approaches in order to understand and predict behavior in real life situations. The term "field theory" has been given to the general approach used by Lewin and his associates in their attempts to analyze causal relationships regarding the conditions of change. As he states, *"Field theory is probably best characterized as a method:* namely, a method *of analyzing causal relations and of building scientific constructs."*[7] Emphasized in his method is the importance of viewing the "life space" of the individual, which includes both the person and his environment, as one psychological field.

A basic principle which has been stressed by the field theorists is that "Any behavior or any other change in a psychological field depends only upon the psychological field *at that time*."[8] What is meant here is that man's purposive behavior can only be governed by what he perceives. Asch summarizes this very poignantly:

> We act and choose on the basis of what we see, feel, and believe; meanings and values are part and parcel of our actions. When we are mistaken about things we act in terms of our erroneous notions, not in terms of things as they are. To understand human action it is therefore essential to understand the conscious mode in which things appear to us.[9]

In order to apply this theoretical principle in predicting an individual's health behavior in any situation, one must first of all determine the nature of the psychological field he perceives. How does he define the situation? Does the problem or concern exist in his private world? Is it seen as being of personal significance? Of what action possibilities is he aware? How does he evaluate these different alternatives? What barriers to effective action exist in his mind? What possible outcomes does he anticipate?

Lewin suggests that the traditional or historical approach, similar to the case study method of medicine, yields information regarding the events that have led to the present situation, and will therefore help us understand what has led the individual to describe the situation as he does. This traditional approach, however, is not adequate for obtaining the most significant information required for understanding the individual's interpretations and for predicting his reactions.

In addition to the background information obtained by means of the historical approach or the case history, some tests of the present situation are required—a diagnosis of current status. Such a diagnosis of the present situation will sometimes yield the most significant data necessary for predicting future behavior. Resort to the historical approach may not even be required. How an individual perceives the present situation depends in good part upon his past experiences. Yet one may obtain from him a description of definition of the current situation as it appears from his point of view and the meaning it has for him personally without either knowing or needing to know the vast range of experiences that have led him to perceive the present in his own particular way.

For example, a man may fail to respond to an invitation to obtain a free multiphasic examination. Through an interview one may learn from him how he interpreted the invitation. Does he see the invitation as one of personal significance? Is his reaction one of interest, curiosity, indifference, fear, or doubt? Does he believe himself to be well and healthy so the examination would serve little personal value? Or does he fear knowing what he already suspects—that he may have some serious malady that could cause him to be removed from his family, job, friends, and all that is of prime importance to him? Does he hold doubts about the intent of the offer, the quality of the methods, or the reactions of the staff?

If one had such information about the individual's reactions to the situation—information that could be obtained in a diagnosis of current status—it might be possible to adapt the program to his needs or to find a means of encouraging him to participate without delving at length into the varied experiences that have led him to question the significance of the examination, to distrust the methods employed, or to fear the outcomes.

OBJECTIVE AND SUBJECTIVE FACTS

In applying such an approach to an understanding of man's behavior it is imperative to distinguish clearly between facts as they are experienced by the perceiving or knowing individual and facts as they may exist in reality or as others may perceive them. Failure to make this distinction may lead to serious error in research or program.

The term "subjective facts" may be used to refer to facts as they are directly perceived and experienced, as distinct from the "objective facts" which may actually exist in reality. Subjective facts are experienced as part of one's private world and exist for him whether they are present in objective reality or not, and whether or not they exist in anyone else's private world.

Each man perceives, knows, and experiences subjective facts in all areas in which objective facts exist. They may concern physical, biological, or social aspects of environment, both concrete and abstract, and may, like objective facts, be concerned with the past, present, or future. Of particular significance to understanding man's health behavior are those subjective facts concerned with his hopes, fears, expectations, values, norms, standards, goals, incentives, and other variables which govern the flow of his social and personal life.

The subjective facts that exist for an individual may be different from reality and may also be different from the subjective facts that are experienced and known by other persons. For the perceiving and knowing individual, however, the facts experienced are real, more real in fact than what may actually exist in either objective reality or in the private worlds of others.

One should not infer from this discussion that a clear and sharp distinction separates objective facts from the subjective facts—that objective facts are the "real, stable things." As Charles Bird once observed, "A fact is a function of your method."[10] All facts seem to have both objective and subjective qualities. Even objective facts for one person may be subjective facts for another.

Objective facts do change as methods of observation and validation change. While we now hold, as an objective fact, that the sun is a star, the earth a sun satellite, and the moon an earth satellite, these facts are of recent origin and were not present in the factual world of ancient man. Only in the present decade have we begun to question the fact that "what goes up must come down."

In health, as in other matters, objective facts change. Each year new techniques of observation and diagnosis yield new objective facts about man's physical, social, and mental well-being. One must recognize, however, that such facts are often present only in the minds of those who have the professional knowledge and training to appreciate the methods whereby they are derived.

APPLYING THE APPROACH OF FIELD THEORY

Adapting Kurt Lewin's approach to understanding an individual's health behavior in any situation requires knowing:

1. How does the issue of concern exist in his private world? How does he perceive or define the situation? What subjective facts exist for him regarding the situation? As Lewin has suggested, this involves understanding his "life space," that is, the person and the psychological environment that exist for him.[11] We usually have this field in mind if we refer to needs, motivations, moods, goals, anxieties, ideals.

2. How does the issue exist in the private worlds of others who are concerned? How do they define the situation? What are their subjective facts as related to the problem? To what extent are their subjec-

tive facts in agreement with, or in opposition to, the subjective facts of the individual they are seeking to understand?

3. What are the objective facts about the issue or situation of concern? How do the objective facts relate to the subjective facts experienced by the individual involved? Are there facts in the objective world that do not exist in the private world of the individual or that are perceived in ways different from objective reality? What accounts for these differences?

4. How have the subjective facts of the different individuals been acquired? What accounts for their being different from objective reality? In what areas are subjective facts and objective facts in agreement? What experiences would be helpful in bringing facts more closely in agreement with the facts of objective reality?

In brief, then, in order to understand man's health behavior in any situation one must know how the situation exists in his private world as related to (a) the way it exists in the private worlds of those who seek to influence him, (b) the way the situation exists in objective reality, and (c) historically how both came about. For most program purposes it is not necessary to have full understanding of the historical basis for the subjective facts and the objective facts even though these may be required for full understanding of the individual's behavior. One may be able to predict future behavior or to plan actions to influence future behavior without such historical information.

From this point of view, the first step in investigating the health behavior of any individual involves understanding how he defines the problem. This applies whether the purpose of the investigation is to understand his past actions and to predict his future behavior or to develop programs to influence his health practices, attitudes, beliefs, or knowledge. It is wasteful, often futile, to begin without first knowing how he perceives the world about him as it is related to the health action under consideration.

Application in Dental Health

Applying the approach described above in an attempt to influence man's health behavior involves first determining whether or not an individual perceives a problem of concern to his health. An individual is not likely to seek medical assistance to improve his eyesight or hearing unless he is first aware that physiological changes have occurred and that his eyesight or hearing is inadequate. He is not likely to seek dental help to avoid the loss of his teeth as he grows older if the idea of preventing the loss of teeth does not exist as a subjective fact for him. If the idea that the loss of teeth can and should be prevented is not present in his private world, if the idea simply does not exist in his mind, he is not likely to take even the simplest preventive action. Such a person is neither opposed nor in favor of preventive dentistry. It simply does not exist for him. He may have a sense of futility about the idea of losing his teeth. He may expect to have artificial teeth sometime and may never have considered the possibility of avoiding this presumably inevitable event. Such a person says, "False teeth. Everyone winds up with them. False teeth are just a matter of necessity. You have to have them."

Personal interviews have indicated that there are some people who actually look forward to getting rid of their teeth, not having to go to the dentist any more. For them, false teeth seem to represent an escape from pain and discomfort. As one man said, "I wouldn't mind false teeth. Then I wouldn't have to have toothaches and wouldn't have to go back to the dentist. I don't think it would make much difference. You can't tell these days. Most of them look so nice."[12]

It is not known to what extent such ideas are currently held in various groups of our population. To the extent that they are held, however, they indicate a lack of full awareness of the possibilities of preventive dentistry. This lack of awareness may be a more important barrier to fluoridation than the active opposition of the special interest groups.[13]

Application in Program Development

The public health worker who plans an action program within the framework of his own private world and does not take into account the subjective facts held by the public regarding the program may miss significant opportunities for program development. In one instance a health educator in a local community sought to identify the needs on which to build a sound program and made her survey using a traditional public health terminology to obtain data for program development. She was unhappy with her findings because many health problems of which she knew were not being reported.

She reviewed her approach and found that she had used questions about health needs and public health problems that meant more to the public health professional than to the public she was interviewing. Her approach had encouraged responses in terms of existing services only, and these in terms that were unfamiliar to her public. She changed her approach and tried a more open interview which encouraged her respondents to discuss freely "the little things that families run into when they first move into a neighborhood" and "the kinds of problems they discuss when they get together," things "something ought to be done about."

Using this new method, she found that many were concerned about uncontrolled dogs roaming the neighborhood, although few had mentioned the need for rabies control. Others who had not mentioned accident prevention for children called attention to the need for some type of recreation facilities for preschool children who were playing in the streets because there were no sidewalks in the neighborhood. Expectant mothers did not know where to reach the nearest physicians or nurses, yet had not mentioned the value of a medical register. Mothers with young children desired help on behavioral problems, yet had not expressed an interest in the mental health program. Thus the open approach, which provided an opportunity for obtaining responses within the framework of the layman's private world, yielded data of great value in defining the goals for community action.[14]

Communicating Health Concepts

At times a concept that has one meaning for the professional public health person may have a different, even opposite, meaning for a lay group. Use of this concept elicits a pattern of subjective facts in the mind of the layman that may be quite different from the subjective facts known by the professional person. Serious error may result. For example, in one instance a pretest of a pamphlet drew attention to the disagreement, and serious error was avoided.

Shimberg interviewed a group of laymen to determine whether a pamphlet on the use of salt-soda solution as a substitute for blood plasma for shock for severe burns would be understood by the general public. His subjects were given the pamphlet to read and were then asked questions like these: How would you know a person was suffering from shock? Is there anything you can do for a person suffering from shock?

From the responses it was learned that even after reading the pamphlet most of the persons interpreted "shock" as meaning psychological or mental shock rather than physiological shock. As a result, many failed to relate the use of the salt-soda solution to the treatment of severe burns even though this was a major point of the pamphlet. Several commented they would give the injured person the solution to drink so that they would not feel shocked looking at each other's injuries. These comments suggested that confusion about the concept of a shock was a real barrier to understanding the health practice recommended. Clarification was clearly needed. The term "shock" elicited a much different pattern of subjective facts in the private world of laymen than existed as salient in the private world of the professional persons preparing the pamphlet.[15]

Diagnosis and Treatment

In the clinic or community situation serious barriers to program development often hinge on the difficulty of obtaining a valid picture of the private world of the patient. This is particularly true in dealing with groups who by reason of minority membership, low income, low education, illness, or other reasons are unable to communicate effectively with the public health professional worker. Adair and Deuschle, in their study of the problems of physicians working on the Navajo reservation, observe:

> . . . The Navajos are so called "good patients" because they accept and endure certain painful procedures stoically; this may mislead some unwary physician into thinking that the Navajos do not experience pain as sharply as his Anglo patients. Occasionally a physician will continue a difficult venipuncture or some other minor surgical procedure because of the patient's seemingly high threshold to pain.
>
> A notable illustration of this point had to do with an obstetrician who administered a minimum of analgesics to his Navajo patients in labor on the assumption that the Navajos had very little pain since they "probably experienced a more natural reaction to childbirth." After this obstetrician completed his tour of duty the physician who succeeded him administered much larger doses of analgesics. Very soon thereafter, the obstetrical patient load at this Navajo hospital increased sharply. When some of these Navajo women were queried as to why they were coming into the hospital they replied: "To have a baby without pain."[16]

It is not surprising to learn that serious errors in diagnosis may also be traced to failures to communicate accurately and fully when patient and physician come from different ethnic groups and possess different patterns of subjective facts.

Patient Instructions

An intensive study by Caron of a small group of patients on low-sodium diets dramatically illustrates some of the ways in which differences between the subjective facts held by patients and the subjective facts held by professional persons lead to difficulty in communicating vitally important information. The study was carried out in cooperation with nutritionists and health educators who were eager to learn ways of improving a booklet on low-sodium diet and wished to identify difficulties that patients have in understanding, following, and maintaining low-sodium diets through the use of the booklet.

The booklet was developed (a) to serve as a reference source for dieters to use in selecting or rejecting foods, (b) to teach the dieter to control his daily intake through the preparation of a satisfactory meal plan, and (c) to teach the principles of sodium restricted diet.

Caron interviewed 31 patients on low-sodium diets selected in the outpatient clinics of six hospitals. Since the purpose was to identify barriers to communications rather than to obtain a representative sample of reaction, no attempt was made to sample systematically. The median education of patients was approximately ninth grade. Ten of the patients had been on low-sodium diets for six months or more. The remainder were new patients. Eight were male, the remainder female.

Caron's first research question was: "Is the patient able to use the booklet as a reference book?" Each patient was asked to find a list of foods in the booklet and to determine whether or not these foods were appropriate for his diet. These were foods that had been recognized in preliminary exploration as foods with which patients were having difficulty. Each item was scored as "failed" if the patient could not locate the food or drew an incorrect conclusion as to whether or not it was permitted or prohibited in the diet.

> From among 42 instances in which patients looked for corn, cold cuts and peanut butter, there were 22 failures. For those who correctly located corn, cold cuts, and peanut butter, the average amounts of time required were 42, 50, and 26 seconds, respectively. These performances may be contrasted with those on locating fruits and vegetables. Here, patients successfully located the foods in all instances and required an average of only 11 seconds.[17]

A primary source of difficulty was related to the titles of the index. Patients had difficulty in locating peanut butter, for example, because they were unfamiliar with the nutritional concept of "fats." Few patients identified peanut butter as a fat. Consequently most were able to find it only through random searching in the booklet. Since some of them did not understand the term "bread and its exchanges," they had difficulty looking up "cereals." Even some patients who were acquainted with the terms "starchy foods" or "carbohydrates" had difficulty finding the entry "corn" or "lima beans," since they tended to look under "vegetables." Thus the terms familiar to the private world of the nutritionists caused difficulty to the patient who had a different pattern of terms in his own private world.

The booklet offered a daily meal plan as a help to the dieter in controlling his daily intake of sodium. Description of the nutritional contents of the foods presented was under symbols "C," "P," "F," "Na," "Cal." These symbols, common to nutritionists, had no meaning to patients.

Findings regarding the research questions, "Does the patient know what sodium is?" and "Does the patient know how to recognize foods with high and low sodium content?" yield information of particular relevance to those interested in comparing the worlds of professionals and laymen. Interviews with 27 patients revealed that only three, all older patients, indicated in their answers that they realized that sodium appears in foods both as a constituent of salt and independent of salt. The tendency to identify sodium with salt led to considerable confusion. The patients said they tended to avoid salty foods in order to avoid sodium. They were unaware that some foods that do not taste salty also contain sodium and that sodium may be present in baking powder, bread, canned vegetables and meats having preservatives, animal proteins—meats, milk, eggs, and so on. Their confusion was increased because at times professional people tend to refer to a "sodium-free diet" as a "salt-free diet." This may have contributed to the misunderstanding of many patients.

> A consequence of this poor learning is that patients fail to perceive that foods that are not actually or apparently salty may still be high in sodium. They will not bother to check on the suitability of foods that are not perceived as "salty" (or "very salty"). This distortion in the diet was observed in all but three of the ten patients interviewed who had been practicing the diet over a long period. Some patients were "killing the salt" in bacon, ham, sausage, and salt cod by boiling or pouring hot tea over the food. . . . Few patients bothered to check on the sodium content of popular drugs such as Alka-Seltzer. . . . Few patients maintained the restrictions on bread and milk. "Saltiness" is subject to a wide range of subjective interpretation. Some patients did not consider boloney, a high sodium food, to be salty.[18]

Other Implications

It should not be implied, however, that complete harmony between the professional health worker's private world and the private world of the layman in the particular area of concern is essential if appropriate action is to occur. Actions appropriate to the situation may be taken for reasons other than agreement on subjective facts. The layman may act not because he is concerned about his health but for any of a wide range of other reasons. In fact, he may act because he has incorrectly interpreted the intended message in some unexpected way. When this occurs, the long-range effects of his action may be quite different from those hoped for by the public health worker.

Pedro Martiz cites an interesting illustration of this in regard to a spraying program in Mexico: "In a remote little town in Mexico we discovered during an observation and evaluation trip that many people had cleaned their walls a few days after other workers had sprayed them with dieldrin. When we asked them about it, they said they believed that this thing was to kill cockroaches and after several days all the cockroaches had been killed so they did what they thought was needed and cleaned the walls. They perceived that dieldrin spray in a different way from that which was intended—without any relation to the malaria eradication program. We had failed because we did not change their attitudes toward the spray before the beginning of the campaign. We did not think to find out about their past experience with insecticides. They were not able to appreciate the important role that the insecticides had in the fight against malaria."[19]

SUMMARY

Each new study of man's health knowledge, values, beliefs, attitudes, or behavior identifies new ways in which subjective facts held in regard to illness and its treatment or control tend to influence health action. The subjective facts people hold regarding the existence of disease, its cause and course, their own susceptibility to it, appropriate sick roles and behaviors, the efficacy, feasibility, and social implications of treatment, the possibilities of lasting cure, control, and rehabilitation, the personal and social costs of health action—all are of significance to health program effectiveness.

The concept of man's private world and the methods of description and analysis suggested by field theory are useful in viewing such differences in the subjective lives of people. Bearing such a concept in mind in planning health actions may suggest the value of including more and more varied viewpoints for consideration. Representation from different age or sex groups, different sociocultural and social class groups, education and occupational groups, when matters being considered will concern their health actions, may help to assure that more significant subjective facts are represented in planning.

NOTES TO CHAPTER 13

1. Cantril, Hadley, *The Politics of Despair.* Basic Books, New York, 1958, pp. 16–17.

2. Lewin, Kurt, "Defining the 'Field at a Given Time,'" initially published in 1943; in Lewin, Kurt, *Field Theory in Social Science: Selected Theoretical Papers,* edited by Dorwin Cartwright, Harper and Bros., New York, 1951, p. 57.

3. Cantril, Hadley, *op. cit.;* Idem, *The "Why" of Man's Experience,* Macmillan Co., New York, 1950.

4. Frank, Lawrence K., "Projective Methods for the Study of Personality," *Journal of Psychology,* vol. 8, October, 1939, pp. 389–413. Reprinted in Kuenzli, Alfred E., editor, *The Phenomenological Problem,* Harper and Bros., New York, 1959, pp. 96–125.

5. MacLeod, Robert B., "The Phenomenological Approach to Social Psychology," *Psychological Review,* vol. 54, July, 1947, pp. 193–210. Reprinted in Kuenzli, Alfred E., *op. cit.,* pp. 149–181.

6. Snygg, Donald, "The Need for a Phenomenal System of Psychology," *Psychological Review,* vol. 48, September, 1941, pp. 404–424. Reprinted in Kuenzli, Alfred E., *op. cit.,* pp. 3–27. Also discussed in Combs, Arthur W., and Donald Snygg, *Individual Behavior: A Perceptual Approach to Behavior.* rev. ed., Harper and Bros., New York, 1959. (The first edition of this text was published by Harper and Bros. in 1949 under the title *Individual Behavior: A New Frame of Reference for Psychology,* by Donald Snygg and Arthur W. Combs.)

7. Lewin, Kurt, *op. cit.,* p. 45.

8. *Ibid.*

9. Asch, Solomon E., *Social Psychology.* Prentice-Hall, Inc., Englewood Cliffs, N.J., 1952, pp. 64–65.

10. Bird, Charles, Lecture Notes, University of Minnesota, 1938. See also in this context Cohen, Morris R., and Ernest Nagel, *An Introduction to Logic and Scientific Method,* Part II, Harcourt Brace, New York, 1934. See also Kohler, Wolfgang, *The Place of Value in a World of Facts,* Liveright Publishing Corp., London, 1938; republished as a Meridian Book, World Publishing Co., Cleveland, 1959.

11. Lewin, Kurt, *op. cit.,* p. 57.

12. Starbuck, Nancy, "A Study of the Perceptual Factors Associated with a Particular Decision of Leaders in Six Selected Communities." Unpublished doctoral dissertation, Cornell University, 1953.

13. Knutson, Andie L., "The Layman's Interpretation of the Dentist's Advice on Fluoridation," *Bulletin of the American Association of Public Health Dentists,* vol. 13, February, 1953, pp. 13–21; Starbuck, Nancy, *op. cit.*

14. Galiher, Claudia, Personnel communication and study with the author; Knutson, Andie L., "Evaluating Program Progress," *Public Health Reports,* vol. 70, March, 1955, pp. 305–310.

15. Shimberg, Benjamin, Unpublished manuscript, Bureau of State Services, U.S. Public Health Service, Washington, 1952.

16. Adair, John, and Kurt Deuschle, "Perception of Pain," *Human Organization,* vol. 16, Winter, 1948, p. 21.

17. Caron, Herbert S., "An Evaluation of the Booklet: Planning Low Sodium Meals." Unpublished manuscript, Behavioral Studies Section, U.S. Public Health Service, Washington, 1955, p. 16.

18. *Ibid.*

19. Martiz, Pedro, Personal communication, 1958.

Part Four

Social Motivation

Part Four

Social Motivation

SINCE MAN is a purposive animal whose health behavior is governed by needs, concerns, desires, fears, hopes, and expectations, understanding human motivation seems basic to any attempt to plan action for his health improvement. Effective public health planning requires knowledge of motive patterns that exist or may be emergent. It requires awareness also of the means people themselves identify as most likely to satisfy their motives. Such information would permit planning in terms of specific patterns of striving.

The search for meaning in man's social behavior has led behavioral scientists up many avenues of theory. Some have focused their efforts on gaining an understanding of his biochemical processes; others have sought the answer in man's sense of self, in his interpersonal experiences, or in the value patterns of his sociocultural heritage. No one has found an adequate explanation.

Motivation research is often viewed as a panacea for those who seek to influence man's health behavior. It excites the imagination with sophisticated techniques that seem to offer promise of easy solutions to complex problems. The public health official should be warned, however, that some of its spectacular successes have been offset by dismal failures. The unwillingness of man to be swayed to act blindly, contrary to his past patterns of behavior, protects him against undue pressure or enticement.

The behavioral sciences offer public health no social pharmacopoeia for planning dynamic action programs, nor sure-fire approaches for disclosing the complex motivations underlying healthy and unhealthy behavior. Much progress has been made, however, in both theory and research. Some of the approaches to an understanding of social motivation that have emerged from these theoretical and research efforts would seem to deserve far greater attention than they now receive.

Chapter 14

The Search for the Sources of Man's Energy

THERE has been much philosophical speculation regarding the process whereby the newborn infant obtains the motives and purposes that help to make him a functioning member of his social group. The issue is of crucial significance to the health of society, for it bears directly on the questions: Can human nature be changed? If so, how and to what extent?

If man inherited his value and motive patterns, it would be futile to plan and conduct educational programs oriented toward influencing improvements in his health behavior. Only the most limited changes in behavior could be anticipated to result from such program efforts. Health leaders might then better spend their efforts in direct program actions—doing things *for* the less fortunate members of society who had inherited less desirable health values, motives, and practices.

To the extent that man's health values, beliefs, and attitudes are learned, however, it is realistic to focus major public health effort on ways of helping people to work for their own health betterment. The questions, then, do not concern *whether* people can learn new health ways, but *how* they learn, and how more effective means can be developed to help them learn. Public health leaders need to focus attention on major issues concerned with ways of determining the kinds of improvements in health values and beliefs that are really necessary for the betterment of society. What criteria can be employed to judge which changes are really necessary? What tests can be employed to assure the validity of such value decisions? How can such value decisions best be made? How can effective programs of social change then be initiated within a group in a manner that protects the prerogative of people to make and carry out their own value decisions by the individual and collective means available to them?

199

INSTINCTS AND INSTINCTUAL TENDENCIES

At one time the confusing evidence available, together with the almost insurmountable difficulties of research to obtain valid evidence regarding the origin of man's motives, led to the positing of a wide range of instincts and instinctual tendencies as explanatory principles. James, McDougall, Warren, Thorndike, and many other psychologists developed long lists of behaviors they considered to be "instincts or instinctual tendencies." Even such social characteristics as curiosity, gregariousness, cleanliness, modesty, secretiveness, and aggressiveness were included in one or more of these lists.

This tendency to draw upon instincts in explaining man's social behavior led Dunlap in 1919 to question, "Are there any instincts?"[1] He was soon supported by Bernard, who reacted to the tendency to conceal ignorance through the use of scientific label by publishing an article on "The Misuse of Instinct in the Social Sciences."[2] Bernard followed this up with a report of a survey on the uses made of the concept by 500 writers in the social sciences and related fields. Almost 6,000 human urges or activities had been referred to as instinctive in nature.[3] Bernard's critical reviews, along with the startling experimental conditioning research of Pavlov, Watson, Dunlap, and other early behavioristic psychologists contributed to a discrediting of the loose use of the concept of instinct as scientific explanation. They helped to stimulate intensive efforts by behavioral scientists to gain a more adequate understanding of the dynamic processes involved. Research has since established that many of the social behaviors once labeled instinctive are actually learned prior to birth or in infancy.[4]

Instincts are still posited by some outstanding scientists as tentative explanations of the origin of man's motivational system. Freud, Jung, Adler, Horney, Fromm, Murray, Maslow, and a host of others have leaned in varying degrees on innate tendencies or forces in developing their theories of motivation. Other scientists who reject the idea that infants are equipped at birth with specific instinctual tendencies still tend to agree that the newborn infant does possess some general innate sources of energy, or drives. They disagree, however, regarding the origin, number, pattern, and priority of any such drives. They disagree also as to the relationship of these general drives to any specific patterns of wants, needs, or desires the child may possess.

Generalized theories of behavior often treat motivation as a life force rooted in biological tensions and seeking expression in predetermined directions. Freud, for example, conceived of the libido as such a generalized source of energy which expresses itself through both conscious and subconscious channels. Janet's "psychological energy," McDougall's "hormic" principle, and Bergson's "élan vital" are in many ways similar to Freud's libido, in that they, too, are generalized instinctual sources of energy.

Such general theories have proved useful to psychological and psychiatric clinicians in their efforts to explain their therapeutic activities. They tend to be of less value as one moves out of the clinic into normal life situations. Attempts to translate these theories into specific form for purposes of prediction and action have resulted in long lists of instincts, drives, needs, demands, wants, motives, and incentives. Although these lists have served useful purposes in research and action, their use more often than not has been limited to the specific setting, population, and purpose for which they were compiled. They are not likely to provide satisfactory answers to the health official who needs conceptual tools for dealing with problems of human motivation of many sorts and in widely varying circumstances.

HOMEOSTASIS

Any theory of motivation concerns the sources of energy underlying man's actions. Attention must therefore be centered on the most complex of internal states, states that involve physiochemical as well as neuropsychological processes, for as Murphy summarizes current thought, "All behavior seems to be motivated, and all the tissues of the body seem to be important in motivation."[5] The terms "physiological needs" and "tissue needs" have been employed to refer to these requirements of the body.

Cannon introduced the concept of homeostasis to refer to the capacity of the organism to maintain an equilibrium of its internal-external environment.[6] Many aspects of the internal environment of the organism require regulation if the organism is to survive. These include the water and sugar content of the blood, salt content of the blood, hydrogen ion concentration, oxygen content in the blood, calcium content, and so forth. Mechanisms for maintaining homeostasis include the lungs, circulatory system, kidneys, digestive tract, nervous system, and the many duct and ductless glands. When imbalances occur, reactions take place to return the body to an inner stability.

It has been hypothesized that the tension states produced by changes in the homeostatic state provide inner stimulation to the organism. The discomforts of tension are said to "push" the organism toward tension reduction activities, leading it to "seek" a return to adjustment or homeostasis.

HOMEOSTASIS AND SOCIAL MOTIVATIONS

Such an approach to motivation theory may satisfy certain biological requirements, but it is less than adequate for describing and understanding motivation from a psychological or social point of view.[7] While we may be sensitive to the tensions of extreme imbalances, such as dehydration or starvation, we lack awareness of the constant chemical changes our bodies undergo. There is no evidence, furthermore, that the subjective states of comfort and discomfort, rest and tension are conscious subjective states for the fetus or newborn infant, nor that the latter are in any way "aware" of biochemical processes taking place. Accordingly, it would be naive to imply that either adults or infants seek or strive for a state of homeostasis. This is not to say that these changes in homeostasis do not influence our feelings and cognitions. As L. K. Frank observes:

> To the extent that we are aware of these sometimes subtle, evanescent internal alterations—which may occur as a brief contraction of the stomach or intestine, a quick spasm of the muscles, a moment's alteration in the heart rate, or else as a sudden relaxation of tension and a release which may persist for a while—we say we "feel" toward a person or a situation in ways we describe by various terms: happy, sorrowful, apprehensive, expectant, etc. These are the ever-changing responses that occur in every situation as our physiological processes change. Whether we are aware of and pay attention to them, or ignore or deny them, they participate in all our activities and often dominate our thinking and acceptance or rejection of people.[8]

He draws attention to ways in which homeostatic imbalances develop in response to imbalances in the environment, so that under conditions of perceived danger or other emergencies, emotional energies become temporarily mobilized to prepare the individual for action. "In this way emotional reactions are channeled into effective action; when the emergency is past, the individual recovers his equilibrium, often with enhanced confidence and ability to meet the next crisis."[9]

In considering this important concept of homeostasis, it would be folly to imply that the individual constantly seeks to reduce tension.

Much of our activity is deliberately focused toward increasing tensions and the creating of conditions that offer suspense and excitement. The capacity to develop, maintain, and release tension is basic to personality development, and through the management of tensions one learns to cope with new life situations.

> Thus, even young babies like to play peek-a-boo and soon are engaged in a variety of such play, building blocks higher and higher until they topple down, and engaging in similar tension-creating activity. Dramatic play and stories likewise serve to build up tensions which they enjoy, and they postpone the climax and release of tension as long as possible. School children and adolescents likewise enjoy tension-creating games, teasing, running away with each other's hat, wrestling, mountain-climbing, etc. Much of the avid interest in radio and TV programs may be interpreted as an expression of this deliberate seeking of the increase of tensions, as does all goal-seeking, purposive striving of human living.[10]

Today few, if any, behavioral scientists would relate these complex inner forces or physiological drives, whether innate or resulting from homeostatic imbalances, directly to *specific social* behaviors. Tendencies, to the extent that they do exist, seem to be nonspecific or general. The human organism is at once more complex and more plastic than lower animals at birth. The longer period of maturation and development, and the wider range of modifying influences during growth, cloud distinctions between drives of biogenic, and drives of social, origin. Inherited tendencies seem highly flexible and subject to almost infinite individual variation during maturation and use.[11]

BIOGENIC AND SOCIOGENIC MOTIVES

There have been many attempts to distinguish between motives that seem to have a biochemical origin and those that appear to be socially or culturally based. The research and theoretical literature is filled with summaries of efforts to group motives in terms of such a dichotomy. The terms "biogenic" and "sociogenic" are among those frequently used to indicate this difference in origin.

Those who make this differentiation between biogenic and sociogenic motives tend to view biological sources of energy as basic or primary sources. Among the biogenic motives or drives are such tensions or "tissue needs" as hunger, thirst, the need for oxygen, rest and sleep, sex, adjustments to temperatures, and so on. Such drives are rooted in biochemical deficits or demands. When present, they are assumed to lead to fairly systematic responses on the part of the individual.

Sociogenic motives, on the other hand, tend more frequently to be defined in terms of the goal rather than in terms of the tension. Included here are strivings for security, gain, power, prestige, and the almost infinitely long list of specific wants, interests, and desires that distinguish us as social beings.

From this point of view one may speak of a biogenic hunger drive and a sociogenic food motive. As Newcomb has observed, it is somewhat easier to identify motives in terms of their goals than in terms of their state of drive, for we do not as yet have the means to distinguish between the various states of drive that exist in an individual at any particular time. As Newcomb puts it:

> We do not have the means, for example, of distinguishing between the drive states of a given individual when he is motivated to win at poker and when he is motivated to win at tennis. The goals can easily be distinguished, but the drives can not. Hence we shall speak of a *hunger drive* and a *food motive,* but not of a food drive or a hunger motive. The phrase "food motive" does not deny the influence of the hunger drive but stresses the directional aspect of whatever behavior is involved. Likewise, the phrase "hunger drive" does not imply that no food motive is present but simply emphasizes the tension or energy aspect of the behavior.[12]

ARE SOME MOTIVES "BASIC"?

The assumption that one group of drives is more basic in origin than another is somewhat tenuous. Efforts to trace social motives to their presumed-to-be innate bases have thus far proved fruitless. Almost insurmountable difficulties seem to block any attempt to infer from observed behavior what specific motives are primarily responsible and where these might fall on some type of a continuum between innate and acquired. Any single action may satisfy more than one motive—both social and biological. Likewise a single motive, or group of motives, may express itself through a variety of behaviors even though several drives or motives are known to be present. It may be impossible to differentiate their effects.

The hunger for food, for example, may have a biological base but tends to have specific social meaning for an individual. As Murphy describes it:

> . . . The concrete activities of preparing and serving meals in human cultures are always more than food-gratifying tendencies. They

are not explained by referring to food need. The need for gratification or titillation of the senses of smell, taste, touch, and the thermal gratifications of hot soups and ice cream, etc., and the web of associations between food needs and the need for company, make it forever impossible to explain etiquette, the food style, the ceremonial aspects of the "date" and the banquet, the social meaning of eating with one's own group (excluding the person of lower status), all of which are intelligible only by considering the fusion of many tendencies.[13]

Motives tend to be unique to the individual in any particular setting and at any particular time. Regardless of origin they are seldom purely biological or primarily social when expressed in action. Their relative biological and social weightings cannot be determined in practice. Attempts to make such distinctions imply a degree of scientific sophistication we still lack.

Man does not want for food or drink, biologically defined. He wants a particular kind of food or drink, cooked or prepared according to his specific taste, served in the manner or quantity appropriate to his particular culture. Under such circumstances, to treat the search for food as evidence of a biogenic motive has limited validity. Its predictive value is nil. The researcher or theoretician who ignores social motivations in attempting to predict man's eating behavior is being quite as ridiculous as one who attempts to predict his eating behavior on the basis of social stimulation and social motivation alone, without recognizing biological requirements.

What applies with respect to man's eating behavior applies equally with respect to other aspects of his health. He is not likely to exercise for the purpose of exercise alone, but rather because he finds satisfactions of many kinds. He awakens by the clock, eats by the clock, and goes to sleep by the clock, and is thus controlled as much in his sleeping and eating patterns by the norms of the culture as by the needs of the body. In fact, biological requirements in the areas of eating, sleeping, and exercise show only the slightest relationship to the patterns of behavior of even the best informed persons. In such situations biogenic drives are hidden deep in the background and sociogenic motives dominate the action.

MOTIVATION IN INFANCY

Although the question regarding the nature of any instinctive tendencies within the fetus remains debatable, each scientific breakthrough during the past century has tended to support a naturalistic explana-

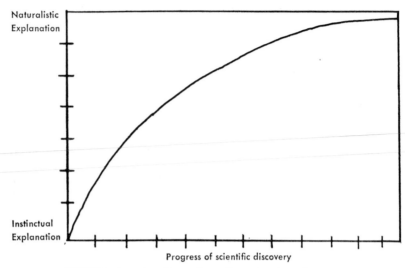

FIGURE 8. Asymptote Decay Curve Illustrating Scientific Progress Toward a Naturalistic Interpretation of Man's Social Behavior

tion of man's social behavior. Progress in this direction might be described in terms of an asymptotic growth curve, with scientific discovery slowly approaching, but never quite reaching, naturalistic explanation. Many research gains have been made, but the goal of adequate understanding remains elusive.

It must be recognized that knowledge of the social world does not yet exist for the fetus; any pattern of genetic capacities or potentialities it may possess must therefore lack specific social orientation. The kind and range of opportunities provided the infant for learning about the social world will tend to have a determining influence on the way these general biological tensions become expressed in patterns of specific social tendencies.

Such opportunities for learning are now known to occur in ways and under conditions early researchers could not have anticipated. Recent research yields evidence that the prenatal environment may significantly influence the child's development in numerous ways. Maternal fatigue, maternal emotional states, maternal dietary and smoking habits, maternal infection (German measles, for example), all have a bearing on the activity and well-being of the fetus. Landreth suggests: "In fact it would appear that after decades of disproving misconceptions that maternal impressions mark the unborn child, we may be on the threshold of discovering a much closer relationship between the physiology and functioning of the mother and her child than we previously thought existed."[14]

Research using anthropoid subjects, previously discussed, yields striking evidence that even organs of sensation and perception require maturation and use before they can function adequately. Environmental factors like diet, drugs, climate, and opportunity for exercise and training may accelerate or retard this process of maturation, and may enhance or limit possibilities for use.[15]

The crucial problem facing scientists concerned with identifying the wellsprings of man's motive structure is the lack of valid information sources. It is as yet quite impossible for science to tap and record the inner mental life of the fetus or of the newborn infant. Our only evidences are obtained through biochemical and neurophysiological research and through observations of behavior. A rigorous scientific approach does not permit imputing motives, concerns, hopes, fears, and other subjective states on the basis of observable data alone. Logic and research both point to the folly of such efforts.

DIFFUSED CHARACTER OF INFANT BEHAVIOR

Through observation we learn that the newborn infant's first physical movements are diffused, undifferentiated, and seemingly trial-and-error efforts. Present evidence suggests that his sensory equipment is also lacking in precision. Insofar as we know, his eyes, when first opened, cannot organize light waves into meaningful forms. His ears do not seem to find meaning in the sound waves of his environment. Just as he must learn through trial and error to differentiate his own body parts from parts of his external environment, he must learn to identify the noises he makes as distinct from sounds about him. His sensory equipment is available to him, but it has to mature through use, and he must learn to make use of it.

The generalized energy sources of the newborn infant seem to lack direction toward specific purposes, goals, or concerns. The pattern of energy is structured to some degree by the unique pattern of glandular organization with which the individual has been endowed. There exists the potentiality for a wide range of output, but the way in which the energy potential is directed and developed into the intricate pattern we know in later years seems to be the result of long and continuous transaction between the infant and its environment. The orchestration of these varied potentialities—the matrix of personal and social motives, the modes of coping with misfortunes and challenges, the details of personality style—all these things that comprise the richness of human life grow out of the experiences of socialization.

To the extent that the child is born with a "motive structure," as Murphy contends, "motives" or "drives" present at birth are energy imbalances.[16] They cannot become object oriented or socially directed until the child has acquired object and social meanings through the experience of transacting with his environment. Thus it is meaningless to say that the newborn loves, hates, fears, wants, desires, seeks, or strives. For all these terms imply the knowledge of a love object, a hate object, a feared object, a wanted object, and so on. Knowledge of the presence or absence of these objects and of their nature is not available to the infant until he has had experience in living.

CONCLUSIONS AND IMPLICATIONS

Present knowledge concerning the role of heredity and environment in human development leads to an unequivocal rejection of instinct explanations for social motivation, social beliefs, social attitudes, or social behaviors. The child is not born with a set of values, or with a pattern of goals, or with a set of rules of human conduct, or with a sense of love, affection, or trust for other human beings. These are man-made things that are imparted to him in early childhood.

The wide range of interests, concerns, and wants we call human, and the intricate means each man develops for attaining satisfactions or for coping with difficulties, were not presented to him at birth. They cannot be passed along from generation to generation through the germ cells. They must be learned anew by each infant through the slow, tedious, but remarkably efficient process known as socialization.

Children learn to be clean or dirty, active or sloven, cooperative or competitive, submissive or aggressive, tender or cruel. They learn to love and to hate, to share and to steal, to run or to fight. Their health behaviors, no less than other behaviors, are acquired.

Is the Concept of Motivation Necessary?

One cannot leave this discussion of motivation without recognizing that some psychologists, Skinner and Gewirtz, for example, question the need for positing any theory of motivation, and deny the necessity of explaining behavioral responses in terms of motives.[17] Proponents of the view feel that one can adequately describe and explain human behavior without resorting to such hypothetical constructs as drives, needs, or motives. They prefer to speak of response repertoires which become conditioned to cue stimuli in the environment. Further attention to this point of view will be given in the discussion of principles of learning in Chapter 24.

Implications

Controversy regarding the primary sources of man's motivation is of little interest to public health officers who are primarily concerned with helping people to make better health choices. An awareness of the deep and confusing currents of man's subconscious life may, however, help them understand the difficulties that confront individuals in making health decisions. As yet, however, our knowledge of the pattern and organization of these subconscious undercurrents is not adequate to form the basis for a mass program planning.

Perhaps, rather than being concerned with the origin of the primary sources of man's motivation, public health officials need to focus their attention on the directions through which these sources of energy are expressed. Knowing the "why" of man's motivation is of use primarily insofar as it is helpful in identifying the direction of his behavior and ways of influencing the direction that behavior may take. Research regarding the nature of tissue needs and their sources, whether genetic or environmental, is not likely to yield such answers.

Serious errors may result from limiting an analysis of motivations underlying some health action either to internally derived tensions, desires, or instincts, or, contrariwise, to external goals or incentives. The relationship between the two is paramount to understanding. Internal tensions may lead the individual to act. He may or may not be aware of the causes of his tensions. Previous experiences, however, aid him in determining the direction and pattern of his action. The ultimate goal may be clear and demanding. Yet in spite of a high level of tension, he may fail to move toward this goal if the intermediate steps are perceived as threatening, unpleasant, untrustworthy, or in some way potentially damaging to his ego.

Man is not an independent isolate. The transactions between man and environment are continuous from conception to death. The growing evidence regarding the influence of environmental transactions, both physical and social, on the nature of the responses of the individual even during the earliest hours of life lead one to question whether it is any longer reasonable to classify motives into primary and secondary groups. Particularly must one question the assumption or implication that those of biological origin are of primary concern and those that seem to have their bases in the culture are secondary or are derivatives of the former. Rather than one group of motives developing out of the other group, the two seem to be reciprocal in their transactions and inseparably bound together. Rather than some actions being governed by biological motivations and others by social motivations, all actions seem to be governed by indissectible fusion of both types of motives.

How strange it is, then, that even among the scientists who most strongly question the instinct theory and would deplore its use in explaining the complexity of adult life are some who still tend to react toward man as primarily a biological rather than a social being, and tend to treat him and to study him without reference to the social world that has helped to shape him and of which he is an integral part.

NOTES TO CHAPTER 14

1. Dunlap, Knight, "Are There Any Instincts?" *Journal of Abnormal and Social Psychology,* vol. 14, December, 1919, pp. 307–311.

2. Bernard, Luther L., "The Misuse of Instinct in the Social Sciences," *Psychological Review,* vol. 28, March, 1921, pp. 97–119.

3. Idem, *Instinct.* Henry Holt Co., New York, 1924.

4. Young, Paul T., *Motivation and Emotion.* John Wiley and Sons, New York, 1961.

5. Murphy, Gardner, "Social Motivation" in Lindzey, Gardner, editor, *Handbook of Social Psychology.* Addison-Wesley Publishing Co., Reading, Mass., 1954, vol. 2, p. 628.

6. Cannon, Walter, *Wisdom of the Body.* W. W. Norton and Co., New York, 1932.

7. Toch, Hans H., and Albert H. Hastorf, "Homeostasis in Psychology," *Psychiatry,* vol. 18, February, 1955, pp. 81–91.

8. Frank, Lawrence K., *Feelings and Emotions.* Doubleday Papers in Psychology, no. 3. Doubleday and Co., Garden City, N.Y., 1954, p. 4.

9. *Ibid.,* p. 5.

10. *Ibid.,* p. 18.

11. Allee, Warder C., Henry W. Nissen, and Meyer Nimkoff, "Re-examination of the Concept of Instinct," *Psychological Review,* vol. 60, September, 1953, pp. 287–297.

12. Newcomb, Theodore M., *Social Psychology.* The Dryden Press, New York, 1950, p. 83.

13. Murphy, Gardner, *op. cit.*, p. 609.

14. Landreth, Catherine, *The Psychology of Early Childhood*. Alfred A. Knopf, Inc., New York, 1958, p. 42.

15. Riesen, Austin H., "Arrested Vision," *Scientific American*, vol. 183, July, 1950, pp. 16–19.

16. Murphy, Gardner, *Personality: A Biosocial Approach to Origins and Structure*. Harper and Bros., New York, 1947.

17. Skinner, B. F., *The Behavior of Organisms*. Appleton-Century-Crofts, Inc., New York, 1938; Idem, *Science and Human Behavior*, Macmillan Co., New York, 1953; Gewirtz, Jacob L., "A Learning Analysis of the Effects of Normal Stimulation, Privation and Deprivation on the Acquisition of Social Motivation and Attachment" in Foss, B. M., editor, *Determinants of Infant Behavior, Proceedings* of a Tavistock Study Group on Mother-Infant Interaction Held in the House of the CIBA Foundation, London, September, 1959, John Wiley and Sons, New York, 1961, pp. 213–303.

Chapter 15

Motivation Research:
An Elusive Challenge

HEALTH BEHAVIOR seems so inseparably linked to motivation that logic impels one to orient any discussion of health practices to human needs and human motives. This applies whether we seek understanding of an individual's overt health practices, insights regarding his health beliefs, knowledges, attitudes, and perceptions, or some understanding of his personal and group activities that may be of concern to cooperative efforts in the community. Even an appreciation of interpersonal and intrastaff relations and communications involves knowledge of personal and group dynamics.

Unfortunately, an enormous gap exists between knowing that health behavior is motivated and identifying the specific motivational components of any particular act. Lest behavioral science approaches be grasped by public health leaders as the quick and easy means of determining health motivations, it seems essential that some attention be drawn to the complexities of research in this area. Behavioral sciences have made remarkable progress during the past few decades in developing theory and method for studying the dynamics of behavior, but the best of approaches still yield only partial answers.

Outstanding scientists who concur in their conclusions regarding the significance of motivation to understanding behavior disagree strongly regarding the current state of scientific knowledge and theory. They often disagree also regarding the most appropriate research approach to take in attempting the solution of any particular problem. Each of many research centers can offer partial answers that have proved useful for specific purposes; thoroughly valid generalized conclusions remain elusive.

PROBLEMS OF DEFINITION

The study of motivation pertains to the *why* of man's behavior.[1] It is therefore concerned with identifying complex causal relationships in situations that usually preclude experimental variation and control. Precise validation of findings is seldom possible, for such research is far more difficult to conduct than is research that is concerned with descriptive data.

Man is ever part of the content he studies when his efforts concern research on human motivation. No way has been found to isolate completely the research subject matter from experimental and social biases. We do not, as yet, know how to parcel out any single motive and examine it apart from the constellation in which it is embedded, or to determine the relative weights and priorities of motives within the constellation. Nor have adequate techniques been developed for separating motives from the behavior through which they are expressed. Baffling indeed are the problems related to separating goals, means, and ends, distinguishing short-term motives from enduring value constellations, differentiating conscious desires from subconscious pressures.

Even the definition of "motive" may involve fundamental assumptions about man's behavior. As English and English note, "Originally, *motive* strongly carried the meaning of a *conscious* factor, something of which one was aware. The psychoanalytic schools preserve the distinction but postulate conscious and *unconscious* motives. Currently, *motive* tends to lose all connotation of that which can be known by the actor: it is employed even in animal experimentation and by behaviorists. . . . Partial synonyms, often used interchangeably, are *drive, want, need, incentive,* each of which has specific meanings."[2]

As in many situations that involve theoretical considerations, apparent inconsistencies or disagreements may reflect differences in levels of conceptualization. A different pattern of assumptions and meanings is involved, when attention is focused on human motivation at the physiological or biogenic level such as physiological drives, needs, and tensions, than is of concern when social motives are the focus of discussion, as in the present instance. MacKinnon notes: "The problem of motivation, narrowly conceived, is the problem of discovering the motives of human beings; but, broadly viewed, it is the problem of determining the forces which impel or incite all living organisms to action."[3]

Personal motives are unique to the individual. Seldom, if ever, in daily life does there seem to be a clear-cut one-to-one relationship between a single motive and a single action. Rather, each individual tends to react as a total organism and a complex of conscious and subconscious motivating forces seem to underly his every action. The dominating motives of the moment seem to be those that are germane in terms of the immediate situation as he perceives it.

CONFLICTING MOTIVES

Conflicts between motives are ever present and need to be resolved as best they can by the acting individual. Conflicts between short-term and long-term goals, for example, are of frequent occurrence. An immediate demand for social stimulation and the enticement of exotic food and drink may be at odds with vague desires for a long and healthy maturity. The challenges of peers and the need to "belong" frequently lead one to take risks in the water, on the mountains, or on the highways that threaten achievement of occupational pursuits toward which one has high strivings. Immediate desires for short-term satisfactions often lead to expenditures of time, effort, and monies that are not in keeping with sincerely held long-term aspirations. Predicting behavior from knowledge of existing motives when such conflicts are present is hazardous indeed.

An individual may at once love and hate, desire and reject, want and fear the same thing. He may, for example, want and seek help, yet reject it when offered through fear or distrust of the way help is provided, or fear of the consequences of action. He may suffer undue tension from feelings of conflict between strong desires for treatment of a persistent pain in the chest, a lingering sore throat, a dull abdominal pain, or severe genital discomfort, and fears of learning the cause of his malady. This is particularly likely to occur if he believes the illness is one that cannot be cured, or if he thinks it could be one which, if identified, might threaten his acceptance by his fellow men. Failure to accept diagnosis when strong social pressures exist may reflect such fears of the consequences of identifying the cause of illness.[4]

INFERRING MOTIVES

Since individuals are unaware of all the dynamic factors influencing their reactions, motives cannot be studied directly. Motives are slithery things and creep into our lives in ways we can neither always anticipate nor identify. They must be inferred from observations concerning behavior, including, of course, verbal responses.

It is hazardous, however, to infer motives from observed behavior, for individuals frequently perform similar actions for different, even conflicting, reasons. Among a group of people lined up for voluntary x-rays, for example, one person may feel certain he is healthy, and volunteer to demonstrate his ability to "pass the test"; another may fear he has tuberculosis and seek to find out for certain before serious complications develop; a third person may have minimal interest or concern about his health, but volunteers in order to be like and with his friends; a fourth may seek to demonstrate to his friends that he is different from the rest.

It is equally hazardous to predict specific behavior from similar motives, for persons with apparently similar motives may express themselves in conflicting ways. One who fears he is ill may seek early diagnosis and treatment; another with like fears may try to conceal from others—and even from himself—that he might be ill; others with similar concerns and a desire to obtain help may avoid diagnosis and treatment because they distrust the methods of detection or lack faith in the possibilities of effective treatment.

MOTIVE—RESPONSE RELATIONSHIPS

In order to make effective use of information obtained about health beliefs, interests, and concerns, it is necessary, therefore, to know not only the patterns of motives, but also the ways the individuals concerned see as the most effective means they have of satisfying these concerns. The person who wants to know whether or not he has early symptoms of tuberculosis may not volunteer for a chest x-ray in a survey unless he perceives this to be the best means *for him* to find out. He may rather seek diagnosis from a private physician or from some other source in which he has faith.[5]

The relationship between motive and response patterns is an intricate one, far less sharply defined than might seem apparent to the rational observer. Each reaction of an individual seems to have emotional and value attributes that cannot meaningfully be isolated for purposes of research or analysis.

Either in attempting to identify motives, or in making plans to tie programs to existing motive patterns, we need, therefore, to be sensitive that "motives and mechanisms for their expression constitute a psychological whole."[6] It is in some ways as meaningless to speak of a person's motives without considering his manner of striving for them as to speak of his actions without attempting to consider the purposes they serve.

THE VALUE QUALITY OF EXPERIENCE

A person may eagerly strive to maintain good physical condition through frequent home exercises or through participation in a recreation program, but may have no interest whatever in reaching the same goal by working in the garden or following a better nutrition program. The process of striving in a particular way may yield greater satisfactions than achievement of the goal.

Cantril has suggested that "an outstanding characteristic of man is his capacity to sense the value in the quality of his experience" and that this is "a pervasive and inseparable aspect of every experience. All human wants, urges, desires, and aspirations are permeated with some value attribute."[7] Cantril continues:

> You sense the satisfying value of experience from a job well done; from helping to accomplish a community, national, or humanitarian task; from having met or exceeded your own expectations or the expectations others have of you. You sense a value attribute in the exhilaration, the sense of well-being you may get, from climbing a mountain, from a swim in a lake or the sea, from a good game of tennis or golf. You feel a richness of experience as you watch your children grow and develop. You sense a high quality from the experience of helping a friend or doing a deed which you know is good. You sense a value attribute in creativity whether that creativity involves baking a tasty loaf of bread, making your garden grow, raising hogs, cattle, or grain, putting together a homemade radio, repairing a broken machine, painting a picture, or writing a poem or a sonata. You sense a value attribute in experience when you learn something useful for your purpose, when you make sense out of something; and you share the value attributes of a child's experience when you see his sense of satisfaction in learning to tell time, in learning to read, in learning his first simple additions. You sense value attributes in the humble, ordinary activities of life: in saying "hello" to a neighbor, in cleaning your house, in taking a bath after a hard day's work. You sense the value attributes of disappointment, disturbance, or sorrow when things go wrong.[8]

The process of participating in some group or community activity may yield satisfactions distinct from the satisfactions of group achievement. Persons may participate for these group satisfactions even though they are not initially concerned about the community problem.

Interest in the goal may actually grow out of the participation.[9] Understanding how an individual or a group of individuals behaves requires an understanding of the process of that behavior as well as the nature of individual or group strivings.[10]

VALIDITY OF RESPONSES

Researchers have long recognized that the reasons people give for their behavior, or for the wants, concerns, or intentions they express cannot safely be taken at face value. Man has a remarkable capacity for concealing from others, and even from himself, the intimate purposes underlying his actions. He may forget, suppress, or repress disturbing fears or socially unacceptable desires. He may rationalize away threatening self-evaluations, or reasons for error, failure, or weakness. He may seek to escape responsibility for motives, feelings, or actions by projecting them on other persons.

An individual who is sensitive about being queried about his health feelings, beliefs, actions, or intentions, or other matters of deep personal significance may consciously evade questions by lying, distorting, or exaggerating. Also, without intending to be evasive, but actually by trying to help the interviewer do a better job, he may give answers he thinks the interviewer is seeking rather than those that best apply with respect to his own behavior. But in addition to these fairly direct ways of distorting responses he may unconsciously employ any one or all of a wide range of techniques for evasion or defense, such as those referred to above. Thus the researcher is left with a most difficult task of trying to uncover truth in a maze of conflicting evidences.

INDIRECT METHODS

Psychologists have responded to these challenges of motivation research by inventing a wide array of indirect, nondirective, and projective techniques for eliciting information. Among the best known of these are depth interviews, word association tests, incompleted sentence techniques, the Rorschach or ink-blot test, and the Thematic Apperception Test in which the patient is asked to tell a story about each of a series of pictures. Hundreds of other novel approaches are also in use.

Projective techniques have become indispensable tools for the diagnosis and treatment of mental illness, and for research on problems of mental illness. By using them along with more conventional methods of inquiry, the trained clinician is often able to uncover hidden meanings of behavior, conflicts in personal and social desires and purposes, and problems the patient may be unable or unwilling to verbalize. He may thus disclose emotional blocks, fears, or concerns which interfere with effective personal and social functioning.

These techniques are also employed by behavioral scientists to study social issues in which there may be high public involvement and long traditional commitment to certain patterns of behavior and response.[11] Such issues may not be susceptible to research by more conventional methods of inquiry and analysis. When people are emotionally involved in issues, they are often hesitant, unwilling, or even unable to speak openly about them, or to give frank answers to direct questions regarding their own attitudes, opinions, and beliefs. Matters that involve accepted values, standards, and norms are most difficult to study because respondents cannot free themselves from the sociocultural environment that clothes them, so they answer questions in stereotyped ways. A skillfully employed projective approach often helps such persons escape from such traditional blinders in providing information.

A Study of Attitude Formation

Horowitz employed an ingenious projective approach to study the formation of social attitudes. He developed two sets of photographs showing identical settings and activities. In one set of the pictures five white children were engaged in an activity, whereas in the matched set, one to three Negro children were included as substitutes for white children. Children were presented with the pictures and asked to indicate whether they wanted to participate. From their responses it was possible to complete a "willingness to join in" score, by which reactions to the all-white and the mixed-group pictures could be compared. By employing this indirect approach in his study of children in northern and southern grade schools, he learned that white children acquire their social prejudices from contact with persons holding such prejudices rather than as a result of direct experience with Negroes.[12]

The Study of Rumor

In a somewhat similar manner, pictures of white and colored persons in various roles were used by Allport and Postman to study the development and spread of rumors during World War II. Their research holds many implications for the practice of public health. Pictures developed in this research have been widely used in group discussions of racial attitudes and their effects.[13]

Marketing Research

Marketing and advertising agencies employ many projective methods in efforts to improve their services. The publication of various techniques in use,[14] together with a popular exposé of the extent of the practice and of dangers to the public presumably inherent in research designed to take advantage of subconscious responses,[15] has resulted in much public interest in motivation research.

A novel experiment by Haire illustrates the value of projective techniques when employed by the expert to explore personality factors related to behavior. He was interested in learning how housewives characterize women who buy instant coffee as compared with those who use regular coffee, and recognized that direct questions on such an issue would tend to yield stereotyped or defensive responses. A projective method was therefore indicated.

Two shopping lists were prepared similar in all ways except that one included Nescafé and the other Maxwell House Coffee. In an interview with women shoppers, alternate respondents were asked to read one or the other shopping list and write a brief description of the personality of the woman using the shopping list.

Haire found that women described the Nescafé shoppers more often as lazy, poor planners, poor wives, and spendthrifts. In follow-up visits to the homes of women interviewed, it was determined whether they had Nescafé or regular coffee on the shelves. The findings from these home visits generally validated the information obtained from the projective approach. Women who described the Nescafé shopper as economical, a good housewife, and one who plans balanced meals were more likely to be using Nescafé than were those who described the Nescafé shopper as a poor housewife and one who does not like to, or cannot, cook.[16]

Uses in Public Health Research

Thus far projective methods have not been widely used in public health research, even though many issues of concern to public health seem to require indirect approaches. The intimate nature of personal health and health actions, the social sanctions and controls tied to health behavior, the social meanings and implications of various illnesses, the experiential and status differences both among members of the public health team and between professional and laymen, all contribute to the difficulty of obtaining frank and valid information by means of direct inquiry.

An interesting example of the effective use of this approach in public health research may be found in Hochbaum's study of public responses to mass surveys. In this study illustrations of various aspects of the chest x-ray survey were presented to laymen who were asked to interpret the actions of persons observed. Comparison was then made between the responses of persons who had obtained x-rays at mobile units, those who had obtained x-rays elsewhere, and those who had never received chest x-rays.

One illustration showed a mobile unit in service with some persons lined up to obtain x-rays, one leaving the unit, and several passing by the line. Interviewers conducting the study said: "I have several pictures I'm going to show you. The first is a picture of a place where

FIGURE 9. Illustration of Mobile X-ray Unit Employed as Projective Device

Reproduced with permission of Godfrey H. Hochbaum, Chief, Behavioral Study Section, United States Public Health Service.

people can get x-rays of their chests. You will notice that some people are getting x-rays, others seem to be passing by. Why do you think some of these people are passing by without having an x-ray?" [The worker displays the picture.]

In response to a direct question asked early in the interview, about 80 per cent of the subjects correctly stated that x-rays could detect tuberculosis in a person before he would be aware of any symptoms. However, many of those who correctly answered the information item revealed, in response to the projective question above, that they did not fully accept and believe this fact.

Answers such as the following reveal a lack of conviction that x-rays do *really* detect tuberculosis before symptoms appear: "They seem healthy—there'd be no need for them." "He probably feels O.K. It would be a waste of time." "They all seem to be healthy and strong— I don't know about this one—but the others. They don't look like they have tuberculosis." "Some may just be afraid to find out, but some don't need them, I guess. At least, they don't look like it."

By combining data obtained in response to the direct question on information with that obtained through use of the projective question, Hochbaum obtained some striking results which yield validating support for the projective approach in this situation: 76 per cent of those who were correctly informed and accepted the information (N=211) had obtained a voluntary x-ray. Only 30 per cent, however, of those who were correctly informed but did not accept the information (N= 543) had obtained an x-ray; and 20 per cent of those who were incorrectly informed and did not accept the information (N=177) had obtained an x-ray.[17]

Limitations

While these indirect ways of studying health behavior offer great promise when employed by the expert, a word of caution seems warranted. Clinical and projective tools seem to hold a special fascination for the novice who often employs costly indirect means when direct approaches would better serve his purpose. Persons untrained in the use of such clinical approaches make serious errors in the collection, analysis, interpretation, and evaluation of information obtained by these means. Findings obtained by indirect methods are often most difficult to validate, and when not adequately validated may lead program directors seriously astray.

Allport cautions that projective techniques are less appropriate for studies of "normal" subjects than they are for the study of patients who are mentally ill:

> . . . The direct responses of the psychoneurotic cannot be taken at their face value. The defenses are high; the true motives are hidden and are betrayed only by a projective technique. The normal subjects, on the other hand, tell you by the direct method precisely what they tell you by the projective method. They are all of a piece. You may therefore take their motivational statements at their face value, for, even if you probe, you will not find anything substantially different.[18]

Some psychologists would disagree with this point of view, and point to studies such as those mentioned above as evidence of effective use with normal populations. Few, however, would disagree with Allport's general conclusion that a psychodiagnostician should never employ projective techniques without at the same time employing direct methods.[19] They would insist, as does Allport, that these direct methods include depth interviewing, autobiographical reports, personality inventories, paper and pencil tests, or any other approaches oriented toward obtaining the "conscious report" of the subject:

> In speaking so frequently of "direct" methods, I have referred chiefly to "conscious reports." To ask a man his motives, however, is not the only type of "direct" method that we may employ. It is, however, a good one—especially to start with.
> When we set out to study a person's motives, we are seeking to find out what that person is trying to do in this life—including, of course, what he is trying to avoid and what he is trying to be. I see no reason why we should not start our investigation by asking him to tell us the answers as he sees them. If the questions in this form seem too abstract, they can be recast. Particularly revealing are people's answers to the question, "What do you want to be doing five years from now?" Similar direct questions can be framed to elicit anxieties, loyalties and hostilities. Most people, I suspect, can tell what they are trying to do in this life with a high degree of validity, certainly not less on the average than the prevailing validity of projective instruments. Yet some clinicians disdain to ask direct questions.[20]

IMPLICATIONS

Public health administrators cannot hope soon to have at hand simple tools for identifying the human concerns, wants, and aspirations so important in public health planning. Methods are available for obtaining partial answers, and research employing these methods is already contributing significantly to program improvement. The most valid and useful contributions can be expected to come from the efforts of skilled researchers employing a variety of approaches adapted to the specific requirements of the program.

At present, an excessive orientation to method development in motivation research tends to cloud an even greater need for theoretical development. Major contributions of motivation research to public health planning await the development and testing within public health settings of conceptualizations more adequate than those currently available.

NOTES TO CHAPTER 15

1. Cantril, Hadley, The "Why" of Man's Experience. Macmillan Co., New York, 1950.

2. English, Horace B., and Ava C. English, A Comprehensive Dictionary of Psychological and Psychoanalytical Terms. Longmans, Green and Co., New York, 1958, p. 331.

3. MacKinnon, Donald W., "Motivation" in Boring, Edwin G., Herbert S. Langfeld, and Harry P. Weld, editors, The Foundations of Psychology. John Wiley and Sons, New York, 1948, p. 112.

4. Hoyt, Cyril J., Andie L. Knutson, and C. Mayhew Derryberry, "What the People Know," Monthly Bulletin, Indiana State Board of Health: Part I, vol. 53, November, 1950, pp. 250 ff.; Part II, vol. 53, December, 1950, pp. 281 ff.

5. Hochbaum, Godfrey M., Public Participation in Medical Screening Programs: A Socio-Psychological Study. Public Health Service, U.S. Dept. of Health, Education, and Welfare, Publication 572, Government Printing Office, Washington, 1958.

6. Bird, Charles, Social Psychology. Appleton-Century-Crofts, Inc., New York, 1940, p. 30.

7. Cantril, Hadley, op. cit., p. 22.

8. Ibid., p. 23.

9. Allport, Gordon W., "The Psychology of Participation." Originally published in Psychological Review in 1945. Reprinted in Allport, Gordon W., Personality and Social Encounter: Selected Essays, Beacon Press, Boston, 1960, pp. 181–198.

10. Stock, Dorothy, and Herbert A. Thelen, Emotional Dynamics and Group Culture. New York University Press, New York, 1958.

11. Selltiz, Claire, Marie Jahoda, Morton Deutsch, and Stuart W. Cook, "Data Collection III: Projective and Other Indirect Methods" in Idem, Research Methods in Social Relations. Rev. ed. Henry Holt and Co., New York, 1959, pp. 279–314. The authors present an excellent discussion of the use of projective techniques in social research. An excellent bibliography on behavioral science research methods is included.

12. Horowitz, Eugene L., "The Development of Attitude Toward the Negro," Archives of Psychology, no. 194, 1936. See also Mussen, P. H., "Some Personality and Social Factors Relating to Changes in Children's Attitudes

Toward Negroes," *Journal of Abnormal and Social Psychology,* vol. 45, 1950, pp. 423–441.

13. Allport, Gordon W., and Leo J. Postman, *The Psychology of Rumor.* Henry Holt and Co., New York, 1947. Slides, and instructions for their use in rumor clinics, are available through Anti-Defamation League of B'nai B'rith, New York, N.Y.

14. Smith, George H., *Motivation Research in Advertising and Marketing.* McGraw-Hill Book Co., New York, 1954.

15. Packard, Vance O., *The Hidden Persuaders.* David McKay Co., New York, 1957.

16. Haire, Mason, "Projective Techniques in Market Research," *Journal of Marketing,* vol. 14, April, 1950, pp. 262–268.

17. Hochbaum, Godfrey M., *op. cit.,* p. 16.

18. Allport, Gordon W., "The Trend in Motivational Theory." Originally published in *American Journal of Orthopsychiatry* in 1953. Reprinted in Allport, Gordon W., *Personality and Social Encounter: Selected Essays, op. cit.,* p. 99.

19. *Ibid.,* p. 106.

20. *Ibid.,* pp. 100–101. Readers interested in considering various other discussions concerning the problems of measuring motives, and the relative usefulness of direct and indirect approaches, are referred to Lindzey, Gardner, editor, *Assessment of Human Motives,* Grove Press, New York, 1960; Stacey, Chalmers L., and Manfred F. DeMartino, editors, *Understanding Human Motivation,* Howard Allen, Cleveland, 1958; Nebraska Symposia, *Current Theory and Research on Motivation,* University of Nebraska Press, Lincoln, nos. 1–10, 1953–1962; Young, Paul T., *Motivation and Emotion,* John Wiley and Sons, New York, 1961.

Chapter 16

Motivation in Health Action

MAN is a purposive animal. His life is a constant struggle to satisfy wants, concerns, desires, hopes, or aspirations, and to avoid, minimize, or escape from pain, discomfort, or injury. He may, at times, be aware of the motives or concerns that govern his behavior, but often these are below the threshold of his conscious awareness, so that even he may not understand the dynamics underlying his daily reactions. Thus his day-to-day behavior is ruled by needs and purposes of which he may be unaware, as well as by his conscious decisions and intentions.

This purposive man has at his disposal a wide range of means for achieving his goals or for protecting himself from real or imagined threat or discomfort—for coping effectively with his physical and social environment. Some of these means are acquired in infancy and have become so thoroughly integrated into the response patterns of the individual that he may be quite unaware of the wide range of responses he has at his disposal. Nor is he likely to realize how much he resorts to their use, often for unrecognized purposes.

The relationships between conscious and subconscious motivating factors and the many direct and circuitous means taken to satisfy motives are confusing indeed. Those who seek to describe such relationships must wallow in the muddiest of theoretical waters. Yet attempts must be made to organize present knowledge if we are to advance in our efforts to understand man's health behavior and predict his responses to opportunities provided for health action.

Those concerned with the solution of practical public health problems sometimes argue that they have greater need to know *what approach* will work rather than *why* it will work. Many of their decisions must be based on empirical evidence. When empirical data are not available, however, decisions must be made on the basis of theoretical evidence alone. The theory must then prove itself by yielding practical returns. Most useful is a union of practice and theory, with theory

225

yielding general principles to employ in making decisions that can be tested by empirical observation.

For most purposes in public health practice it is not necessary to distinguish between needs, drives, or wants. It is not essential to know the exact language of the behavioral scientist who must make distinctions in order to test his theories; nor is it particularly useful to know, for most purposes, whether the motivation involved stems from innate or acquired sources, is primary or secondary in origin, biological or social in nature. For those interested in the mass of conflicting evidence in support of, or in opposition to, various theories of motivation currently under debate there are excellent sources available.

Any theory of social motivation should help us understand the selective nature of perception, emotion, and action. What determines the choices we make in giving primary attention to this or that feature of environment? What leads us to respond differently to what may seem to be similar situations? What factors underlie the priorities we give on matters concerning health, education, occupation, entertainment, dress, family life, and so on?

Such a demand is most difficult for any theory of motivation to satisfy. Similar motives may be expressed through many kinds of behaviors, and any single action may be the expression of many motives. The theory would also need to be one that applies equally to avoidance or escape behavior and to behaviors oriented toward search and attainment. It should not be necessary to employ what has been referred to as a "pitchfork theory" to explain one, and a "carrot theory" to explain the other.[1]

Behavioral scientists do not agree at present on any single theory of motivation that fully satisfies such criteria. Much progress has been made, however, and many approaches have proved useful in prediction and understanding.

Attention here is given to one approach that seems particularly useful in understanding and predicting those social behaviors with which public health workers are most concerned in their daily work. It may serve also as a point of departure in evaluating one's own daily transactions with staff, peers, or superiors and in interpreting the health decisions of primary recipients of the public health programs, community opinion leaders and decision-makers, and other agency representatives.

AN OVERVIEW

The motives that underlie social behavior are not independent forces guiding or directing behavior. How motives are expressed in any situation depends upon the nature of that situation and the way the situation is perceived, interpreted, and judged, as well as upon the pattern of concerns, wants, hopes, or expectations the individual brings to the situation. It is therefore not usually useful to consider health motivations apart from the network of situational factors present and perceived.

Some attention has already been given to the uniqueness of each man's subjective life and to the way each person develops, through experience, his own private world which serves him in judging the significance of alternatives. It has been emphasized that the first step in understanding his health behavior and in predicting future health action involves determining how he defines the situation, what significance he recognizes in it for himself and others, how he defines his role, and what alternative possibilities he perceives for action. Such a step in obtaining his definition of the situation and its significance for him is a long step toward understanding his motivations in that particular situation.

When we speak of social motivation, then, we are concerned with man as a social animal, acting as a unified social being, enmeshed in, and part of, his biological, physical, and social environment. His health behavior, no less than other behavior, is caused behavior, even though the precise nature or pattern of causation can seldom, if ever, be specifically identified. There is purpose underlying such actions as participating in a health survey, taking a medical examination, or discussing a significant problem. Motives are also expressed both through one's feelings and emotions, and through one's perceptions, rememberings, knowings, beliefs, and attitudes.

In general, man's behavior tends to be future oriented. It tends to be governed by his expectations regarding the actions most likely to be effective in protecting, extending, or enhancing his own position as he defines it.

Within his private world man reflects upon himself as well as others and things. He observes, judges, and directs his own behavior. To the extent that he is aware of the alternative choices for action and their significance for him, he tends to be governed by what he expects these alternatives to mean to him personally. His behavior thus tends to be guided in terms of the expectations he holds regarding the actions most likely to protect, to extend, or to enhance his self or ego as he perceives it.

Man's ego-orientations may guide his behavior by subconscious as well as conscious ways. Undercurrents of self-interest so cloud perceptions, judgments, expectations, and anticipations—and in such subtle, hidden ways—that neither oneself nor others can ever be fully aware of the extent or manner in which personal interest is involved in any particular decision or action.

THE FUTURE ORIENTATION OF BEHAVIOR

Man constantly seeks the meaning that future events hold for him and for persons or things of significance to himself. He reviews and evaluates past and present happenings in order better to deal with the future. In Kelly's words, "He lives in anticipation; we mean this literally; *he lives in anticipation!* His behavior is governed, not simply by *what* he anticipates—whether good or bad, pleasant or unpleasant, self-vindicating or self-confounding—but by *where* he believes his choices will place him in respect to the remaining turns in the road. If he chooses this fork in the road, will it lead to a better vantage point from which to see the road beyond or will it be the one that abruptly brings him face-to-face with a blank wall?"[2]

The assumptions that serve man as the basis for anticipating and expecting a particular pattern of future events tend to evolve from his evaluations of past and current situations and events. The assumptions are, in one sense, based upon his best estimates of probabilities regarding future alternatives, as suggested by what has occurred in the past.[3] Man seems to select and act upon those future alternatives that make the best sense in terms of his own situation and purposes without being fully aware of the intricate weighing and judging process that takes place below the level of his conscious awareness.

Man's social behavior, whether in private or public life, seems predicated on what he expects the future to be and on what he expects others to do in the moments, days, or years ahead. This applies with respect both to simple actions such as extending one's hand, offering an arm, or opening a door, and to the more complex behaviors such as going to school, learning a trade, rearing a family, building a home, writing a book, investing in stocks and bonds, obtaining health check-ups, or buying health insurance. Even the thanks man offers his God for past bounties are tied to hopes and prayers for future support, guidance, and protection.

The future orientation of man's perceptions and actions is well illustrated by the manner in which he drives a car. The man who drives his car on the highway is continuously governed in his behavior by what he expects others about him to do. He stops if he expects the car ahead to stop, or speeds with it if he expects its driver to continue to move fast. He turns to avoid the path he expects an oncoming car to take, and in doing so may guide his own car directly at some other car, with a sense of assurance that the other driver will move out of his way at the appropriate moment. Error in any of these expectations would lead to disaster. Yet what frightening confusion would exist if man did not act in terms of such expectations!

Man's subjective life also tends to be future-oriented. By night and by day he dreams of the future, building and destroying castles or dungeons at will. In reliving the day's events in thought or in dreams he glows over achievements and broods over failures, changing outcomes at will. He speculates on the future his dreams may foretell or worries about possible vague implications they may forebode. In his imagination he may examine the various alternatives suggested by his previous experiences and thus pretests in his own mind the effectiveness of different courses of action. By anticipating outcomes in this way, he tries to become better prepared to deal with difficult problems that may arise and to reject opportunities that could lead to failure, injury, unpleasantness, or other damage to his ego.

The health officer may anticipate the inquiries of members of his advisory board and pretest, in his own mind or with others, the manner of dealing with the issues that may come up. A staff member may test out in his own mind the probable reaction to a question, and may withhold even the most insightful of observations if he anticipates a negative or critical response. A quiet, sensitive staff member may fail to contribute either critical insights or creative ideas rather than expose himself to the discomfort of a verbal defense of his position. The expectations of the staff determine whether the open-door policy of the health officer is identified as an additional channel for upward communications or as a technique for identifying and screening out the trouble-makers.

Narrow, indeed, are the gaps between jest and threat, humor and mockery, assistance and charity, deference and submission, curious probing and diagnostic technique. When an action, a comment, or an experience permits alternative interpretations along such axes, the expectations of individuals tend to govern the manner of interpretation that results. When false, therefore, the assumptions that guide our expectations may lead us to serious error in judgment and response.

THE SELF OR EGO

The self or ego each man seeks to defend, extend, or enhance may bear only the slightest relationship to his physical self. It includes all his feelings of identification with, and loyalty to, other persons or groups, places, things, or ideas, whether present or past, tangible or intangible, real or imagined. Thus it includes all those attachments he has acquired as the acting center of his private world. The self or ego, so defined, exists for man as a subjective fact, specific for each individual, compelling in its demands, the core of all that is important to him. Every individual's subjective self or ego is a product of experience in his own private world. It is personally defined through the give-and-take experience of growing up in a particular situation. One man's private world is likely to have certain characteristics similar to those of other persons growing up in like circumstances, but the features held in common with others do not completely overshadow the significance of individual differences.[4]

A person reflects upon his self and gives recognition to himself as distinct from other persons or things in using the pronouns "I," "my," "we," or "ours"; he also implies the presence of a self in distinguishing "you," "yours," "theirs," or "its." Sherif and Cantril identify ego-attitudes as including attitudes "toward my parents, my school, my gang, my church, my nation, my boss, my friend; toward my friend's rival, my father's competitor, my country's enemy, and so on. Most attitudes have the characteristic of belonging to me, of being part of me, as psychologically experienced."[5]

Man begins to develop his ego in childhood as he acquires an awareness of the significance of the world to him. In his search for meaning he learns to attach value to objects, to things, to people, and to ideas in terms of the significance they appear to have for future action. The self or ego becomes the center of his universe. All things are perceived and judged in relation to it. As he learns more about his environment and identifies certain things as goal objects or incentives, it is *he* who wants them; it is *he* who seeks them, who may be satisfied by them, who may use them to defend himself. He avoids things he perceives as dangerous or potentially dangerous because they may hurt *him* or what is important to him. Thus ego-extension, ego-enhancement, and ego-defense do seem to be the focal point for most human effort.

Ego-Involvement versus Egotism

To say that man tends to judge success or failure, satisfaction or disappointment, according to such a standard of ego-threat and ego-satisfaction, does not imply, however, that he is always ego-centered and egotistical. It should not be interpreted to mean that his actions tend to be self-seeking, preoccupied with personal interests, or insensitive to the desires and feeling of others. Nor does it mean that he is in love with his self-image, conceited in his orientation, or dominated by excessive self-regard.

Man may become ego-involved in many far-flung and diverse things. His concerns are often with matters remote from his body and remote even from his social self as others may perceive it. They may be centered in past or future events, ideological, scientific, or religious issues, objects of unique personal significance. Great importance may be given to matters that seem to have little immediate bearing upon daily life, or to things having no apparent social worth. Or prime significance may be given to the most idealized of goals and the most altruistic of behaviors.

It is not unusual to find individuals who have a high stake in ideas or events that may lead to their destruction. Intangible though these identifications may be, they may cause the individual to act in ways that can only with great difficulty be linked in any way to personal gain or defense. One man may starve or make great personal sacrifice so that some distant battle may be fought; another, so that some explosive idea may be tested; a third, so that appropriate tribute may be paid to an unseen God. Each by his actions has placed a higher immediate value on the idea identified with than upon his own physical well-being.

Ego-Involvement and Health Behavior

Nor is it difficult to note ways in which ego-involvements influence health behavior. The man having little ego-involvement in the ideas of personal responsibility and self-reliance may show slight evidence of concern with having his children supported by public funds and make no effort to seek employment in order to support them. Another may be so involved in the idea of self-reliance that he would rather watch his children starve than to permit them to touch public funds. A third, fearful of the loss of love and pride that might accompany the identification of some "social disease," may conceal serious infection, avoid medical examination, and thus threaten the lives of those whose love and respect he seeks to hold.

Whether a mother will take recommended health action to protect her infant may not depend only on her expectation regarding the effectiveness of this action. Of even deeper importance may be the mother's orientation regarding the value to the child as an extension of her self. If children are highly prized in her value system, and she identifies strongly with her child, her action may be different from the way it would be if she conformed to the values of a society in which children are not highly prized, or where male infants have a high value and female infants little value. Different, too, may be the behavior of the mother in a culture in which infants are not considered members of the family until they have managed to live through the diseases and injuries of childhood. Then they are welcomed as full members of the group. In such a situation a mother may protect her ego against the possible injury resulting from identification with the child who becomes disabled or dies by refusing to accept the infant as a member of the family until he has survived long enough to permit safe attachment.

CHANGES IN THE SELF OR EGO

The self, or ego, man seeks to protect, extend, and enhance is a product of his private world, and like other subjective facts of that private world is constantly changing. His anticipations and expectations also change with growth and experience, for new experiences that influence the pattern and intensity of an individual's identifications and loyalties will tend to influence also the nature of his anticipations and expectations. What appears most interesting or significant today may be tossed aside tomorrow.

Man's expectations regarding the future are frequently in error, for he must often anticipate situations or things with which he has had no previous experience. For lack of experience he may be unaware of useful cues for planning effective actions and unable to evaluate appropriately the outcome of matters of current importance. His ties to environment change with each new step in growth and with each meaningful transaction, and each change influences his assessment of present and coming events.[6]

Changes During Adolescence

For example, as an adolescent boy grows into the new social world which includes girls, his group identifications change and many specific ego attitudes may be influenced. His awakened interest in the mixed groups may lead him to have increased concern about his acceptance by others and about the image they may hold of him. The image he holds of himself is likely to undergo a change in focus as he becomes interested in whatever he perceives about himself that may lead him to attract and to hold dates. What barriers seem to stand in his way? Acne? Unattractive teeth? Blemishes? Physical defects? Being overweight or underweight? Speech defects? Difficulties in social adaptation?

To the adolescent, these are urgent concerns. They may even be of such intimate significance that he may be fearful of admitting them, or quite unable to express them rationally to persons who could be of help. His self-image is threatened, and he needs support as well as assistance. An older confidante who treats such concerns lightly, feeling that the youth will grow out of them, or that they will become less important with age, may be seen as expressing an indifference and lack of interest in the individual himself.

An Illustration: The Various Meanings of "Hospital"

The manner in which age and family differences influence health definitions may be seen in the responses of two teenagers, a young mother, a middle-aged father, and two older women to questions about the meaning to each of them of "hospital." Each responds from a different perspective which reflects his own ego-involvement in hospitals.

In an exploratory interview the following three questions were employed to determine the meanings people hold for the concept "hospital." The interviewer was well trained in the use of nondirective probes such as "anything else?" "so?" "uh huh," "and?" "how do you mean?" and the like. Unless specifically indicated in the text, no direct questions were used. The use of a nondirective probe is indicated by "?" The brief interviews reported verbatim below were selected to illustrate wide variance in meanings given to the word "hospital." They were not, however, atypical interviews for their age groups.

QUESTION 1: "I've been asked to find out what people think of when the word 'hospital' comes up. What would you say most people think of in connection with the word 'hospital'?"

QUESTION 2: "What kinds of questions come to your mind when the word 'hospital' is mentioned?"

QUESTION 3: "Now I wonder if you would give me a brief statement of what the word 'hospital' means to you."

Subject A: A fifteen-year-old high school boy, son of a university professor, interviewed at home.

Answers to Questions

QUESTION 1: I don't know, if I had never heard the word . . . (?) The place where sick people go to get treated; where injured people go for help. (?) You think of medicine, pills, doctors, nurses. (?) Of the operation rooms and things like that, I guess, and another thing—of everybody wearing white. (?) Just about run out—whatever that means. I don't know. Regarding hospital beds—they have those cranks on it. (?) Shots—Gee, I don't know—that would be about it, I guess.

QUESTION 2: Oh well, I wonder what people are doing there—I mean they come there for treatment for . . . black eye or treatment for . . . being at the door, you want to look in and see what is happening. (?) Just curiosity to see what the patient looks like—it's just curiosity to see what the patient looks like. It's just curiosity to see what happened to the patient. (?) I suppose you wonder what the equipment is sometimes—that is all of the questions I have; most of the question would be looking at the people—what happened to them.

QUESTION 3: Would be about the same as the first time. The hospital was the place where sick people and injured people would come for treatment to make them well again.

Subjects B and C: A seventeen-year-old Negro boy and a sixteen-year-old Negro girl interviewed together in a park in a low socioeconomic neighborhood. The boy was employed and had to leave for work before the interview was completed.

Answers to Questions

QUESTION 1: *Girl:* I think it should be a quiet area. Around here wouldn't be good. *Boy:* It should be where there's not much traffic. (?) *Boy:* Maybe if you talk more. *Girl:* I've never given it much thought. *Boy:* Well, people want a small playground. (?) *Boy:* For kids that are not sick. Something like a gymnasium for grown-ups too. They like to get exercise. And library they ought to have. (?) *Girl:* It's a place for the sick people. (?) *Girl:* I can't think of something else. *Boy:* I worked at a hospital, Veterinarians, on Milvia. People like to have a place to park, in emergency. *Girl:* It's something you take for granted, they have everything. *Boy:* Most of them have radios, newspapers. Some like to have ministers to come around. People in hospital like conveniences, such as telegraph, telephone, so they can reach people, handy man around.

QUESTION 2: *Girl:* I can't think of anything. Oh, the food. I know when I was in hospital all food had medicine in it, taste was terrible, no salt in it, taste was terrible, no salt in it either. (?) Three, four years ago. It was nice, I liked it. Visiting hours should be short. What about age limit? You have to be 16 I think to visit. *Boy:* I just wonder why it is so expensive for women to have a baby. (Excused himself, had to go to work).

Subject D: A 35-year-old housewife, a mother of two children, interviewed in a park.

Answers to Questions

QUESTION 1: I just got out. What do you mean? Not wanting to go! That's the first reaction of everybody. Antiseptic, you mean word associations or do you mean actual statements? I think of cleanliness, of efficiency, I guess you think of accidents. (?) Oh, dear, what do you want it for? Oh, doctors, nurses, help, aid. I thought you meant word associations first. (?) Gosh, main thing is help in time of need. I really haven't had much association, I guess I've been lucky. I guess you think of having children. Certain stereotypes come to mind. (?) They were looking for a malignancy they didn't find. I go to hospital with apprehension; I think everyone does. I have extreme faith in my doctor. (?) I'd worry about what might happen, but I'd like to be there. When you're there you think of everything that is going on there and how fortunate you are. (*Interviewer*) Cleanliness, efficiency? (R): I think that impressed me, new hospital, a big job going on all the time.

QUESTION 2: Best possible place to be if you're sick.

QUESTION 3: Hospital means to me the best type of aid in the time of medical need.

Subject E: A 35-year-old mother of two children, interviewed at home.

Answers to Questions

QUESTION 1: Sickness. To me it is nothing to think about until it happens. (?) Money, money. At least that's one of my thoughts. (?) Well, I thought I had my hospitalization covered, but I didn't. So they got the money. They wanted me to call my husband at once at his job. (?) He came next night and wrote a check. (?) Collapsed lung I had. They fixed it up in 3 days. (?) Gosh, I can't think of any. I've never been in a hospital, except for babies. I think of hospitals, doctors, nurses. (?) Oh, they were wonderful. Treated me like a queen. (?) Sick people, doctors, nurses, money. Like I said.

QUESTION 2: Like I said, I've never had anything except emergency one time. We brought my girl with her mouth bleeding. She was bleeding inside mouth and nose. I had to wait 45 minutes! The bleeding stopped in the meantime. (?) No. After you leave I will think of a million things.

Subject F: A 39-year-old father of three children, interviewed at home.

Answers to Questions

QUESTION 1: Trouble, health. (?) Money, expenses. (?) Sickness, of course, hospitalization. (?) That just about covers it. My first impression. (?) It's rather self-explanatory: If you are sick you have to go to a hospital . . . payment down before going in . . . quite a matter of finance unless you have a plan that covers it. The problem is so large. . . . You could write a thesis on that word. I worked for the Department of Public Health in _____. Sanitarian. I have been here for about one month. Thought of getting an M.P.H. I have got a year already—got to go another year.

QUESTION 2: No, I have been quite familiar with the hospital working procedure so there is no question that arises in my mind about it.

QUESTION 3: A hospital in my mind is a grouping together of highly trained personnel trained for the benefit of those who are ill and . . . population as a whole . . . refuge of those who are subject to disease, accident and birth. Takes a lot of personnel to maintain a hospital.

Subject G: A 65-year-old widow with two children, interviewed at home.

Answers to Questions

QUESTION 1: Illness, I suppose. I am not articulate. (?) I really can't think of anything but illness. (?) I don't think of a hospital any more than I have to. (?) They handle a real need, of course, and that sort of thing. (?) I carry health insurance. (?) Three-quarters of the hospital bill I carry now. (?) Fortunately, I haven't had to make use of it. (?) I am afraid not. I am not much help to you.

QUESTION 2: Son's family have another hospital plan: Kaiser. He and his family are covered and it's a wonderful thing for them with three children. (?) No.

QUESTION 3: I couldn't summarize them.

Subject H: A 75- or 80-year-old, healthy appearing woman, interviewed in a park. Answered reluctantly; was bothered by the note taking of interviewer.

Answers to Questions

QUESTION 1: What hospital? Do you mean what people wear when they go to hospital? What sick people should do when they are sick? (?) I'll tell you what comes to my mind, I put it away. I don't want to go to the hospital. But it is a wonderful institution for people who are sick. But I have not been sick. I want to stay well. To the last minute. What are you studying, medicine? (?) Hospitals are good, wonderful, but we hope it is not necessary. Personally I don't want to be served, I like to serve myself. To be independent. That is for me the highest thing. It is important to have the right thoughts in one's mind. There are not enough places in the hospital.

QUESTION 2: One reads in the paper that it is not clean enough, is it hygienic? Doctors do a wonderful job, much sorrow with patients, great sacrifices day and night. I only knew wonderful doctors, in Europe and here. I am sorry, but now I must leave. Good-bye.[7]

Thus we see from these quotations that teenagers see the hospital as having little direct personal relevance; the young mother, as a place to have babies or for emergencies; the middle-aged father, as a costly, yet essential service; the older women as a place in which to be ill or to die. Who would question that the actions of these people would be in many ways governed by their evaluation of the significance of the hospital to their personal purposes?

Major Identifications as Anchorages

An individual's age, sex, ethnic group membership, religion, political party, socioeconomic class, occupation, educational status, family membership and marital status are among the major anchorages of his pattern of identifications. They are significant anchorages for many of his values, beliefs, and attitudes, and as such help him judge the personal significance of the happenings about him.

It is not surprising that major changes in the direction or manner in which individual motivation is expressed—in patterns of personal purposes—often occur when these anchorages are disturbed. Such changes are readily observed under conditions of social change, during periods of uncertainty or insecurity, crisis and rebellion, economic or social deprivation, or technical development. Such major shifts in individual purpose are also observed when his own status relative to any of these anchorages undergoes change. Striking changes are sometimes observed following marriage, the birth of a child, a change in occupation, movement into a different social group, movement into a new community, the loss of a job, or change in job status.

Conditions such as these, whether of broad social significance or of unique personal importance, may lead to a major change in the pattern and order of his private world. Things once overlooked or thrust aside become important; things formerly of compelling significance may go unattended. Such a critical upheaval of one's private world forces a reevaluation of what is of future significance in terms of the protection, extension, and enhancement of his self-image.

CONSISTENCY–INCONSISTENCY

As we observe the actions of others we may be struck by the apparent inconsistencies, and impute their inconsistent behavior to a certain instability or uncertainty of motive. A person's actions may vary from day to day in what appears to be the same situation or a similar situation. We may sense no thread of constancy in purpose, for his actions are not in accord with the way we might expect him to act were he constant in his purposes.[8]

When, on the other hand, we examine our own actions introspectively, we note a remarkable constancy of purpose that must be expressed in almost numberless ways because the rest of the world does not remain constant. We usually feel that we know why we do things. Even though our actions may appear inconsistent to others, we can usually sense a common thread of purpose that binds many efforts together.

Even though a man may appear uncertain as to his wants, confused in his efforts, fickle in his attachments, and inconstant in his loyalties, his behavior may still be wholly consistent from the standpoint of his personal anticipations regarding what the future holds for him. Seemingly conflicting acts may serve similar undercurrents of purpose. On the other hand, uncertainties regarding the significance of future actions may lead to all sorts of inconsistencies in observed behavior. This may be illustrated by considering the reactions of a driver to a campaign to further the use of seat belts.[9]

A man is not likely to buy seat belts for his automobile unless he anticipates that they will protect him, or those with whom he identifies, from possible injury. He may feel that they are important to have in the car when he drives on the "freeway" but not necessary for use in the city. If so, he may not consider it worthwhile to equip his car with them unless he himself uses the freeway or unless those with whom he identifies use his car for such a purpose. He may, however, purchase seat belts under pressure if persons with whom he identifies feel that they are important and he wishes to "stick with the crowd." He may feel that possession of seat belts will enhance his status with others or will protect him from criticism. He will be consistent, then, if he purchases the seat belts for such a reason but does not use one himself because he does not consider seat belts useful or necessary while driving in the city.

On the other hand, a man may have a high regard for car safety and may fully recognize that driving, even in the city, is a hazardous venture. To be consistent under these circumstances one might expect him to buy seat belts for his car. Yet he may believe that in case of an accident a seat belt may block his escape from fire, water, or the like. He may not, therefore, buy the seat belts even though they will help to protect him and those who ride with him from injury per se. Here he is likely to act on the basis of his expectation regarding the relative chances involved in the two alternatives—injury due to being obstructed by the seat belt as opposed to injury caused by not using one.

A man may feel that there is no likelihood at all of his having an accident while driving his car because he considers himself a good driver and in the past has always been able to avoid accidents. Then why should he purchase the seat belts? Under these circumstances he may subconsciously protect his ego by being unwilling to admit even to himself that an accident might occur. If this be the case, why should he purchase and have the seat belts in his car as a constant reminder of the possibility of injury? Why should he pay for the annoyance of having something in his car that would remind him of danger he is trying to block out of awareness?

In all these instances the behavior may be consistent within the motive framework of the individual yet appear most inconsistent to an outsider. The key to understanding rests in the knowledge of the individual's expectations regarding the meaning of the action for his own future and the future of others of significance to him. Knowing what he perceives the future to hold for him will help to predict how he will act relative to that possible future. One might expect that action to be the one he perceives as being most likely to protect, to expand, or to enhance his self-image.

HEALTH GOALS AND PERSONAL RELEVANCE

Members of the health professions tend to value long-term health goals as having greater motivational significance than the intermediate steps or means that must be taken in order to attain the desired goal.

Great significance in planning and promotion may be attached to ultimate values or outcomes, health protection for example. Less attention is oriented toward the motivational significance of immediate action processes. One may say, "Why should anyone become so concerned with such minor annoyances as waiting in the clinic, answering a few socioeconomic questions, and following a few instructions when he can so easily obtain long-term protection and guidance?"

What is of primary motivational significance, however, is the actions the individual himself identifies as essential to the protection, extension, or enhancement of his self-image. Immediate, seemingly minor issues, may have far greater ego significance for the individual than life itself.

The insult to the ego that may result from intimate socioeconomic questioning, from a means-test classification, from caste, class, or social status definition, from the embarrassment of indifferent treatment, may be perceived as being of greater personal importance than any possible ultimate threat of disease to the body itself. Such a perceived or imagined affront to the extended self-image may outweigh in motivational importance the offer of a multitude of excellent services.

A woman whose modesty is threatened by the intimate personal examination required in cervical cancer examinations may find the loss of personal privacy too great a payment to make for ultimate safety. The food handler who sees the health department's request for a checkup as implying that he has transgressed in tabooed social areas may cringe at the prospect of an excellent free examination. The workman who perceives failure in a medical checkup as threatening to his future work status, hence seriously endangering his family's income, well-being, and stability, will not easily be induced to accept such an examination regardless of its ultimate value as judged from someone else's point of view.

OTHER EGO-SATISFACTIONS AND THREATS

Man's efforts to protect, extend, and enhance his ego-image may find expression in an almost infinite variety of ways. Such ego needs may lie behind the value satisfactions represented in being accepted as a group member, in "belonging," in being able to participate as a team member, in the sought-for positions of status, power, and responsibility, and in the achievement of physical and social rewards of all sorts. They may be represented in efforts to gain attention, recognition, and acclaim through dangerous ventures, unknown challenges, or new discovery. They may be found, too, in efforts to escape from danger, uncertainty, or discomfort and to gain a higher level of safety, security, and comfort.

Ego-satisfactions may also derive from the very process of activity, or from the excitement of the search itself. As Cantril has suggested, the process of seeking value satisfaction rather than the goals themselves may be the object of man's search.[10] Man does not seek stability—at least not always. He may be challenged by the new or uncertain and may actually relish the insecurities of exploring the unknown. The process of the chase may yield greater value satisfactions than any rewards gained.

A man may avoid the opportunity to obtain a blood test if he fears it may disclose some personal weakness, or if he fears that the giving of blood may lead to a loss of virility. In spite of such fears, he will risk the loss of blood in battle to defend his or his country's "honor," or may give blood to a mobile unit for the sense of power and superiority the process yields. He may even be challenged to accept the test if he feels confident he can "pass," for to him the blood examination may be viewed as a challenge to his strength. Ego-satisfactions and threats may thus come from the process of action itself. The acting individual may have but slight awareness of the goals of health and welfare.

Each person is unique in the pattern of his anticipations regarding future events. What one person judges to be unworthy of attention, may be identified by another as having urgent and fearful meaning, while yet a third person may view it as offering a challenge. Furthermore, all may differ in their definitions of the situation along a needs-means-ends continuum: one man's search often stems from another man's supreme achievement.

From the standpoint of the general theory of motivation considered here, therefore, the primary question regarding any future situation is, "What is significant to the individual from *his* point of view?" What others consider to be the urgent problem, the effective means, or the desirable goal may be outside his knowledge or concern. Critical issues, unless so defined by him, will not be of motivational significance to him; simple, effective, and desirable means of solution, unless so recognized by him and identified as significant in his private world, are not likely to have directive bearing on his actions.

NOTES TO CHAPTER 16

1. Kelly, George A., "Man's Construction of His Alternatives" in Lindzey, Gardner, editor, *Assessment of Human Motives.* Evergreen Edition, Grove Press, New York, 1960, pp. 33–64. For a more extensive discussion of Kelly's conception of motivation, see Kelly, George A., *The Psychology of Personal Constructs,* W. W. Norton and Co., New York, 1955, 2 vols.

2. Kelly, George A., "Man's Construction of His Alternatives," *op. cit.,* p. 59.

3. Cantril, Hadley, *The "Why" of Man's Experience.* Macmillan Co., New York, 1950. See also Cantril, Hadley, *The Politics of Despair,* Basic Books, New York, 1958.

4. Snygg, Donald, and Arthur W. Combs, *Individual Behavior: A New Frame of Reference for Psychology,* Harper and Bros., New York, 1949; see also Combs, Arthur W., and Donald Snygg, *Individual Behavior: A Perceptual Approach to Behavior,* rev. ed., Harper and Bros., New York, 1959. Both of these books will be valuable to public health people interested in fuller discussion of the significance of the ego in man's behavior, and the readable style of the authors makes the books particularly helpful to those interested in the applications of ego-psychology to health action. See also Goffman, Erving, *The Presentation of Self in Everyday Life,* Doubleday Anchor Books, Doubleday and Co., Garden City, N.Y., 1959, for a most interesting analysis of the use of self in interpersonal transactions, and of ways in which man reflects on the "self."

5. Sherif, Muzafer, and Hadley Cantril, *The Psychology of Ego Involvements, Social Attitudes, and Identifications.* John Wiley and Sons, New York, 1947, p. 93.

6. *Ibid.*

7. Unpublished interview material obtained with the assistance of Olof Murelius.

8. Chein, Isidor, Morton Deutsch, Herbert Hyman, and Marie Jahoda, editors, "Consistency and Inconsistency in Intergroup Relations," *Journal of Social Issues,* vol. 5, no. 3, 1949, pp. 1–61.

9. Switzer, John, and Steven Polgar, "A Study on the Use of Seat Belts." Unpublished study, Berkeley City Health Department, California, 1962.

10. Cantril, Hadley, *The "Why" of Man's Experience, op. cit.*

Chapter 17

Patterns of Striving

FOR EACH MAN what is significant in any situation tends to depend upon the special pattern of endowment and growth experience which has helped him create his own private, subjective world. The meaning of his action choices can best be understood when considered from the special vantage point of his own position in any situation. Since many of man's actions are without conscious awareness of purpose, however, even he personally may be unaware of the meaning a particular course of action implies regarding the fulfillment of personal purpose.

Man strives to protect, extend, and enhance his ego in many ways. Some of these patterns of striving seem to be common to all men; others are specific to peoples with common geographies, economics, and political, social, and cultural experiences; still others are unique to peoples living or working together under particular circumstances. While certain patterns of striving may appear generally to influence the behavior of a particular society or group, however, one needs ever to be alert to individual variation in pattern among members of the group. The specific weights or significances given to alternatives tend to vary for each individual. These significances tend to be governed by the expectations of the individual regarding the actions most likely to be effective in protecting, extending, or enhancing his self-image.

Social motives, which at once grow out of and guide man's activities, are ever changing in accord with his transactions in living. Insofar as he shares life experiences with others, he holds common patterns of striving with them. Yet, to the extent that his background, growth, development, and life experiences are unique, his strivings tend to be unique.

Deficiency and Growth Motives

Maslow suggests that personal "needs" and "drives" may be grouped into the two major categories of "deficiency" motives and "growth" motives. He suggests that a person who is hungry or cold, or who lacks care, safety, or love will be guided in his strivings by a need to satisfy these deficiencies. Once he achieves adequate satisfaction of these deficiency motives, he will reach out in creative or self-actualizing ways.[1]

These deficiency and growth motives to which Maslow refers tend to be subjectively determined, based on subjective facts of the individual rather than on objective reality, although a close tie to objective reality is often present. Thus what one person identifies as a deficiency may not be a deficiency for someone else; one man may starve on another man's feast. A man's image of himself and of his self-potentialities and barriers to their achievement tend to guide his strivings whether for comfort and safety, affection and support, status, power, and esteem, or self-actualization and value satisfaction. Self-evaluation regarding areas of insecurity tend also to influence the priority he gives to alternative courses of striving.[2]

Krech and Crutchfield have drawn together a limited grouping of motives which seem to encompass the behavior of most people. They have divided these motives into two major groups, "Survival and Security" and "Satisfaction and Stimulation," in a manner similar to that suggested by Maslow, and have further classified them in terms of their primary locus for the individual.[3]

In viewing such a list, one can readily observe some of the complexities involved in any attempt to relate specific motives to actions. Not only are multiple motives and multiple actions likely to be involved, but conflict between motives is of common occurrence. One may not at once be able to attain certain enjoyable experiences or possessions and avoid dangerous experiences, or to attain close identification with some groups without risk of conflict with others, or to conform to group standards and values and maintain independence of thought and action.

The Krech and Crutchfield outline could serve as a useful tool to health leaders and members of their staffs in making a critical analysis of some of their activities. Analysis of some specific activities or situations might help to bring to light strivings that demand satisfaction or methods of administration that block personal growth.

For example, what strivings lead volunteers to contribute so much time and effort to public health programs? Do the services they are asked to perform yield the ego-satisfactions they seek? What procedural changes might facilitate greater ego-satisfaction, and thereby yield more significant contributions?

TABLE 3. THE HUMAN MOTIVES

Listed in this table are some of the principal human motives, classified under the general aims of survival and security (deficiency motives) and satisfaction and stimulation (abundancy motives). Under these general headings the motives are further classified according to whether they mainly pertain to the body, to relations with the environment, to relations with other people, or to the self.

	Survival and Security (deficiency motives)	*Satisfaction and Stimulation* (abundancy motives)
Pertaining to the body	Avoiding of hunger, thirst, oxygen lack, excess heat and cold, pain, overfull bladder and colon, fatigue, overtense muscles, illness and other disagreeable bodily states, etc.	Attaining pleasurable sensory experiences of tastes, smells, sounds, etc.; sexual pleasure; bodily comfort; exercise of muscles, rhythmical body movements, etc.
Pertaining to relations with environment	Avoiding of dangerous objects and horrible, ugly, and disgusting objects; seeking objects necessary to future survival and security; maintaining a stable, clear, certain environment, etc.	Attaining enjoyable possessions; constructing and inventing objects; understanding the environment; solving problems; playing games; seeking environmental novelty and change, etc.
Pertaining to relations with other people	Avoiding interpersonal conflict and hostility; maintaining group membership, prestige, and status; being taken care of by others; conforming to group standards and values; gaining power and dominance over others, etc.	Attaining love and positive identifications with people and groups; enjoying other people's company; helping and understanding other people; being independent, etc.
Pertaining to the self	Avoiding feelings of inferiority and failure in comparing the self with others or with the ideal self; avoiding loss of identity; avoiding feelings of shame, guilt, fear, anxiety, sadness, etc.	Attaining feelings of self-respect and self-confidence; expressing oneself; feeling sense of achievement; feeling challenged; establishing moral and other values; discovering meaningful place of self in the universe.

SOURCE: Krech, David, and Richard S. Crutchfield, *Elements of Psychology*. Alfred A. Knopf, Inc., 1961, Table 2, p. 279. Reproduced with permission of the authors.

What does the outline suggest regarding the likely concerns and strivings of patients or clients? Are any procedures or processes of the health department unnecessarily damaging to the self-images of persons served? What are the implications of employing a means test? Of asking personal questions in the presence of "outsiders?" Of disrobing in public clinics? Of being used as a demonstration in a teaching situation?

Are there ways in which the self-images of members of the staff may be threatened? Are there unrecognized ways of obtaining greater ego-satisfactions? How do the opportunities for growth perceived relate to expectations? What possible factors may be reflected in inefficiency, absenteeism, tardiness, or high turnover?

It should be recognized that the saliency for any one of these specific motives does not remain constant. A specific threat to an individual's self-image, or a newly recognized possibility for ego-enhancement may consume his prime attention. Yet as an individual moves from group to group or situation to situation his specific concerns or strivings are not likely to remain constant. The groups in which he lives offer different opportunities for self-expression and yield different types of satisfactions, depending on his roles, involvements, and expectations. Generalizations regarding motives and responses from one group or situation to another are hazardous indeed.

While a list such as the above may serve a useful analytic or discussion purpose, its use in the analysis of an individual's behavior may lead to serious difficulty. Underlying strivings are not easily identified and interpreted. For each person they are personal and subjective. The source of praise or criticism, for example, may be of greater significance than its content or apparent meaning; the individual meaning of an award may bear slight relation to its objective value.

Maslow's Hierarchy

Man seems to be an insatiable animal whose patterns of striving are ever in flux. Under normal circumstances his major wants do not long remain constant, for each change in environment tends to bring with it new imbalances between wants and their satisfaction. Satisfied wants do not remain wants, at least in the sense of immediate urgency. Yet the satisfaction of one want or group of wants tends to result in the emergence of other, often equally compelling, urges.

Maslow suggests that a hierarchic pattern may be discerned regarding the order in which an individual's strivings demand satisfaction. He suggests that human motives can be ordered into a hierarchy from those directly tied to physiological needs on the one hand, moving on up through needs for safety, love, and esteem to the need for self-actualization and creativity.[4] Although considerable individual variation may be observed, such a general ordering of human needs into a hierarchic pattern has theoretical merit. The present author prefers the term "strivings" as better representing his point of view than do Maslow's terms "needs" and "drives."

Maslow treats the physiological needs of hunger, thirst, and sex as a starting point for his motivational theory. "For the man who is extremely and dangerously hungry, no other interests exist but food. He dreams food, he remembers food, he thinks about food, he emotes only about food, he perceives only food, and he wants only food."[5] All other strivings are pushed into the background until this want for food is satisfied.

Man's safety needs, which include comfort from heat and cold, job security, and protection against the possibilities of illness or disablement, come into greater significance once physiological needs have received minimum satisfaction. Infants and children within our society often lack the undisrupted routine or rhythm of the organized environment necessary to satisfy needs for safety. Maslow suggests that on the other hand, "The healthy, normal, fortunate adult in our culture is largely satisfied in his safety needs. The peaceful, smoothly running, good society ordinarily makes its members feel safe enough from wild animals, extremes of temperature, criminal assault, murder, tyranny, etc. Therefore, in a very real sense, he no longer has any safety needs as active motivators. Just as a sated man no longer feels hungry, a safe man no longer feels endangered."[6] Such an observation by Maslow may deserve the attention of public health leaders who wonder why public health programs rank so low among the urgent concerns of people.

Thus "the need for safety is seen as an active dominant mobilizer of the organism's resources only in emergencies, e.g., war, disease, natural catastrophes, crime waves, societal disorganization, neurosis, brain injury, chronically bad situations."[7]

The needs for love, affection, and belongingness tend to emerge into prominence once the physiological and safety needs are fairly well gratified. Maslow notes that thwarting of these needs is commonly found in cases of maladjustment such as in severe psychopathology. Love, in the sense outlined here, is not synonymous with sex but involves both the giving and receiving of affection.

The individual becomes more concerned about self-esteem, prestige, status, recognition, attention, and power after the three groups of needs mentioned earlier are satisfied at some minimal level. Satisfaction of these esteem needs leads to feelings of self-confidence, worth, strength, capability, and adequacy, and in this way prepares the individual for creative growth.

The need for self-actualization, self-fulfillment, or creative development is viewed by Maslow and others as an ideal goal sought by persons who have achieved a certain level of satisfaction of other motives. What is ideal for each person will be individually unique. Maslow suggests: "A musician must make music, an artist must paint, a poet must write if he is to be ultimately at peace with himself. What a man can be, he must be. This need we may call self-actualization."[8]

Krech, Crutchfield, and Ballachey, who use the term "wants" in preference to Maslow's "needs," have schematically illustrated the change in relative saliency of these groups of wants in the process of

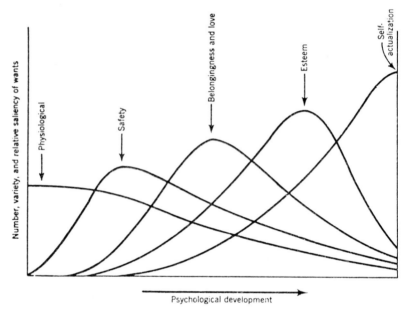

FIGURE 10. Schematic Portrayal of the Progressive Changes in Relative Saliency, Number, and Variety of Wants as Described by Maslow

Note that the peak of an earlier main class of wants must be passed before the next "higher" want can begin to assume a dominant role. Note also that as psychological development takes place the number and variety of wants increase.

SOURCE: Krech, David, Richard S. Crutchfield, and Egerton L. Ballachey, *Individual in Society*. Copyright 1962. McGraw-Hill Book Co., New York, 1962, Figure 3.1, p. 77. Used by permission.

psychological development. Note that while one group of wants may be dominant at a particular period, a considerable overlap with other wants tends to occur.[9]

Maslow's theory regarding this sequential pattern through which individual strivings emerge has enormous potential for those in public health who are concerned with program planning and community development, particularly those working with deprived peoples at home or abroad. Each of us can think of many exceptions to the general pattern Maslow describes. Stereotypes of starving musicians and creative artists living in garrets come immediately to mind. We overlook the many artists and musicians with great potentiality who have been compelled by more urgent demands to seek other forms of occupation, or who, driven by more basic requirements, have moved into commercial art pursuits.

An individual who has strong strivings in one of the more creative areas may move forward with a minimum of satisfaction of other wants. Since an individual's patterns of striving are guided by his image of himself as related to others within the sociocultural setting, what constitutes adequate satisfaction regarding any area of striving remains a matter of individual assessment, being relative rather than an absolute. It is a subjective matter determined on the basis of the subjective facts of one's private world rather than upon objective reality.

Patterns of Security–Insecurity

The significance of this theory for public health action leads one to raise questions as to whether the theory is supported by other than clinical evidence. Is personal security a dynamic concept in the sense that an individual's areas of insecurity are at once areas of striving? Do an individual's subjective estimates regarding his needs differ from what might be judged by others on the basis of his observed station in life? To what extent are there parallels in the way a man perceives the world about him in terms of need satisfaction and the objective situation observed by others? Do feelings of insecurity, by influencing the areas in which man strives, at the same time guide his perceptions, cognitions, emotions, and responses?

Thus far Maslow's theory has not been tested within a sufficient range of conditions to permit definitive answers to all of these questions. Preliminary data, however, tend to support positive responses to these issues.

Many studies conducted during periods of unemployment, depression, or economic stress or disaster reveal that people lose confidence in their abilities, lack feelings of status and belongingness, and sometimes even lose hope. Significant reversals in personality are observed under these conditions. Creative energies are often diverted to the solution of the problems of existence.[10]

In an earlier attempt to obtain empirical answers to some of the questions raised above, Knutson carried out a study of six occupational groups employed in the Veteran's Hospital.[11] Personal security was studied relative to ten areas of striving:

> Having a chance to develop some special talent, interest, or hobby.
> Having a good social standing and the right kind of people as friends.
> Having a good ability to understand things, good education, and general information.
> Being sure of a job or steady income with good living conditions.
> Being satisfied in your relations with members of the opposite sex.
> Having good looks and appearances, good build, height, etc.
> Being liked and respected, and feeling you "belong."
> Having a good religious understanding and faith.
> Being in good physical and mental health.
> Being satisfied with your work or job.[12]

A ranking of the significance of these areas of striving for the individual was obtained by asking them to identify which three they considered most important or cared most about, and which three they considered least important or cared least about. Comparison was then made between the rankings of these areas of striving and subscores on a personal security inventory that included scales for each of these areas, thus providing an estimate of the level of personal security the individual subjectively rated himself as holding in each area.

A person's feelings of security or insecurity were measured in this situation in terms of "his own subjective evaluation of his success, satisfaction, and surety or confidence with respect to carrying out his purposes in past and present situations and group relationships; also, his expectations, hopes, fears, or uncertainties about the carrying out of his purposes and aspirations in future situations and group relationships."[13]

It was found that security is indeed a dynamic concept.

> People strive for security. By and large, the things they consider most important, that they care most about, tend to be the things about which they feel most insecure. Conversely, the things they care least about tend to be the areas in which they feel most secure. This rela-

tionship, while consistent, was revealed to be somewhat less pronounced for persons of higher professional status, possibly due to a more objective attitude on the part of such persons.

There are functional areas within which people feel secure or insecure, and unique patterns of security exist within even a fairly homogeneous employee population. In addition to these unique individual patterns of security and insecurity, broader group patterns are present. The patterns of security of very similar occupational groups are more alike than are those of more distantly related occupational groups. Occupation, income, education, etc., were all closely related within the population studied, so that occupational status provided but one measure of what might be called a person's *station in life;* therefore, it is concluded that an individual's patterns of security and insecurity are closely related to his station in life.

A general level of personal security tends to be present in addition to the levels of security within the individual areas of striving. This seems to occur because the areas of personal striving are interrelated and overlapping, even though some are of greater importance than others to the security of the individual.[14]

Changes in Strivings During Starvation

It is interesting to review, within the framework of Maslow's theory, the Minnesota study of experimental starvation conducted during World War II. The purpose of the Minnesota study was to investigate under strictly controlled conditions the relative effectiveness of different types of diet in bringing about recovery from prolonged starvation. The group studied included 36 normal, young, male volunteers between the ages of twenty and thirty-three years. The experiment lasted about one year. Controlled data were obtained during the first three months, and this was followed by six months of semi-starvation during which the daily intake was reduced to 1,570 calories. This semi-starvation period was followed by three months of controlled rehabilitation. The average loss of weight by the men during the starvation period was about 24 per cent of gross body weight.

As the study progressed, the subjects gradually acquired an absorbing concern with food and eating.

> Food in all its ramifications became the principal topic of the subjects' conversations, reading, and day dreams. More dreams about food were reported as the stress continued. When subjects read books and attended movies, they were deeply impressed by the frequency with which food and eating were mentioned. Cookbooks, menus, and information bulletins on food production became intensely interesting reading matter to many of the subjects who previously had little or no

interest in dietetics or agriculture. Some men went so far as to re-plan their lives according to their newly-acquired respect for food. For example, one man became impressed by the importance of developing efficient methods of food raising and decided to go into agriculture as a vocation. A few planned to become cooks. In some men there appeared, particularly toward the end of the experiment, a reaction against this "tyranny" of food; they became annoyed by discussions of food and related subjects. One man expressed disgust at this "animal attitude"; another referred to such engrossment as "nutritional masturbation."

. . . The persistent clamor of hunger distracted the subjects when they attempted to continue their cultural interests, hobby activities, and studies. The discrepancy between what the men wanted to do and what they were able to do resulted in frustration."[15]

The men showing a large degree of personal and social deterioration as the study progressed became objects of aggression for the rest of the group. By their own ratings they were relatively lacking in self-discipline, self-control, restless, indecisive, sensitive to noise, unable to concentrate, and so on. Their personal appearance and care began to deteriorate.

The men often neglected to shave, brush their teeth, and comb their hair. Even those who had been careful or even particular in their grooming now dressed carelessly and presented a slovenly appearance. . . . Social initiative, and sociability in general, underwent remarkable change. Their earlier interest in having a voice in the making of policies and rules for the conduct of the non-scientific aspects of the experiment dwindled. The men became indecisive, unable to make personal plans, and unwilling to participate in group activities. The subjects spent more and more time alone. It became "too much trouble" or "too tiring" to have to contend with other people. With the decline in the interests which had previously been held in common with others and with the growth of feelings of social inadequacy the men became self-centered.[16]

It is not surprising under these conditions that the men lost interest in the educational program which was to prepare them for foreign relief work. The decline in sex drive was so dramatic that the subjects themselves were struck by the change and used colorful language to describe it.

Not until the latter part of the rehabilitation period and near the end of the experiment was there a noticeable improvement in morale. At this time humor, enthusiasm, and sociability gradually reappeared and irritability decreased. The sexual interests were very slow in regaining their preexperimental intensity.

In quite the pattern outlined by Maslow, the heightened physiological demands resulting from removal of food led to a gradual social withdrawal, narrowing of interests, and decrease in sexual drive. Food and eating became the dominant concern. Activities that are normally identified as being related to maintaining a social belongingness and gaining the acceptance of others were ignored during this period. There was an obvious disregard for many of the status symbols of their social group. While starving they had little concern for social esteem and, as has been indicated, there was a striking decrease in strivings for intellectual development or self-actualization. When food was once again available in quantity enough to satisfy minimum physiological requirements, "Feeling of well-being, range of interests, emotional stability, and sociability were regained more rapidly than strength, endurance, normal eating habits, and sexual drive."[17]

Possible Implications for Public Health

To the extent that there is general validity to Maslow's theory regarding the hierarchical pattern of man's strivings, many questions may be posed concerning its applicability to public health practice. Are programs in public health centered in areas where people have deep concern? Is public health practice adapting as quickly as it might to emerging concerns of the people served? Are our national and international programs flexible enough to permit program adaptation in terms of the specific patterns of concern found in local areas? Are we in some situations attempting to guide people to be concerned about what we believe to be important rather than focusing program efforts to equally significant areas in which they are striving?

Issues like these deserve intense analysis in local settings. Broad generalizations regarding all populations are doomed to failure. Maslow's observation, for example, that the safety needs of adults in our culture are better satisfied than the safety needs of children may not be everywhere applicable.

To the extent that Maslow's general theory holds under normal circumstances for communities in North America, it may account for the greater readiness on the part of some of our populations to support mental health programs and services in areas where many of the so-called "basic public health services" are lacking. In such areas strivings for love, affection, and belongingness may have emerged into prominence for a significant proportion of the public.

On the other hand, the growing concern on the part of some groups for greater action to develop man's creative potentialities may reflect adequate satisfaction of their strivings for affection and esteem. They feel society must move forward rapidly in developing its maximum potentialities for creative work. It may be difficult at times for such persons to recognize the urgency of taking community action on matters that less fortunate groups consider critical.

Since motives tend to guide perceptions and cognitions, the public health team might profit by looking critically at disparities that may exist between their own feelings of security-insecurity and those of the people they serve. In a clinic situation, for example, the public health physician and nurse are usually working in areas of great personal security, whereas the patient tends to be in an area of his greatest insecurity when he comes to the clinic. The greater personal security of the public health staff in this area of striving may lead them to evaluate the situation more critically and objectively. Yet, at the same time, it may be more difficult for them to empathize with the patient and fully understand his problems. The implications of this disparity between the professional staff and the patient regarding the definition of a situation and alternative action possibilities have scarcely been explored.

In the mental health hospital study described above, it was found that attendants and service workers who as a group have the greatest contact with patients were the most insecure members of the hospital staff. At the same time, they were most similar to the patients in their areas of striving. They were, perhaps, best able among the staff to communicate effectively with the patients. Since they were as a group so much less secure in their feelings than professional staff members, one might wonder to what extent their communications with patients were supportive or aggressive. This issue deserves a most critical study.[18]

Maslow's theory may help us have a better understanding of the reaction of hospitalized patients during the course of recovery. While they are seriously ill their concerns relate to physical survival and satisfaction of minimum physiological requirements. As recovery proceeds, one might theoretically expect an increasing number of complaints regarding nursing attention and nutrition services and increased demands for attention. Indeed, a growing pattern of complaints may better reflect the progress and recovery of the patient than low patient morale. Dissatisfaction with hospital food or services may not necessarily mean that services are inadequate or food is poor in kind or quality.

NOTES TO CHAPTER 17

1. Maslow, Abraham H., *Motivation and Personality.* Harper and Bros., New York, 1954. See also Maslow's *Toward a Psychology of Being: An Insight Book,* D. Van Nostrand Co., Princeton, N.J., 1962.

2. Knutson, Andie L., "Personal Security as Related to Station in Life," *Psychological Monographs,* vol. 66, no. 4, 1952. Whole number 336.

3. Krech, David, and Richard S. Crutchfield, *Elements of Psychology.* Alfred A. Knopf, Inc., New York, 1961, p. 279.

4. Maslow, Abraham H., *Motivation and Personality, op. cit.*

5. *Ibid.,* p. 82.

6. *Ibid.,* p. 87.

7. *Ibid.,* p. 88.

8. *Ibid.,* p. 9.

9. Krech, David, Richard S. Crutchfield, and Egerton L. Ballachey, *Individual in Society.* McGraw-Hill Book Co., New York, 1962, p. 77.

10. Bakke, Edward W., *Citizens Without Work,* Yale University Press, New Haven, 1940; Idem, *The Unemployed Worker,* Yale University Press, New Haven, 1940; Hall, O. Milton, "Attitudes and Unemployment: A Comparison of the Opinions and Attitudes of Employed and Unemployed Men," *Archives of Psychology, New York,* no. 165, 1934; Rundquist, Edward A., and Raymond F. Sletto, *Personality in the Depression: A Study in the Measurement of Attitudes,* University of Minnesota Press, Minneapolis, 1936; Stouffer, Samuel A., and Paul F. Lazarsfeld, *Research Memorandum on the Family in the Depression,* Social Science Research Council, Bulletin 29, New York, 1937; Zawadzki, Bohan, and Paul F. Lazarsfeld, "The Psychological Consequences of Unemployment," *Journal of Social Psychology,* vol. 6, May, 1935, pp. 224–251.

11. Knutson, Andie L., *op. cit.,* p. 11.

12. *Ibid.,* p. 4.

13. *Ibid.,* p. 24.

14. *Ibid.*

15. Franklin, Joseph C., Burtrum C. Schiele, Josef Brozek, and Ancel Keys, "Observations on Human Behavior in Experimental Semistarvation, and Rehabilitation," *Journal of Clinical Psychology,* vol. 4, 1948, pp. 28–45. Abridged article also found in Stacey, Chalmers L., and Manfred F. DeMartino, editors, *Understanding Human Motivation,* Howard Allen, Cleveland, 1958, pp. 348–349.

16. *Ibid.,* pp. 350–351.

17. *Ibid.,* p. 362.

18. Knutson, Andie L., *op. cit.*

Part Five

Values, Attitudes, and Beliefs

Part Five

Values, Attitudes, and Beliefs

VALUES, ATTITUDES, AND BELIEFS have a pervading influence over all of man's behavior. When strongly held, they contribute to social, industrial, and personal harmony, efficiency, and well-being, or, conversely, to conflicts that directly end in the death or disability of members of society. Their many indirect influences on man's health behavior, while less spectacular and obvious, are often of equal significance.

When we speak of values, attitudes, and beliefs, we are concerned with tendencies to respond to environment, including other men, in particular positive or negative ways. Such tendencies are rooted in cultural, social, and personal experiences, either directly or indirectly acquired. They may be openly or secretly held, and the individual having such tendencies to action may or may not be aware of holding them and of their influence on his actions. How they influence the acting individual tends to vary according to the intensity with which they are held and the urgency with which they impel him to act.

Man's personal and social values, his beliefs regarding himself and the world about him, and his attitudes toward other persons and things, and toward himself, at once guide and limit his health behaviors. Together, they form a significant part of the self he seeks to defend, extend, and enhance.

Values, attitudes, and beliefs have many characteristics in common. An inability to distinguish sharply between them and their individual effects on man's health actions leads us to group them together in this section. However, illustrations of their influence appear throughout the text.

Chapter 18

Values and Value Patterns

MAN, more than any other creature, is a valuing animal. A subtle network of values, which he begins to develop early in life, guides both the direction and mode of his thought and action, and gives meaning and significance to his efforts. The intensity with which these values are held may at once impart fervor to his strivings and blind him to other possible, even more fruitful, alternatives. Unless shaken up by some unusual situation or value conflict, he may be unaware of their guiding, and restricting, influence.

Sylvia Pankhurst, the woman suffragist, fought her cause on the streets of London where she met people from all walks of life. It is said that she once bent down to console a small boy who was sobbing as though his heart would break. As she patted him on the head she advised, "There, there, little boy. Tell your trouble to God. *She* will help you."

An American tourist while shopping in the Middle East came upon a craftsman who was selling baskets of a rare quality and design. Delighted with his find, he offered to buy them all. "You cannot buy them all," the merchant replied. "Then I would have nothing left to sell."

A physician from India was asked, "How many children do you have?" He hesitated a moment, then replied, "You should have asked how many sons and daughters we have. A short time ago, I should have answered your question by saying 'we have but one,' for we have only one son. We also have two daughters. In my country, until recently, a man might not include his daughters in answering such a question."

As these three stories illustrate, values are expressed in action and response without the individual who is holding them necessarily being alert to their presence and significance. While we are accustomed to think of values as varying according to sociocultural group, they

261

also vary according to sex, occupation, age, and many other factors. Their presence and significance for the individual come into focus when disagreements or conflicts in value occur.

Our assumptions about God as male are so firm, it comes as somewhat of a shock to hear someone refer to God as "She." We are so accustomed to thinking of a merchant as one who is selling to make a profit that we are taken aback at the thought that selling may serve as a satisfying social activity for the individual. Without understanding the religious significance of male children for the Indian father, we cannot understand his exclusion of daughters in making a family count.

PROBLEMS OF DEFINITION

The term "values" is a much used, generally understood, but seldom precisely defined, term. Like the term "public health," theoreticians, researchers, and action-oriented leaders have employed the term in different ways in accordance with their research or action purposes, theoretical orientations, or personal preferences. Operational definitions have also varied, depending upon the purposes of research or analysis. Thus findings in regard to the nature or significance of values in any setting can best be understood by learning what the researcher or author meant by the term in that specific setting.

When one attempts to be precise in the definition and use of the term "values," one is aware that much meaning is lost in the attempt to be exact. It appears to have no single concise meaning, but many abstract implications. In this sense it is like the cotton candy we eagerly buy at the circus but find, when we bite into it, that it dissolves into nothingness.

English and English define value as "an abstract concept, often merely implicit, that defines for an individual or for a social unit what ends or means to an end are desirable. . . . These abstract concepts of worth are usually not the result of the individual's own valuing; they are social products that have been imposed on him and only slowly internalized—i.e., accepted and used as his own criteria of worth." A value system, then, is "the more or less coherent set of *values* that regulate a person's conduct, often without his awareness that they do so."[1]

"A value," Allport suggests, "is a belief upon which a man acts by preference. It is thus a cognitive, a motor, and above all, a deeply propriate disposition."[2] Yet a man may respond in a value-oriented way without being, even to the slightest degree, aware that his values are guiding his choice of action.

On the other hand, Kluckhohn, Murray, and Schneider hold that "The values embedded in a culture have special weight among the group membership determinants. A value is a conception, explicit or implicit, distinctive of an individual or characteristic of a group, of the desirable which influences the selection from available modes, means, and ends of action. It is thus not just a preference, a desire, but a formulation of the *desirable,* the 'ought' and 'should' standards which influence action."[3]

If we were to accept all these different definitions of value, we would be expressing values when we say "I would like to do this" or "I would prefer to do that." Also when we say "I ought to do this," or "you should do that," or "we must do it." We would still be expressing values, however, by acting in relevant ways in areas of approval or disapproval, acceptance or rejection, by our manners, or gestures, or subtle reactions of which we may be unaware.

The public health official who has tried to apply information regarding community values in making decisions will recognize that these different expressions of value are not consistent with one another. What an individual *prefers* may be quite different from what he considers *ideal;* what he *desires* may have little to do with what he thinks he *ought* to have; what he *wants* to do may be in conflict with what he feels he *ought* to do, *should* do, or *must* do.

In evaluating the significance of information on community values for predicting community response to some projected course of action, therefore, it is necessary to know what value definition was employed by the researcher who assembled the data. It is important to know also from whom and by what means the information was obtained. While no one research approach is necessarily superior to others for the purpose of studying values, the findings reported are likely to have different meanings according to the research method used—whether conclusions are based upon the observation and analysis of behavior, upon responses to direct, indirect, or projective questioning, upon the expressions of choice or preference among preselected alternatives, and so forth.

In discussing the implications of values for public health action, it is also necessary to limit one's definition so that conflicts in meaning and interpretation will be minimized. For the present discussion, therefore, the term "values" will be used to refer to what one feels that one should do, ought to do, or must do, whether or not one is consciously aware that these imperatives, acquired through socialization and learning, are giving direction to thoughts and action. One must recognize, in making this restriction on the use of the concept, that what one feels that one should do, ought to do, or must do, may very well be just what one desires or prefers to do. Sharp distinctions in this ambiguous area are difficult. Heider, for one, has tried to keep these distinctions clear.[4] Even though an attempt will be made to employ this definition in the discussion, some studies employing other definitions will be included in the presentation when germane.

VALUES GUIDE AND LIMIT ACTION

Values influence action and give general direction to behavior, acting as significant forces in man's social environment. They are not sought as goals are sought. Rather, they guide action by orienting and by limiting alternative choices.[5] "The individual does not try to 'reach' the value of fairness but fairness is 'guiding' his behavior."[6]

Thus one's value judgments are judgments concerning the worth of alternatives. Each of us is constantly making evaluations in his daily life, judging the worth of ideas or actions, weighing the pros and cons of arguments, estimating the significance of goal attainment relative to the effort required and the merits of alternative ways of achieving goals. Our values are reflected through such determinations.[7]

Feelings of duty, obligation, and responsibility lead one to take certain courses of action rather than others; they may, in fact, blind one to the existence of alternatives. Yet one may, and often does, deny, ignore, or reject the socially derived pressures in seeking satisfaction of some purpose or avoiding some undesirable position. Accordingly, it might be better to speak of value orientations than value incentives or goals, recognizing however, that when harmony exists between man's feelings of responsibility, obligation, and duty, and his personal or group motives it is impossible at our present state of analytical ability to distinguish personal motive from value forces in the social environment. Values, as ideal goals, may actually have some motivational qualities.

VALUES GIVE LIFE MEANING

Much of man's behavior is indeed governed by the values he holds. They guide him in his transactions with members of his family, friends, neighbors, and co-workers, with members of social, community, and national groups, with members of broad cultural, ethnic, or political groups. They also influence him in his judgment and response to other things, to life and death, to nature and the supernatural, to God and the universe.

While a man's values help to make his present life meaningful and significant, they contribute also to his efforts to piece together remnants of the past, and to identify threads of meaning leading into the future. Thus in the patterns of recorded history, we find values expressed in the day-to-day records of what was significant in the lives of people. They are also expressed in the evaluative analysis of those who are guided by their values as they seek to make meaning of these records in their search for historical trends and developments.

Hopes, fears, and anticipations rooted in values have implications for a man's judgments and actions. As ideal goals of which he may have scant awareness, they may lead him to accept his position in nature or society with a fatalistic submission, or, on the contrary, to battle adversity in attempts to invoke improvement. They may lead him to center his interests and standards in the traditions of the past or in the urgencies of the immediate present, or to strive with determination in anticipation of rewards in the distant future. They may lead him to fear and avoid the mysterious or unexplored, or to seek out the unknown as a challenge to be understood and harnessed.

Values are one of the most important and enduring products of our social heritage, and provide continuing standards that serve as a basis for judging social behavior and thus help to maintain group order. "If one asks the question, 'Why are there values?' the reply must be: 'Because social life would be impossible without them; the functioning of the social system could not continue to achieve group goals; individuals could not get what they want and need from other individuals in personal and emotional terms, nor could they feel within themselves a requisite measure of order and unified purpose.' Above all, values add an element of predictability to social life."[8]

THE EARLY ACQUISITION OF VALUES

It is not surprising, then, that societies everywhere place a high premium on the teaching of values in schools, in churches, in political and social groups. Yet some of the most deeply held values are taught to infants without conscious intent, for those who teach during the process of socialization are likely to be unaware of the significance of the values they impart.

The "whys" and "what fors" of children reflect an early search for value orientations:

Why am I here? Where did I come from?

What will happen when I die? Why?

What should I do this for? Do I have to? What will happen if I don't do it?

Why did you do that? Why did you do it that way?

Where are we going? Why do we have to go?

Where did Daddy go? Why?

Where does the sun come from? Why does it come?

Where did yesterday go?

Many values, however, are acquired before the child has grown old enough to ask such questions. As Smith has noted, before a child develops a reflective self or self-image he lacks direct awareness of values, but responds to parental sanctions in the way of rewards or punishments.[9] "Superego values" may thus become established through this experience with parental sanctions before the child has acquired the language necessary to discuss and understand abstractions of this type. Such superego values would be more difficult to identify through interviews, since they are not easily verbalized even though they do guide or restrict the individual's behavior.

An individual is likely to be most aware of the role of values in his life while he is learning them, when he is trying to understand their significance for himself and others, and how he should act with respect to them. Once acquired, they tend to become second nature to him to the extent that he will pass them on to his children without awareness. Only when value or action conflicts arise through new experience or through transactions with persons having a contrary system of values do they again leap into prominence.

In a provocative study of parent education, Brim observes that such questions as who should teach the child values, what values should be taught, and how they should be taught are themselves questions of value of great significance for any society. While science may be able to provide information useful in making such value judgments, science cannot supply the standards needed for making such judgments.[10]

VALUES ARE INFERRED FROM BEHAVIOR

One does not always verbalize his values, and when he does speak of them may lay claim to values different from those that are truly guiding his behavior. In fact, as has been noted, some of the most basic values we hold may be held without our being fully aware of the ways they are guiding judgments and actions. Accordingly, in defining the value patterns of an individual or of a group, one must infer values from behaviors observed as compared with alternatives available, and by looking behind verbal expressions in search of validity.

Individual values are inferred from individual behavior; group or community values are inferred from the behavior of members of the group. When we speak of the values of a group or of the dominant community values, we mean the values identified by observing the modal behaviors of the members. Such group values serve as group standards and give general direction to group behavior, facilitating group order and unity of purpose. One infers them from observations of the patterns of group life, the institutions and organizations, together with their manner of functioning, the communications symbols employed, the justifications given for decisions made, and the assumptions that seem to be accepted regarding what is right or wrong, just or unjust, good or evil, worthy or unworthy. While individuals within the group vary considerably in their personal values, these tend to be restrained by the limits of the general values of the group.

In discussing the role of values in public health, Burton writes, "A nationalist leader opposes the destruction of mosquitoes in West Africa because he says they are the only sure defense against the white settler. An English county prays for divine intervention to solve its inadequate water supply. Pressure groups in America resist fluoridation of water supplies because they believe it interferes with the liberty of the subject. A Bantu resists hospitalization of his family with T.B. because it would imply that his daughter who spread the disease was a witch. Here at the heart of social medicine we find the battle of values."[11]

Each of the situations Burton describes is an action guided by certain assumptions people have about man in his relation to the universe and man in his relation to other men. From observing these behaviors one may infer something about the values that appear to guide them. One assumes that the acting individuals are doing what they feel they should do, ought to do, or must do, and that human values are therefore guiding their actions.

DIFFICULTIES OF RESEARCH ON VALUES

The same characteristics of values that make them so significant to an understanding of group stability, social functioning, and social change create countless difficulties for the researcher interested in defining them and in determining the extent of their impact on group members. The subtle way in which values become internalized by the individual during the socialization process leaves him unaware of their presence, perhaps without words to describe them. Since they tend to crop to the surface of awareness when threatened by conflict, outside pressures, or new experiences, one cannot judge their apparent significance for the group by their influences on current actions or by the extent to which they are being discussed.

Some values may be protected from exposure and analysis by formal or informal taboos, often of unknown origin. Even inquiring about them may be viewed as dangerous, immoral, or sacrilegious. Responsibility for matters pertaining to other values may be seen as resting with some particular group within the society, such as the clerical, the military, the legal, and the medical professions. Permission and support from members of such groups may be required or expected before such values can be investigated.

Attempts to identify or investigate values involves the use of symbols that have high emotional components, often so potent as to make rational discussion difficult for both subject and interviewer. In our society, for example, objective discussion and rational judgments are difficult when they include reference to health, honesty, God, the flag, the cross, our national anthem, taps, or even a handclasp or kiss—value symbols involving several of our senses. Group values communicated by such symbols may be protected from exposure and analysis by unwritten norms of long standing.

The researcher needs to be constantly aware that the values represented by such symbols are not precise things; they may be ambiguous in their meanings for different members of the group. They are likely to be differentially distributed among members of the sociocultural group according to the institutional patterns of the group, varying widely both in their meanings and significance for group members, and in terms of the directives for actions they imply. Thus significant members of the group may hold values dissimilar from, and even in conflict with, those held by the majority.

STUDIES OF AMERICAN VALUES

A wide range of approaches has been used to identify nationally held values and to determine the extent of their distributions within specific groups. For this purpose, use has been made of public opinion polls, attitude surveys, questionnaires, group discussion techniques, professional judgment, and the content analysis of communication materials. These studies have varied widely in quality—in some instances no attempts have been made to distinguish between interests, wants, attitudes, and incentives. Other investigations have shown a high level of theoretical sophistication.[12]

From such studies we learn that middle-class society in America tends to place great value on such things as romantic love, conformity, activity, speed, verbal abilities, personal wealth, personal achievement, material comfort, progress, humanitarianism, science, equality, freedom, democracy, and so forth.

The Process of Identifying a Social Value

In discussing the value we place on cleanliness, Williams illustrates the range of source materials put to use in making such determinations.

> Suppose we assert that cleanliness is a major focus of value in American society. We could establish or refute such a statement by recording the following types of observations: (1) In this society, people often choose between activities that promote cleanliness and other types of activity (for example, cleaning house *versus* going to church or enjoying leisure). A great deal of time and effort is lavished on washing hands, taking baths, preparing clean clothes, scrubbing and sweeping, collecting and disposing of trash, and so on. (2) Newspapers and magazines devote much space to news, articles, and advertising dealing with cleanliness and ways of promoting it in various areas of life. (3) Comments asserting or implying a bias in favor of cleanliness are extremely common, not only in response to direct questioning but also in the form of unprompted statements. (4) Analysis of a wide sampling of spoken and written materials reveals an extraordinary number of instances that assume "cleanliness is desirable" as an implicit concept underlying the assertions. (Thus, in the frequent articles on new housekeeping methods, there are many that never make the value statements directly.) (5) Children are approved and otherwise rewarded for cleanly behavior, but meet frowns, censorious speech, minor deprivations, and physical chastisement for certain violations of this pattern. Although the rewards and penalties may be less obvious in later life, adults, too, face sanctions for conduct disregarding this value.[13]

Using such an approach, Williams identifies some of the dominant value orientations in our American culture as achievement or success, activity and work, a moral orientation, humanitarianism, efficiency and practicality, progress, material comfort, equality, freedom, conformity, scientific and secular rationality, nationalism-patriotism, democracy, and individualism. It should be recognized that the number and nature of value orientations identified by a researcher within any culture depends upon the level of his conceptualization and the methods of his approach. As Williams points out, one might expand or contract this list in accord with the conceptual tools he employs.

Influence on Public Health Programs

American value orientations influence public health programs in many ways. Of significance is the value we place on health and on the control of illness and also the relative importance given to health as compared to education, welfare, employment, recreation, or other services. We seem to be guided at times also by a deep-seated Emersonian tradition to which Mountin was referring in discussing the "Evolving Pattern of Tomorrow's Health."

> Traditionally in this country, a man's illnesses have been regarded as his personal affair—something he may endure if he prefers, or from which he may obtain relief if he is both willing and financially able to do so. Gradually, as society has increased its investment in the training and security of the individual, this point of view has become a subject of serious debate. There are signs which clearly suggest that a complete reversal of attitude is in the offing. With such a shift in viewpoint, the means for implementing an enlarged program of medical care assume added importance.[14]

COMPARING THE VALUES OF GROUPS

Serious difficulties arise when one attempts to draw comparisons between groups by using empirical and analytical approaches in the study of values. The level of theoretical formulation or conceptualization employed by the researcher is of significance if such comparisons are to be meaningful. Sociocultural differences exist in language, the content of verbal response, patterns of thought, the structure of social organizations, the patterns of behavior, and many other aspects of society. A search for value similarities or dissimilarities must be conceptualized in such a way as to permit meaningful comparisons of overtly different content of observation and response. Otherwise variation due to differences in experiences and the way of life of the people concerned may conceal basic value similarities.

The fact that one group measures time by the clock, the radio, or the factory whistle; another by the shadows of the mountain or an ancient sundial; and the third by the time it takes to perform a specific pattern of tasks ought not to stand in the way of comparing their orientations to time as a factor influencing community life. Even though members of one group may seek medical diagnosis and treatment from a "trembler" or medicine man, another from a witch doctor, and a third from a family physician, it should be possible to determine through study what significance each places on early diagnosis and treatment for the same condition of ill health (if common to all) and how the decision to take action is reached within the particular family structure.

In any study of values, attitudes, beliefs, and aspirations, one faces the possibility that the manner of interviewing, the alternatives employed in questions, or the terms used to identify alternatives will influence patterns of response. Information must be elicited in the words familiar to the individual and stated in a manner which truly reflects his private world. Otherwise the researcher may obtain no more than confirmation of his own expectations.

A Self-Anchoring Scale

A self-anchoring scale, developed by Kilpatrick and Cantril, has proved to be one creative way of avoiding some of these problems. It is designed to offer the subject interviewed the greatest possible freedom of expression, yet it provides a means of obtaining information in ways that permit comparison between individuals or groups, even though they come from different cultural backgrounds.[15]

Cantril describes the approach as follows:

> In an interview the respondent is first of all asked the following question: "All of us want certain things out of life. When you think about what really matters in your own life, what are your wishes and hopes for the future? In other words, if you imagine your future in the best possible light, what would your life look like then, if you are to be happy? Take your time in answering; such things aren't easy to put into words."
>
> The interviewer records the reply in as verbatim a fashion as possible. When the respondent falters, the interviewer may prompt him with questions, being careful not to ask leading questions, until there is nothing further to report. The interviewer then continues with this question: "Now, taking the other side of the picture, what are your fears and worries about the future? In other words, if you imagine your future in the worst possible light, what would your life look like then? Again, take your time in answering."
>
> Again the responses are recorded verbatim with whatever prompting is necessary. The interviewer then shows the respondent a drawing of a ladder with 10 rungs and says: "Here is a picture of a ladder. Suppose we say that the top of the ladder represents the best possible life

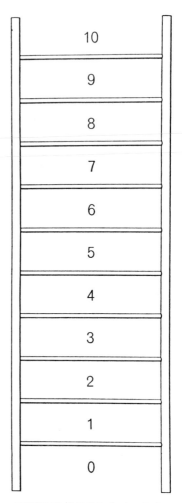

FIGURE 11. A Self-Anchoring Scale

This drawing is presented to a subject after he has established his own "self-anchoring" scale by defining his personal aspirations and fears. The subject is asked to assume that the top of the ladder is the best possible life for him and the bottom the worst possible, and to judge where he stands now and where he was five years ago and will be five years from now.

SOURCE: Cantril, Hadley, "A Study of Aspirations," *Scientific American,* vol. 208, February, 1963. Reprinted with permission. Copyright (c) 1963 by Scientific American, Inc. All rights reserved.

for you. Where on the ladder do you feel you personally stand at the present time?"

As he speaks the interviewer points to the top of the ladder and then to the bottom, and when he comes to the question of where the respondent now stands on the ladder, he moves his finger rapidly up and down it. When the respondent has indicated the appropriate rung, he is asked: "Where on the ladder would you say you stood five years ago?" Then he is asked: "Where do you think you will stand on the ladder five years from now?"

Although there is nothing sacred about the number of rungs the ladder might contain, experience has shown that the zero-to-10 interval is easily understood. There is nothing crucial about the interval of five years either, but we find that many people have difficulty recalling where they were more than five years ago and equal difficulty foreseeing the future more than five years hence. The device of the ladder has proved meaningful and workable in all groups except among certain primitive peoples, where it was tested in the preliminary phases of the study. Some untutored Bantu in South Africa found a crude sketch showing climbers on a hill more intelligible.[16]

Using this approach, Cantril and his associates at the Institute for International Social Research in Princeton, New Jersey, have been able to make comparative studies of population samples in the United States, Cuba, West Germany, the Philippines, Brazil, and other countries. In some of these countries the viewpoints of legislators have been obtained to compare with those of the publics they represent. By developing a systematic method of coding responses it has been possible to make comparisons between groups stratified in various ways: urban-rural, economic status, ethnic group, and so forth. Thus "The self-anchoring scale makes it possible to secure insight into the diverse worlds in which people of different nationalities live and to compare their outlooks on those worlds."[17]

It should be noted that the questions employed in the specific interview recorded above yield information on attitudes, beliefs, values, aspirations, and concerns. With open or free response data such as obtained in this approach, many difficulties are involved in developing meaningful and reliable codes for analysis.

SPRANGER'S VALUE TYPES

One theoretical approach to the study of value orientations has been stimulated by a provocative proposal made by the German philosopher Spranger, who argued that in order to understand an individual's personality one must know what meaning he gives to his experiences and actions, the value or values that help to shape his life. Spranger suggested that there are six ideal value types into which personalities might be ordered. He recognized, however, that a person need not hold value orientations that are exclusive of one type. The six value types he describes were: (1) theoretical man (concerned with truth and knowledge), (2) economic man (utilitarian), (3) esthetic man (art and harmony), (4) social man (humanitarian), (5) political man (power and control), and (6) religious man.[18]

A Scale of Personal Values

The most creative applications of the Spranger theoretical approach have been carried out by Allport and his associates, using a scale known as "A Study of Values."[19] This scale has served as an operational tool for translating Spranger's ideal types into measurable dimensions. An individual taking the scale makes 45 choices between alternative preferences or judgments regarding specific items that relate to broad value issues. On the basis of his response to the scale one may develop a profile of his value orientation.

This instrument for studying values has had more than thirty years of study and application. As the authors and others have warned, several characteristics limit its usefulness—the level of education required, the use of items most familiar to an educated American, and a checklist type of approach which may be unfamiliar to persons in other societies. The instrument presupposes certain broad orientations of values that may not be present in all population groups; therefore some of the values held by the group may be more important than those included on the scale. The identification of value orientations unique to a specific individual may require some approach that offers greater freedom of response. The types of items used, furthermore, are of a choice, preferential, or judgmental type that may be more revealing of attitudes, desires, and hopes than of values.

"A Study of Values" offers choices of two types. In Part I the individual is asked to make 30 choices between the alternatives such as the following: "Which would you consider the more important function of modern leaders? (a) to bring about the accomplishment of practical goals; (b) to encourage followers to take a greater interest in the rights of others." In Part II he is asked to respond to 15 questions, and in each case to rank his order of choice of 4 alternatives: "Which of the following would you prefer to do during part of your next summer vacation (if your ability and other conditions would permit)— a. write and publish an original biological essay or article, b. stay in some secluded part of the country where you can appreciate fine scenery, c. enter a local tennis or other athletic tournament, d. get experience in some new line of business."[20]

In spite of limitations, the instrument has proved to be a valuable research tool. Studies applying it provide convincing evidence that persons of different professional and social class groups tend to vary considerably in their orientations toward content of value significance. Thus use of the instrument confirms what health officers have learned by experience—that engineers, businessmen, social workers, and Catholic leaders are likely to apply different values in judging the significance of action proposals.

Values of Women and Public Health

Of particular interest to public health is a finding that women score higher than men on esthetic, religious, and social values.[21] This finding has been amply verified by other research in this country, although thus far adequate comparisons of the sexes in regard to values have not been carried out in other parts of the world.[22]

Bierman has observed that major changes in legislation of significance to maternal and child health and welfare, both within our individual states and among the nations of the world, have tended to follow the introduction of woman suffrage.[23] A reasonable hypothesis, worthy of rigorous test, is that stronger religious, esthetic, and social value orientations of women, as described by Allport, are of significant political importance in regard to health matters. To the extent that such a hypothesis holds, it suggests the value of involving women in more policy positions, or in positions where policies can effectively be influenced.

Sears, Maccoby, and Levin offer excellent support for this hypothesis with regard to child-rearing practices. They note that with the growth of independence of women and their higher education women have taken a stronger position in guiding their children and in promoting changes both within the home and the school system.[24]

Values of Health Team

There may be other parallels within the public health team that may deserve investigation. How do the different disciplines making up a health team compare in their value orientations? How do their value orientations compare with those of the people they serve, their peers in other agencies, the members of boards and committees to which they may report? To what extent do value conflicts contribute to difficulty in planning, communication, group effectiveness, and promotion?

In a study of the relationship between values held by instructors and their students, Bills reported that "students who held the same general value orientation as their instructor were found to have higher final class marks (as determined by objective examinations). . . ."[25] Such a relationship may be the effect of greater interest on the part of students with like values, or possibly the inadvertent encouragement by instructors of students who agree with them. Whatever the reason, the findings he reports are of interest to public health administrators, since the same type of relationship between their own values and those of staff members may be inadvertently leading to inequities in treatment. As Fiske has reported, the criteria used for hiring, firing, and promotion tend to be based upon the value judgments of the employer and management group.[26]

In the past the issue of values has been dealt with in an intuitive manner by administrators. Yet, as Allport suggests, knowing one's own values and the implications they have for action may be of great significance for an administrator.

> President Lowell of Harvard was once asked how it was possible for an overworked administrator to make so many detailed decisions day by day. He replied that it was not so difficult as it might seem, for each specific issue fits readily into one of a few dominant categories (schemata) of value. If the administrator is clear in his own mind concerning his value orientations, if he knows his major aims, decisions on specific issues automatically follow.[27]

TOP LEVEL BIAS

Kornhauser has observed that there tends to be a narrowing of the value systems held by employees of an organization as we move from the top down to the man at the operating level. As a result, values may become crystallized at the action levels in subtle ways far removed from the intent of the administrator. This narrowing of the value orientation of the organization, Kornhauser suggests, seems to be an almost inevitable effect of the process of selection, appointment, and inservice training, coupled with a tendency on the part of personnel at one level to try to interpret action alternatives as they feel would be desired by their superiors. He refers to this process as "top level bias."[28]

The administrator of an organization, such as a Health Department, is likely to be selected by an advisory group in part, at least, because he seems to represent their values. The deputy he appoints, in turn, is likely to be one to be trusted within the value areas of major concern to the administrator. This is usually true also for key committee members. The deputy, in turn, will probably choose aides whose value orientations are consistent with his own, and so on.

Differences occur within the organization in part as a result of human error and personnel turnover, and in part because requirements other than values are also important. Then, too, some administrators will seek to supplement rather than reinforce their own value orientations in making choices.

To the extent that top level bias occurs, at each step down through the administrative hierarchy there tends to be a narrowing of the value orientations of the individuals in administrative positions. This may be accompanied by a high sensitivity, perhaps, to the significance of the value orientation of the person directly below, since as one moves lower in the organization, the restriction on his activities tends to be increased. When new appointments are made for the purpose of developing new areas of emphasis, significant value issues may need to be resolved before progress can be made. Value conflicts may occur whether the appointment is high or low in the hierarchy.

"BASIC VALUE ORIENTATIONS"

When one seeks to compare the value patterns of social groups, many problems arise in attempting to differentiate values, as standards, from perceptions and assumptions regarding the nature of man and his place in the universe. The term "basic value orientations" has been used by Kluckhohn and Strodtbeck to apply to this amalgam of "principles" that tend to govern behavior. In their research, no attempt has been made to treat values apart from their relationship in this transactional setting.

"Value orientations" they define as "principles . . . which give order and direction to the ever flowing stream of human acts and thoughts as these relate to the solution of 'common human' problems."[29]

Kluckhohn and Strodtbeck assume that "there is a limited number of common human problems for which all peoples at all times must find some solution."[30] They assume also that all societies can solve these common problems in any of a number of ways so that their preferences regarding the solution reveal their basic value orientations.

The five problems they have identified as crucial for all human groups are stated as questions all societies must consider:

1. What is the character of innate human nature? (*human nature* orientation)

2. What is the relation of man to nature (and supernature)? (*man-nature* orientation)
3. What is the temporal focus of human life? (*time* orientation)
4. What is the modality of human activity? (*activity* orientation)
5. What is the modality of man's relationship to other men? (*relational* orientation)[31]

Using this approach, the type of solution members of a group identify as best for themselves and others in their society is considered to be that group's basic value orientation with respect to solving the specific problem. In the research conducted, three possible solutions were offered as alternatives to consider for each problem.

To the extent that groups hold such basic predispositions toward the solution of life's problems, one would expect these predispositions to guide all sorts of daily decisions. Accordingly, Kluckhohn and Strodtbeck designed a questionnaire regarding a series of problems of rural life in order to compare the value orientations of different societies.

It is not possible here to discuss the findings of the Kluckhohn-Strodtbeck research. However, the type of approach they used for studying the predispositions of different societies is one that seems to hold significant potential for public health practice. Their theoretical framework is a particularly useful one, in considering the implications of alternative basic value orientations held by social groups, for public health practitioners responsible for program planning and action.[32]

Orientation to Human Nature

While philosophers and social scientists have discussed at length the orientations of our society toward human nature, relatively little has been done in the way of comparing our society with other societies regarding this value orientation. Nor has consideration been given to the implications such value orientations might have for public health. Three or more different orientations are widely held.

Some of our Puritan ancestors held the view that man is innately evil but can be made pure and good through strict discipline, moral education, and rigid social controls. Change in this innately acquired human nature was considered achievable, but difficult. Such a value orientation offered fertile soil for the belief that illness or misfortune was the just product of sin, that abnormal behaviors reflected the influence of the devil, and that the so-called "social diseases" were God's punishments for transgression.

A somewhat different value position was held by the Machiavellians who regard man as basically evil, selfish, and ruthless and contend that human nature will never change. The philosopher Dunham has referred to this point of view as the "doctrine of selfishness."[33] For those who hold this doctrine, war and conflict are inevitable. Attempts to create a peaceful, cooperative society or to institute lasting social improvement are doomed to failure. Were public health leaders to hold such a negative value orientation toward human nature they would face their tasks with a sense of futility and despair.

Saunders has noted some of the public health implications of the assumption that "you can't change human nature."

> The persistence of crime, war, poverty, willfulness, disease, and virtually any condition that meets with disapproval is ascribed to the operation—usually in others—of a fixed, innate nature which predisposes people to respond in certain ways to social situations. The great utility of this bias is that it can be used both to "explain" behavior and to avoid explaining it, and that it can justify and validate almost any notion about behavior that one wishes to hold. If some people are reluctant to accept the advice or the services of surgeons, it can be said that "it is human nature to be afraid of surgery" and surgeons thus be absolved from any necessity for modifying their approach to patients. If "it is human nature to want to be well," there is no reason to adapt medical programs to fit the needs of different ethnic groups, since their nature will lead members of such groups to recognize superior medical technology and impel them to seek its services. If "it is human nature to want to get something for nothing," then those giving medical services must be careful to keep their fees high or make access to their services difficult by some other means lest they be overwhelmed by demands for service from people who are not "really" sick, but who are merely seeking a medical bargain. Statements such as these illustrate the ways in which assumptions about human nature can be used, either consciously or unconsciously, to defend the *status quo,* support invidious judgments about the behavior of groups and individuals, and provide moral support for engaging in courses of action or inaction which could not be approved if rationalized under a different set of assumptions.[34]

Philosophical leaders of public health such as Shattuck, Winslow, and Mountin have been in the forefront of those Americans who recognize the pliability of the newborn infant, the importance of socialization and learning, and the significance of environmental influences for personality and social change. The value assumption underlying programs in Maternal and Child Health, Mental Health, Rehabilitation, and Environmental Health, for example, is that man is born neither good nor evil and that human nature can and does change with growth, development, and experience.

Value Orientation to Man-Nature

The man-nature value orientation has received much attention from philosophers and social scientists and has been frequently mentioned as a variable significant to public health. Some peoples do seem to take a fatalistic position toward nature, feeling that there is little that they can do to control the winds, the rains, the crops, or life itself. Others feel that man gets along best when he seeks to adapt to the conditions of nature, living in the proper way, adapting his life in accord with what he sees to be the plan of nature. Others, such as most Americans, seem to take the conquest of nature as a challenge, try to change adverse natural conditions, the weather, rainfall, quality of the soil, course of the rivers, and the availability of potable waters.

Most Americans tend to feel that the world is better off because of science, and credit science with improvements in health, medical advance, and longevity. Others feel that science is so powerful in its ability to influence nature that it in some ways threatens society, contributes to the increase in problems of overpopulation, possibilities of war, and destruction. Even such persons as feel that science is a threat, as well as a value, tend to recognize and accept the good effects of science and the value of science as a means on influencing unfavorable natural conditions.[35]

Americans who hold such views regarding man's relation to nature have difficulty understanding or appreciating the logic of members of other groups who are fatalistic in their orientations. Foster tells us:

> In many cultures it is assumed that what is to be is to be, and there is little the individual can do to change things. Pineda (1955) points out that in rural Colombia, when a child dies, the parents often say, "It was his destiny, not to grow up." In the province of Santander, when a child is more beautiful and intelligent than average, the parents sometimes prepare themselves for grief by saying, "This child is not for this world." And, if a sick child recovers without medical attention, the parents say, "See, God did not intend him to die." When Pineda urged parents to take ill children to doctors, they often refused, saying, "The rich also die, in spite of having so much money for medical care."[36]

Saunders, Clark, and others have identified such value orientations among Spanish-American groups.[37] One must recognize, of course, that such a viewpoint taken by members of a group may reflect a true inability to take preventive action for economic, educational, or other such reasons. The response may reflect a history of failure of attempts to influence nature or "the will of God."

Many religious denominations in the United States also place rigid limits on the right of man to interfere with God's will, particularly in such areas of public health concern as family planning, fluoridation of the water supply, surgery, vivisection, or animal experimentation.

Orientation to Time

In considering the public health significance of value orientations regarding time, one must immediately recognize that leaders of the public health professions are among the most futuristically oriented members of society. Public health research is oriented toward predicting the occurrence of illness, disability, or disaster. By anticipating potentially dangerous developments, appropriate actions can currently be taken and public health leaders hope to minimize future risks. The success of public health programs depends upon the quality of actions taken in anticipation of possible future events. If goals of prevention are fully achieved, the feared epidemic or tragedy never occurs.

Many of the publics served by public health professions do not share this orientation toward the future. For some, such an orientation to program planning and development appears impractical, unrealistic, beyond the realm of accomplishment, and indeed even interfering with or diverting funds and efforts from satisfaction of more immediately urgent needs.

Americans are frequently described as a future-oriented people, being, on the whole, less concerned with maintaining old customs and traditions than with keeping up with the latest fads and standards of thought, dress, and behavior. Minimal ego-involvement in the past is reflected in the fact that among leaders in our society are found some who lack even an elementary awareness of social or political history. Few Americans demonstrate a serious concern with the origins of their language, their social, political, and economic ideas, or even their religious practices. They tend to assign almost full responsibility for knowledge and understanding of these cultural areas to specialists. Relatively more Americans demonstrate an urgent need to keep abreast of their neighbors in dress and social behavior. While urging the expert to open new vistas of knowledge and technology, they are quick to take advantage of his discoveries, and try to be "up" on the latest news and fashions, fads and gadgets.

Yet within this future-oriented society are some who are deeply concerned with maintenance of past traditions and values. They find themselves in the conflict situation of favoring science and progress because these things are "good," yet fearing the "threat" that science, scientists, and technology hold for their patterns of value and belief.[38]

Also within our future-oriented society are many who, lacking minimal security or having experienced hardship, center their thoughts and efforts on the urgencies of the present. Such a present-time orientation prevails among many southern Negroes,[39] Spanish Americans,[40] migrant laborers, and other groups of lower socioeconomic status. Even though the economic and social conditions of such people may improve, the serious hardship conditions they have experienced leave deep social and psychological scars. A present-time orientation, acquired during a period of urgent need, retains its hold on thoughts and actions long after urgent immediate needs are satisfied. It is not surprising that public health programs sponsored by future-oriented citizens find a hard core of resistance among such poorer members of society who might most benefit from early identification and control of illness. Nor is it surprising that leaders of communities that have undergone severe economic hardship in past years are hesitant about accepting long-range commitments that might threaten future economic security. For example, the leaders of such communities may feel they cannot afford new health facilities even though the costs may appear to an outsider to be reasonable. While costs seem reasonable in our present economy, the leaders may fear the community will not be able to support them tomorrow, or at some future date.

In such countries as India, where social changes are occurring at great speed, the conflict in value orientation between a future-oriented leadership and a traditionally bound citizenry is likely to become of increasing significance to public health leaders. Awareness of the urgency of forward-looking programs, a high regard for economic and social progress, and an increasing respect for scientific and technical development, all seem to be hamstrung by the overburdening requirements of traditionally bound administrative practices. Manifold dangers accompany such conditions. Complex administrative procedures may frustrate leaders and laymen alike, and continued frustration may give rise to actions inconsistent with a democratic philosophy. Improvements in administrative procedures seem crucial to the development of sound and lasting public health programs.

Orientation to Activity

The activity value orientation concerns the preference people have for particular modes of expression. It is closely tied to the time orientation. Those future-oriented tend to be also achievement-oriented, eager to "get going" on things, anxious to "get things done"; whereas those oriented toward the present may find greater satisfaction in spontaneous activities less oriented toward future goals. Mexican society, with its *fiesta* activities and less concern with time pressures, illustrates the "being" type of orientation. Members of such a society, on the whole, seem to feel less need to compete.

Few frustrations are likely to be greater than those experienced by a person eager to institute change that he believes to be significant when he is faced by those who agree with him philosophically but are personally content to let the world move by them. Helping social change to occur under such circumstances requires infinite patience and tolerance.

Orientations to Relationships

Man's relationship to man, the relational value orientation, is strikingly different within various sociocultural groups and contributes significantly both to the social organization of the group and to patterns of behavior of its members. Those who would seek to adapt health programs to existing patterns of communication, administration, and decision-making need to be sensitive to the value orientations of the group regarding the relationships between people and the significance this may have for planning and action.

It is important to learn early, for example, whether community decisions are customarily initiated and directed by senior members of the traditional families (linear orientation), by majority vote so that action may be taken even in opposition to a strong minority (individual orientation), or by a type of group action that requires almost total support before the decision is final (collateral). Do people look toward an older, important person for leadership? Do they go ahead on their own and try to get cooperation from others, with less regard for what members of the older families think, or do they depend on members of their families for health and support? Knowing how members of the group are accustomed to responding to other situations will suggest to the health worker ways of identifying lay leaders and gatekeepers who ought to be involved in the early consideration of possible health activities.

In developing health facilities, such information is also useful. People who prefer to treat illness and care as a private, personal matter will expect a different approach from those who are accustomed to sharing their illness and treatment with members of the family. This applies to casefinding and diagnostic procedures, and also to hospital care. Those who share their illnesses expect the family to be present in the hospital, and may avoid treatment and care unless such an opportunity is offered.[41]

Possibly in this value reside some of the sources of internal conflicts and difficulties of public health groups. Persons who have one value orientation may be required by the job situation to act contrary to the requirements of that orientation. Older members may resent young leadership and youthful leaders may feel uncomfortable with an older staff. Women may at times have difficulty in gaining acceptance of positions of leadership. Members with individual value orientation may have difficulty in adapting to group functioning, whether in a leadership or membership role. Others oriented to expect group discussion and decisions may resent direction from one who does not share the information.

THE VALUES OF HEALTH AND LIFE

Of great importance to public health practice is the value people place on health and on life. Persons committed to the public health professions are strongly oriented toward the principles of prevention and control. Their professional lives are largely committed to the idea of protecting society from conditions that may threaten to produce morbidity or mortality, in this way preserving health and life. It is not surprising that they feel that everyone ought to be similarly concerned about these issues, particularly insofar as his own health and life may be involved.

To date we lack substantial evidence about the nature of health and life as values. Health has many meanings, and when one speaks of health as a value one must be certain that he and his correspondent share the same meanings. When health is ranked in comparison with other broad areas of importance to man, it may be given a primary ranking. One may say it is more important than income, a sense of belongingness, and so forth. This suggests it has an ideal value quality; in our society one "ought" to give it importance.[42] Yet health, as a significant principle, does not seem to be of equal importance to the individual at all times. It becomes salient in guiding action when health is threatened in some way; otherwise the individual may seriously ignore and injure his health.

Prenatal and Infant Care

This issue comes clearly to attention in the area of prenatal care. Whether or not an expectant mother is realistically concerned about her pregnancy and its outcome and is interested in prenatal care may depend on whether or not she wants the child. How her husband reacts to the idea of parenthood may also significantly influence her ego-involvement in the child and her receptivity to professional assistance. Her acceptance or rejection of him may govern her acceptance or rejection of the child. If she feels closely bound to both him and the child, but he does not want the child, her feelings during the period of waiting may be filled with unresolvable conflicts.

In our society we tend to place a high social value on human life and it is almost sacrilegious in some quarters to raise questions regarding the desirability of preserving and protecting new life. All pregnant women, however, may not want safe deliveries. Whether or not a woman wanted to become pregnant and desires to have her child may have a significant bearing on whether or not she seeks prenatal care. Thus whether a mother will take recommended health actions to protect her infant may not depend only on her expectation regarding the effectiveness of this action. Of even deeper importance may be the mother's orientation regarding the value of the child as an extension of her self. Cultural factors may have an important bearing on this decision. If children are highly prized in her value system, and the mother identifies strongly with her child, her action may be different from what it would be if she conformed to the values of a society in which children are not highly prized. Different, too, may be the behavior of the mother in a culture in which infants may not be accepted as full members of the family until they have managed to live through the diseases and injuries of childhood. In such a situation a mother may protect her ego against the possible injury resulting from identification with the infant, who is given little chance to survive, by not accepting him as a full member of the family until his survival is reasonably assured.

Gadalla, in a study of low-income mothers interviewed shortly after being delivered, found that only about one-third of the mothers said that they had wanted to become pregnant. Of this group, two-thirds had received adequate prenatal care (prenatal care for five or more months of pregnancy), whereas only half of those who had not wanted to become pregnant had received adequate prenatal care. Seventy-eight per cent of those mothers who demonstrated an interest in the baby by beginning to prepare the layette before the sixth month received adequate prenatal care. In general, Gadalla found that mothers who were most favorably oriented toward preventive measures in the area of health, who had favorable attitudes toward their pregnancy, and also had favorable attitudes toward the idea of prenatal care were more likely to have received adequate prenatal care. Mothers with favorable attitudes toward their pregnancies tended also to be more tolerant than other mothers toward waiting in clinics and were more favorable in their evaluations of the behaviors of physicians and nurses.[43]

It should be cautioned that Gadalla carried out his study after the women in the sample had been delivered. Accordingly, their attitudes toward pregnancy may reflect, in part, their satisfactions or dissatisfactions with the experiences of prenatal care and delivery. One can never be sure that retrospective studies fully reflect the feelings and concerns of the individuals at the time they were undergoing an earlier experience.

Family Planning

The increasing involvement of public health agencies in areas of family planning and population control has brought into focus major value conflicts between groups who strongly disagree regarding the value of prenatal human life and the right of man to interfere with natural reproductive processes. Many who oppose the introduction of clinics to provide contraceptives and advice in their use find such actions in direct conflict with strongly held religious values. Of significance to this conflict is the definition of human life: When does a human life actually begin? Is an interception of the process of conception a preventive or a destructive act?

One cannot assume that similar value-guided behaviors regarding such actions necessarily reflect an enactment of similar life values for the individual concerned. Several persons opposing support for family planning may do so on different value grounds: one on the basis of a specific religious dogma, another on the grounds of religious freedom with the fetus viewed as an individual with rights and privileges, another on the basis that one should maintain a harmony with nature and not interfere with natural processes, a fourth on the grounds that his society supersedes the individual in value and needs a larger population for purposes of development or defense.

Value of Animal and Insect Life

An individual's orientation to the value of life could be of prime significance to the way he views public health actions and judges their significance. Among the peoples of the world are some, such as the Jain sect in India, who believe that all animal and insect life is valuable. From their point of view man has no right to injure or to kill even the smallest of insects or microbes, even though they may bear disease that threatens his own health or existence, or consume food he desperately needs for his own nourishment. Such persons are reported to keep their mouths covered after dark so they do not inadvertently kill some flying insect. Such a frame of reference toward the destruction of living things becomes a serious barrier to the introduction of such public health measures as the chlorination of the water supply to protect society against dangerous bacterial life, the use of insecticides to control malaria or other insect-borne diseases, the destruction of diseased animals to prevent the spread of brucellosis, or the control of rodents.

Other Life Value Influences

Among other matters of significance in which life values would appear to be of major concern are legalized abortion and sterilization, euthanasia for the hopelessly afflicted, medical experimentation on man and on animals, space research involving human and animal life, capital punishment, wartime killings, and suicide. The issues of smoking and cancer, chronic illness and restricted life, the use of alcohol with its positive as well as negative effects, all concern the meaning of life for the individual and his definition of a good life as opposed to just living. We do not know to what extent people value the length of life of and by itself, or are concerned about its personal, social, or task utility. Much research is needed before such questions can be answered.

Of concern also are values regarding ideal family size and composition, which involve many questions pertaining to the relative value of different types of human life. A Hindu whose religion requires that a son be available to perform his own funeral rites is not likely to be easily swayed into limiting the size of his own family until his future is protected by having at least two sons, with the hope that at least one will live. Such a person, who at the same time places a high value on social, cultural, educational, and economic attainment for his family, and therefor would otherwise prefer a small family, is faced with a difficult value choice.

Death and Its Meanings

In an exploratory study of attitudes toward death and dying, Kalish draws attention to some of the inconsistencies in attitudes held. He notes that attitudes toward wartime killing and capital punishment tend to be related, but that such attitudes correlate negatively with attitudes toward the prevention of life, suicide, and euthanasia. Thus persons who favor the taking of life for the purposes of society tend to be opposed to the prevention of life or the taking of life by the individual himself for personal reasons. In view of the self-selected nature of Kalish's sample, such findings need to be viewed with caution until more adequately verified.[44]

The meanings of life and of death as matters for both theoretical and action significance have been brought to attention in recent years by Feifel, Shneidman, and more recently in dramatic fashion by Mitford in *The American Way of Death*.[45] Shneidman calls attention to the process of gradually removing oneself or disassociating oneself from the aged or disabled, thus avoiding traumatic experiences associated with death. The gradual reclassification of the aged or disabled out of one's own social world prior to death tends to make dying a process rather than a specific terminal event. Such findings deserve serious consideration on the part of persons responsible for the care and treatment of terminal patients, patients with long-term illnesses, or the aged.[46]

Many questions remain unanswered regarding the value of life, the meaning of life and of health for different groups under varying conditions, how these values and meanings are acquired and changed, and the significance they have for "appropriate" health action. Under what conditions is health a value for the individual, or a salient motivating force toward action or inaction, or part of the "background" in human transactions? While some consideration will be given to health concerns in the chapter on applications of learning, fuller understanding in this area awaits more and better studies.

GENERAL IMPLICATIONS

Values play a role, often unrecognized, in all public health activities. The health officer and his staff need to take into serious consideration the value systems of those with whom they plan programs, but also profit by examining their own values insofar as they relate to public health activities.[47]

Values held by those professionally engaged in public health may be of significance in many ways:

1. The values we hold help to identify the problems to which we give primary attention.

2. They help to determine how we define these problems and the roles we assume in dealing with them.

3. They help to determine whether we see these problems as something that can be solved by man or something that cannot be solved by man, but depend upon the will of God.

4. They help determine how we relate to one another in attempting to solve the problems to which we give attention.

5. They help to define the roles we take in dealing with the problems of concern.

6. They help to identify the approaches we consider the most fruitful in problem solution.

7. They help to determine the criteria we use in determining whether or not we have been successful or have made progress.

8. They help to determine the areas to which we give prime attention in evaluating our progress.

Above all, since the values held by those in public health involve their basic assumptions about man and the universe, they are of primary significance in determining both what constitutes fact in public health, and what facts are significant within the broad field of public health.[48]

In discussing the relationship of values to social theory and social policy, Myrdal summarizes a few of the principles that apply in such situations.

> Let me try in one paragraph to formulate the main rules we should attempt to apply to social analysis. Value premises should be introduced openly. They should be explicitly stated and not kept hidden as tacit assumptions. They should be used not only as premises for our policy conclusions but also to determine the direction of our positive research. They should thus be kept conscious and in the focus of attention throughout the work. This is, incidentally, our only protection against

bias in research, for bias implies being directed by unacknowledged valuations. The value premises should be formulated as specifically and concretely as possible. They cannot be *a priori* self-evident or generally valid. They should be chosen, but not arbitrarily, for the choice must meet the criteria of relevance and significance to the actual society we are living in. Since as a matter of fact conflicting valuations are held in society, the value premises should ideally be given as a number of sets of coexisting valuations.[49]

NOTES TO CHAPTER 18

1. English, Horace B., and Ava C. English, *A Comprehensive Dictionary of Psychological and Psychoanalytical Terms.* Longmans, Green, and Co., London, 1958, p. 577.

2. Allport, Gordon W., *Pattern and Growth in Personality.* Holt, Rinehart, and Winston, New York, 1961, p. 454.

3. Kluckhohn, Clyde, and Henry A. Murray, with the collaboration of David M. Schneider, editors, *Personality in Nature, Society, and Culture.* 2d. ed., rev. and enl. Alfred A. Knopf, Inc., New York, 1956, p. 59.

4. Heider, Fritz, *The Psychology of Interpersonal Relations.* John Wiley and Sons, New York, 1958.

5. Lewin, Kurt, "Constructs in Field Theory," initially published in 1944, in Lewin, Kurt, *Field Theory in Social Science: Selected Theoretical Papers,* edited by Dorwin Cartwright, Harper and Bros., New York, 1951, pp. 30–42; Heider, Fritz, *op. cit.,* pp. 218–243.

6. Lewin, Kurt, *op. cit.,* p. 41.

7. Knutson, Andie L., and Benjamin Shimberg, "Evaluation of a Health Education Program," *American Journal of Public Health,* vol. 45, no. 1, 1955, pp. 21–27.

8. Kluckhohn, Clyde, and Henry A. Murray, with the collaboration of David M. Schneider, editors, *op. cit.,* p. 60.

9. Smith, M. Brewster, "Personal Values in the Study of Lives" in White, Robert, editor, *The Study of Lives.* Atherton Press, New York, 1963, pp. 324–347.

10. Brim, Orville G., Jr., *Education for Child Rearing.* Russell Sage Foundation, New York, 1959.

11. Burton, John, "Soap and Education," *Health Education Journal,* vol. 15, May, 1957, p. 72.

12. Williams, Robin M., Jr., *American Society: A Sociological Interpretation,* Alfred A. Knopf, Inc., New York, 1951; 2d ed., also published by Alfred A. Knopf, Inc., 1960, pp. 388–442; Dukes, William F., "Psychological Studies of Values," *Psychological Bulletin,* vol. 52, January, 1955, pp. 24–50; Morris, Charles W., *Varieties of Human Value,* University of Chicago Press, Chicago, 1956.

13. Williams, Robin M., Jr., *op. cit.,* pp. 407–408.

14. Mountin, Joseph W., "The Evolving Pattern of Tomorrow's Health," *American Journal of Public Health,* December, 1943, pp. 32–39. Reprinted in Mountin, Joseph W., *Selected Papers.* Thomas Parran, Harry S. Mustard, and Dean A. Clark (Editorial Committee), Joseph W. Mountin Memorial Committee, n.p., 1956, p. 35.

15. Kilpatrick, Franklin P., and Hadley Cantril, "Self-Anchoring Scaling, A Measure of Individuals' Unique Reality Worlds," *Journal of Individual Psychology,* vol. 16, November, 1960.

16. Cantril, Hadley, "A Study of Aspirations," *Scientific American,* vol. 208, February, 1963, p. 4. See also Cantril's *The Politics of Despair,* Basic Books, New York, 1958; and Free, Lloyd A., *Six Allies and a Neutral,* The Free Press, Glencoe, Ill., 1959.

17. Cantril, Hadley, "A Study of Aspirations," *op. cit.,* p. 7.

18. Spranger, Edward, *Types of Men.* Translated by Paul J. W. Pigors. M. Niemeyer, Halle (Saale), Germany, 1928.

19. Allport, Gordon W., Philip E. Vernon, and Gardner Lindzey, *A Study of Values: A Scale for Measuring the Dominant Interests in Personality,* 3d ed., Houghton Mifflin, Boston, 1960; Allport, Gordon W., *Pattern and Growth in Personality, op. cit.,* pp. 455 ff.

20. Allport, Gordon W., *Pattern and Growth in Personality, op. cit.,* p. 455.

21. Vernon, Philip E., and Gordon W. Allport, "A Test for Personal Values," *Journal of Abnormal and Social Psychology,* vol. 26, 1931, pp. 231–248.

22. Cantril, Hadley, and Gordon W. Allport, "Recent Applications of the Study of Values," *Journal of Abnormal and Social Psychology,* vol. 28, 1933, pp. 259–273; Hartman, G. W., "Sex Differences in Valuational Attitudes," *Journal of Social Psychology,* vol. 5, 1934, pp. 106–112; Pintner, R., "A Comparison of Interests, Abilities, and Attitudes," *Journal of Abnormal and Social Psychology,* vol. 27, 1933, pp. 351–357; Spoerl, Dorothy T., "The Values of the Post-War College Student," *Journal of Social Psychology,* vol. 35, 1952, pp. 217–225; Triplett, Richard J., "Interests of Commercial Students," *Journal of Abnormal and Social Psychology,* vol. 29, 1935, pp. 409–414.

23. Bierman, Jessie M., Personal communication, 1964.

24. Sears, Robert R., Eleanor E. Maccoby, and Harry Levin, *Patterns of Child Rearing.* Row, Peterson and Co., Evanston, Ill., 1957.

25. Bills, Robert, "The Effect of a Value on Learning," *Journal of Personality,* vol. 21, 1952, pp. 217–222. Cited in Dukes, William F., *op. cit.,* p. 30.

26. Fiske, D. W., "Values, Theory, and the Criterion Problem," *Personnel Psychology,* vol. 4, 1951, pp. 93–98. Cited in Dukes, William F., *op. cit.,* p. 30.

27. Allport, Gordon W., *Becoming.* Yale University Press, New Haven, 1955. Paperbound edition, 1960, p. 76.

28. Kornhauser, Arthur, "The Problem of Bias in Opinion Research," *International Journal of Opinion and Attitude Research,* vol. 1, December, 1947, pp. 1–16.

29. Kluckhohn, Florence R., and Fred L. Strodtbeck, *Variations in Value Orientations.* Row, Peterson, and Co., Evanston, Ill., 1961, p. 4.

30. *Ibid.,* p. 10.

31. *Ibid.,* p. 11.

32. *Ibid.*

33. Dunham, Barrows, *Man Against Myth.* Little, Brown and Co., Boston, 1947, pp. 31–56.

34. Saunders, Lyle, *Cultural Difference and Medical Care: The Case of the Spanish-speaking People of the Southwest.* Russell Sage Foundation, New York, 1954, pp. 234–235.

35. Kirscht, John P., and Andie L. Knutson, "Science and Fluoridation: An

Attitude Study," *Journal of Social Issues,* vol. 17, no. 4, 1961, pp. 37–44; *Idem,* "Fluoridation and the 'Threat' of Science," *Journal of Health and Human Behavior,* vol. 4, Summer, 1963, pp. 129–135; Davis, Robert C., *The Impact of Science in the Mass Media.* University of Michigan, Survey Research Center, Ann Arbor, 1958.

36. Foster, George M., *Problems in Intercultural Health Programs.* Social Science Research Council, Pamphlet 12, New York, April, 1958, p. 30; cited within this quotation is Virginia G. de Pineda's "Causas culturales de la mortalidad infantil," *Revista Colombiana de Antropologia,* vol. 4, 1955, pp. 18–19.

37. Saunders, Lyle, *op. cit.;* Clark, Margaret, *Health in the Mexican American Culture: A Community Study,* University of California Press, Berkeley, 1959.

38. Kirscht, John P., and Andie L. Knutson, "Fluoridation and the 'Threat' of Science," *op. cit.*

39. Davis, Allison, B. B. Gardner, and Mary R. Gardner, *Deep South: A Social Anthropological Study of Caste and Class.* University of Chicago Press, Chicago, 1941.

40. Saunders, Lyle, *op. cit.;* Clark, Margaret, *op. cit.*

41. Mead, Margaret, editor, *Cultural Patterns and Technical Change.* Tensions and Technology Series, United Nations Educational, Scientific, and Cultural Organization, New York, 1955. Reprinted as a Mentor Book, New American Library, New York, 1955.

42. Knutson, Andie L., "Personal Security as Related to Station in Life," *Psychological Monographs,* vol. 66, no. 4, 1952, pp. 1–31. Whole number 336.

43. Gadalla, Fawzy R. A., "A Study of Motivational Factors and Barriers Related to the Utilization of Prenatal Care by Mothers Delivered at Alameda County Hospital." Unpublished doctoral dissertation, University of California, Berkeley, 1962.

44. Kalish, Richard A., "An Approach to the Study of Death Attitudes," *American Behavioral Scientist,* vol. 6, 1963, pp. 68–70; *Idem,* "Some Variables in Death Attitudes," *Journal of Social Psychology,* vol. 59, 1963, pp. 137–145.

45. Feifel, Herman, editor, *The Meaning of Death,* Blakiston Division, McGraw-Hill Book Co., 1959; Shneidman, Edwin S., "Orientations Toward Death: A Vital Aspect of the Study of Life," in White, Robert, editor, *The Study of Lives,* The Atherton Press, New York, 1963, pp. 200–227; Shneidman, Edwin S., and Norman L. Farbarow, editors, *Clues to Suicide,* McGraw-Hill Book Co., New York, 1957; Shneidman and Farbarow, editors, *The Cry for Help,* Blakiston Division, McGraw-Hill Book Co., 1961; Mitford, Jessica, *The American Way of Death,* Simon and Schuster, New York, 1963.

46. Shneidman, Edwin S., *op. cit.*

47. Knutson, Andie L., "The Influence of Values on Evaluation," *Health Education Monographs,* no. 3, 1959, pp. 25–31. See also Lippitt, Ronald, "Value-Judgment Problems of the Social Scientist in Action-Research" (paper originally presented September, 1950), in Bennis, Warren G., Kenneth D. Benne, and Robert Chin, editors, *The Planning of Change: Readings in the Applied Behavioral Sciences,* Holt, Rinehart, and Winston, New York, 1961, pp. 689–694.

48. Benne, Kenneth D., and Guy E. Swanson, editors, "Values and the Social Scientist," *Journal of Social Issues,* vol. 6, no. 4, 1950.

49. Myrdal, Gunnar, "The Relation Between Social Theory and Social Policy," *British Journal of Sociology,* vol. 4, September, 1953, p. 241.

Chapter 19

Attitudes and Beliefs

BY RONALD C. DILLEHAY*

FOR SOME FIFTY YEARS the concept of attitude has had a prominent role in social psychology and sociology. Some behavioral scientists have given the concept singular importance.[1] The behavioral sciences have employed attitudes and beliefs to explain in part such phenomena as perception, learning and forgetting, judgment, and motivation. In this way some roles that attitudes play in the economy of adjustment, broadly conceived, of an individual to his world have been examined. Attitudes are found to play many functions in this process. Attitudes and beliefs affect overt behavior, but caution must be used in inferring attitudes from behavior or in predicting behavior from attitudes. Many factors other than attitudes influence behavior. From another perspective, behavior may determine attitudes, as may perceptions, learning and forgetting, judgment, and motivation.

Attitudes are formed and changed throughout the process of growth, and maturation, being affected by such factors as experiences within the family, the peer group, education, participation in formal organizations, occupational membership, and others. It is possible to view most attitudes and beliefs that people acquire as a result of these and other influences as enduring states of readiness that facilitate transactions between the individual and a complex world. While they induce stability and reduce problems of surprise, attitudes invite difficulty because they are in some degree insensitive to new experiences, to information suggestive of change. In extreme form, closed-mindedness and stereotypic thinking raise serious problems of adjustment. From a motivational viewpoint, a complex of attitudes may serve to protect their host from ideas and feelings that are unacceptable to him.

* I wish to express my thanks to Dr. Andie L. Knutson for editorial suggestions in the preparation of this chapter. A note of thanks is due also to Donald Blandford and David Stimpson for their comments on an earlier draft.

293

Such attitudes may show increasing rigidity, rather than change, in the face of discrepant information.

In the following pages we will explore some of these aspects of attitudes and beliefs. This discussion represents a sampling of, and perspective on, the vast and growing behavioral science literature on social attitudes.

The Concept of Attitudes

Attitudes are tendencies to experience or act toward an object in a way indicating some degree of favorableness-unfavorableness toward that object. An object is anything that exists for the person, and it may be concrete or bounded, such as sanitarians, novels, patients, or it may be less concrete, such as fluoridation of a community water supply or housing integration. The object may be esoteric or abstract, such as God, prestige, or happiness. From one perspective we may view attitudes analytically and concern ourselves with the structure or components of these predispositions.[2] That is to say, we may focus on the elements that comprise an attitude. From another perspective we can focus upon functional effects or outcomes of the tendency to evaluate a given class of objects in certain ways.[3]

Three major components of attitudes are beliefs about the object, affect, and behavioral tendencies. An attitude contains beliefs about the attributes or characteristics of the focal object. A nurse might believe, for example, that "The mothers who come to the clinic don't really care about how nutritious their child's diet is." A sanitarian may think that "Many landlords are unwilling to cooperate with the health department in meeting health codes." In addition to expressing an idea about some object, each of these statements expresses some degree of affect or feeling, if certain conditions are met. In the case of the nurse's statement about mothers who come to the clinic, we may assume or ascertain that nurses consider nutrition important in planning diets for infants, and that therefore this assertion indicates disapproval of the mothers' practices. Similar negative feeling is exhibited toward the landlords by the sanitarian if we make the plausible assumption, or take the trouble to determine, that cooperation with the health department in meeting health codes is positively valued by the sanitarian. Affect may be expressed directly in a statement such as "I dislike sanitarians who come around too often."

The feeling or affect expressed in a statement of belief or opinion may, of course, be positive in tone, as in the case of the following statements about a health officer made by members of his staff: "Doctor does not fail to obtain a better salary for us whenever the issue comes up before the personnel board." "He makes a sincere effort to help the public understand what they are to do in meeting acceptable health standards."

Attitudes cannot validly be discerned or inferred on the basis of only one or a few statements; rarely can a statement be interpreted in a simple way. It is with a pattern of expressions that one may perhaps validly draw an inference about an attitude. The nature of the inference, and the purpose to which it is to be put, are crucial in the confidence that one may have in it.

The third characteristic of an attitude is the kind of action tendency expressed in the attitude. An aspect of the attitudes of local physicians toward a health department might be "We need to restrict the immunization program being conducted at the present time." A health officer may believe that "We should enforce existing regulations that deal with reporting communicable diseases." These statements indicate the action dispositions that are a part of an attitude. Considerable variation is to be expected from person to person in the kind and amount of action tendency that forms a part of a given attitude. Note that this characteristic of an attitude is not action per se but rather a belief about action toward the object.

These action tendencies may or may not be openly advocated as a matter of policy. The policy stand[4] that is expressly adopted will be affected by many factors in addition to the attitude. A person may feel that he should write to his state Board of Health complaining about its policy on some matter, but fail to do so because of the inconvenience of writing, fear of having to support his claims, pressure from significant others to remain silent, and so on. Attitudes and actual behavior will be discussed in a later section.

A rudimentary description of an attitude conveys the beliefs held about the object, the feelings that accompany them, and something of the associated behavioral tendencies. Each of these components can be described as to its favorableness-unfavorableness toward the object. Is the view of the object positive or negative? Are the behavioral tendencies such as to help, harm, or be indifferent toward the object? We may further wish to know the degree to which a person favors or disfavors something: Is he only lukewarm about it, or does he take an extreme stand? Related to extremity of opinion is intensity. How strongly does he feel about it? How aroused is he likely to become in thinking or talking about it? In general, we can expect that more extreme attitudes will be more intensely held. Attitudes may also be differentiated in terms of their salience, or the prominence of the object in the person's psychological field or awareness.

Other dimensions are discussed by various authors.[5] A person may view an object in a simple, uncomplicated way, seeing only one or a few aspects of importance; another person may see many different important aspects in the object. For example, for some individuals contraception may be seen as simply a moral question, something one ought or ought not practice depending upon religious sanction. Others may view this issue in terms of relative expense, ease of obtaining the necessary items, relative responsibility of the sexual partners, convenience in application, restriction in satisfaction, efficiency, or morality. These differences in consideration of the issue will have important implications for programs designed to change attitudes about contraception and family planning.

An aspect of health attitudes that may be of particular importance is their time perspective[6] which is defined as the duration and persistence of concern embodied in the attitude. A person's view of public health practice may be transitory and limited to specific crises, or it may be long-term and future-oriented, containing the notions of planning and lengthy support.

Attitudes are systems, which is to say that they contain interdependent parts: a change of any substance in one part of an attitude (for example, affect) will usually lead to changes in other components (for example, beliefs and behavioral tendencies). As systems, attitudes will exhibit varying degrees of consistency. We expect that attitudes tend toward consistency, that beliefs, feelings, and behavioral tendencies are generally consonant. An attitude that is internally inconsistent will normally be psychologically uncomfortable for the person. This discomfort will likely be stronger when the attitude topic becomes salient. Inconsistency in attitude components may exist with little consequence when the topic is infrequently confronted or unimportant. Fear of submitting to a periodic medical examination may exist side by side within an attitude that contains many positive beliefs about such a practice. If the holder of such feelings and beliefs can successfully ignore the topic altogether, the inconsistent implications of these components may be subdued. If the issue becomes sufficiently salient or important, one or more of the components should change in the direction of consistency. The question of consistency applies not only to consonance among beliefs, affect, and behavior tendencies, but also to elements of each.

Attitudes may also be part of a larger psychological structure, in this way interconnected in various degrees with other attitudes, with values, or embedded within an ideology. A person may hold an elaborate system of beliefs the substance of which is that government has no place in the private lives of its citizens as individuals, while recognizing public health as a governmental institution. This ideology may foster negative attitudes toward public health programs concerning smoking, air pollution, immunization clinics, and so forth. Or certain religious beliefs may lead to negative attitudes and opposition to family planning. Most attitudes are connected in some degree to a larger system of thought or beliefs and form and change on this basis.

Just as attitudes will differ depending upon the belief structure within which they exist, they will also differ according to the characteristic style or manner of expression of their host. Smith and associates[7] attribute these persistent personality differences to innate characteristics or to acquired modes of adjustment to the world, and discern two broad determiners of the expressive nature of attitudes: intellectual qualities and temperamental qualities. Intellectual differences between individuals will lead one person to think of government-sponsored medical care in abstract, ideological terms as a broad humanitarian attempt to deal with an increasing social problem, or in concrete, personal terms of "paying my medical bills." Temperamental qualities such as general optimism vs. pessimism, high vs. low energy level, indecision vs. decisiveness, and the like will serve to set the tone of specific attitudes.

Another important attribute of attitude systems is their openness or closedness.[8] Some persons tend to be closed-minded, clinging tenaciously to their beliefs, with a tendency to perceive exaggerated differences between these favored beliefs and any that differ from them. The closed-minded or dogmatic person fails to admit of the possible merits of alternative points of view while maintaining that "there is only one right way." Dogmatic thinking is not characteristic of any single attitude content, but may be exhibited by individuals with widely differing beliefs. A public health nurse may be closed-minded in her favorable health views just as a patient with whom she deals may be dogmatic in her beliefs that nutrition is unimportant or that immunization is a frill.

In the foregoing we have tried to indicate how attitudes may be viewed both as to content and style. Content can be roughly equated to *what* a person thinks, feels, or is disposed to do with respect to some object; style refers to the *how* of his attitude, his manner of thinking in the matter, his characteristic mood, his persistent way of expressing himself.

Another way of viewing attitudes is in terms of their guiding influences in our experience of and reaction to the physical and social environment. Smith and associates have taken such a view as shown in their definition of attitude as "a predisposition to experience a class of objects in characteristic ways; and to act with respect to these objects in a characteristic fashion."[9] This view of attitudes emphasizes their role in the interplay between the individual and the environment. Such a view also emphasizes the influence of attitudes in personality functioning.

Note that this functional view of attitudes does not conflict with the foregoing view of attitude components, but rather the two approaches are complementary. We may ask in what ways a given attitude affects behavior, such as perception or memory; at the same time we may be concerned with different aspects of attitude, such as behavior tendency or beliefs, and ask how these jointly or separately determine perception or forgetting.

Attitude Measurement

Various approaches may be used to assess attitudes. Any means that taps a person's thinking and affect on a topic might be relevant. Autobiographical material, stories told about specially prepared pictures, open-ended interviews, structured questions, sentence completion, and other approaches have been used in research. Whatever the approach used, it must be reliable, that is, yield consistent results. It must also be accurate, or valid, measuring what it purports to measure. In the final analysis, the selection of a technique will depend upon the requirements of the specific research problem.

The systematic study of attitudes most frequently employs standardized attitude scales. Such techniques have been in use since the pioneering article by Thurstone[10] in which a procedure for developing standardized instruments was put forth. Other techniques have since been developed, with by far the most common three associated with the names of Thurstone, Likert, and Guttman.[11] These three procedures are questionnaires that form scales. The element common to these approaches is the use of statements referring to the attitude object being studied. Such statements are presented to the respondent who is asked to agree or disagree with them. The interpretation of responses to these statements varies, depending on the technique being used, and is based on the steps in the construction of the scale. In addition to the advantages of a standardized procedure, these techniques permit assessment of degrees of favorableness and permit group comparisons dealing with small differences.

Caution must be exercised in the use and interpretation of attitude scales. Generally speaking, such instruments are used in research activities to make statements about groups of individuals, and in some situations a study comparing two or more groups must be made to provide necessary information for the interpretation of scores based on an attitude scale. Such scales are not normally used as diagnostic devices for individual assessment; they have not been constructed with this purpose in mind.

The Formation and Maintenance of Attitudes

The circumstances that contribute to the formation and change of attitudes are complex and multiple; any given set of beliefs may be due to the interplay of a number of factors. We can discern some of the factors and discuss them, even though in so doing we encounter the risk of oversimplification. Such a discussion, however, may clarify the forces that come to bear upon the individual in shaping his attitudes and beliefs.

Cultural values set frameworks within which specific attitudes develop. When a person believes that good health ought to be maintained, and immunizations are seen to facilitate this, then immunization tends to be positively regarded. A fatalistic view of health, even though health is positively valued, may imply that health maintenance activities of a medical kind are inconsequential because "what must happen will happen." If God is seen as the agent of health, then those objects and events that please Him will be highly regarded since they are seen as instrumental to health. Similarly, values opposed to government spending for welfare will tend to induce opposition to a medical care program sponsored by the government and financed through social security.

A person's attitudes and beliefs will be shaped by the forces that act upon him because of his position or status within the social structure. A physician in the United States will, by and large, display certain attitudes that characterize his occupational position. Similarly with other social groups. Such attitudes are probably the result of three kinds of influences: (1) selection of role occupants; (2) socialization; (3) selective exposure to information.

In the matrix of cultural, social, and psychological factors acting upon a person, differential forces affect different economic classes, ethnic groups, and so forth. For example, most professional medical personnel do not come from economically disadvantaged segments of society. Members of voluntary health agencies also tend to be drawn from middle- or upper-class social groups. In this way some selection occurs as to who will enjoy the advantages of access to education, become members of various occupational or professional groups, and hold different social positions in general. These same forces induce differential attitudes, resulting in a tendency toward position-attitude association due to selection of role occupants from certain segments of the population.

A person may be said to be undergoing a period of socialization when acquiring the expected attitudes and behaviors of a given position. In some cases the socialization process may be highly formalized, as in learning the attitudes and skills that are part of being a physician,[12] or it may be more informal, as in the case of being a "mother." The resultant is a certain predictability about positions and the attitudes of their occupants.

A third way in which the social structure shapes opinions is through selective exposure to ideas and information once a given position has been achieved. As we have suggested earlier, part of a person's selective orientation to his world is due to his existing beliefs and attitudes. So also is his exposure limited by his primary groups, the people with whom he has face-to-face contact. A health department employee will have much contact with other employees of the health department. Because of similar spheres of activity and reference groups, these employees will tend to share attitudes and ways of thinking. In this way, one hears from others those things which he hears from himself, a tendency increasing homogeneity of opinions for persons in similar or related role positions.

Just as cultural values and social positions help to determine attitudes, so also do characteristics of a person's psychological makeup. Perhaps one of the most important psychological determinants of specific attitudes has to do with authority. Attitudes toward authority are highly significant in setting a framework for organizing experience. Rokeach[13] has emphasized the role of beliefs about authorities in mediating the acceptance and rejection of information. The authorities that one accepts are looked to for guidance on policy and action, on what is workable or infeasible, on what is right or wrong. Few public health practitioners are able to examine in detail the evidence on any particular health issue. And yet these practitioners must act on health matters in the performance of their duties and also in their personal lives. It is their view of authority that prompts them to base policy and action on recommendations or standards from the American Public Health Association or the United States Public Health Service. Professional and official organizations may also serve as authorities for laymen. How many health personnel or laymen who favor the use of seat belts in automobiles have seen for themselves the evidence regarding their use as a preventive measure in morbidity and mortality in accidents? How many who oppose smoking cigarettes have firsthand knowledge about studies of smoking and lung cancer? It would be obviously impossible for everyone to be expert in many fields, to know the evidence for a particular set of feelings and beliefs that he comes to possess. It is possible, however, to recognize certain authorities and accept as justified the attitudes they impart.

Attitudes toward authority work also in a negative way. For example, some persons may hold in low esteem or be negative toward the American Public Health Association, the United States Public Health Service, or a professional society, such as the American Dental Association. Under these circumstances recommendations from such bodies will likely produce attitudes in these persons that oppose the organizational stand. Reaction by some groups to fluoridation of the community water supply has been interpreted in this light. Simmel,[14] for example, suggests that certain segments of the population oppose fluoridation because of relative deprivation: fluoridation is seen by these individuals as a further example of the exertion of authority by those in power over those who are relatively deprived of social status, economic advantage, and social influence. To the extent that such an explanation is true, it is the *view of authority* that is blocking support for fluoridation rather than information about the issue.

The view of authorities held by some groups may be undifferentiated, so that authorities may be the people with power or influence, the "big people," or those with money. Such a view may be typical of working-class or lower-class culture, as suggested by a variety of studies that link feelings of powerlessness with class status.[15] Lipset's analysis of class differences suggests that the situation of the working class may tend to make their recognition of authority especially important in acceptance and rejection of various health programs.[16]

The Motivational Bases of Attitudes

In examining the etiology of attitudes and beliefs we may look to the cultural, social, or psychological forces acting upon the individual. At the same time, however, it must be recognized that motivational bases within the individual mediate the effects of these forces in the formation and change of attitudes and beliefs. Smith and associates[17] identify three ways that motives induce attitudes. First, a person may relate a current specific situation to earlier experience in an effort to give it meaning. When a person encounters for the first time a request to obtain an x-ray as a screening device for tuberculosis, he may perceive this in the context of his previous medical experience. If this previous experience, knowledge, and so on, is favorable, chances are the person will be favorably disposed toward the x-ray procedure. If the previous experience is negative, so will be the attitude toward x-rays. In this process the person "sizes up" the object and identifies it with ideas, feelings, experiences that already have meaning for him. In this way a ready-made attitude is taken on. It is easy to see also that there are few objects that cannot be related to some aspect of our experience.

Second, one's identification with other persons or groups may determine his attitude in a particular situation. A nurse working in the traditional medical setting may often exhibit the view that she is an assistant to the physician. This attitude helps in her relationships with surrounding medical personnel, and it was acquired in the process of learning the role of nurse, either in nurses training or in this particular situation.

A study by Lieberman[18] illustrates the importance that role can have in shaping one's views. He found that a change in job position from worker in a factory to either union steward or company foreman resulted in attitude changes toward management and toward the union. Some of the findings show the foremen became more pro-management while the stewards became more pro-union. The effect of role, status, or position upon attitudes reflects the generic process of social adjustment. This motivational support for an attitude is not limited to formal role relationships, but may serve in any situation involving important self-other relationships.

Third, some attitudes may be formed in the process of protecting a person's sense of adequacy or self-esteem. From his experience, perhaps accumulated many years previously, a person may feel that admitting weakness, lack of skill, or other inadequacy is tantamount to admission of loss of self-worth. Since this is more than can be tolerated, he rejects these feelings within himself and must cover them up. One way of covering them up is to develop hostility toward someone else, a scapegoat. This accomplishes two satisfying ends. On the one hand, it provides an outlet for the anger generated by these feelings toward oneself, and on the other, it calls attention away from oneself. A health officer who is not able to handle the many and varied tasks facing him, and unable to admit this to himself and others, may become highly critical of the faults of his staff. Needless to say, such a process in the development of attitudes toward the staff does not foster constructive solution to the problems faced. Attitudes developed on this basis are referred to as ego-defensive attitudes, since the service they provide is to protect the holder from a loss of self-worth or ego damage.

One or all three of these motives may serve as the basis for any given attitude. Except in extreme cases more than one motivational substructure will come to bear on an attitude, and these supports may operate in a uniform direction, or they may conflict. The chief of a program division may think that a program suggested by a subordinate would facilitate meeting the overall objectives of the division, but be threatened by the fact that it was a subordinate's idea rather than his own. Some resolution of these conflicting influences will lead to the person's attitude toward the program.

Attitudes, Beliefs, and Psychological Processes

Attitudes have been shown to affect perception, thinking, learning, and forgetting in studies inside and outside the psychological laboratory. These studies grow out of the conception of attitudes as relatively enduring characteristics that enable an individual to bring meaning and order into his life space. The welter of events to which each of us is exposed daily cannot be tolerated as an undifferentiated mass without meaning. Instead we strive to organize events in such a way that they can be understood, and beliefs and feelings supply part of the mechanism that orders experience.

Attitudes have been shown to foster selective perception in the realm of political issues and candidates. Berelson, Lazarsfeld, and

McPhee[19] found that an individual perceived his candidate as taking a policy stand more nearly in keeping with the individual's conception of what is "good." They found the complementary tendency for persons to misperceive opposing candidates as taking a less desirable policy stand. These tendencies are most marked where there is high agreement among individuals generally, regardless of their candidate, as to what represents the desirable policy.

Two recent studies have shown a relationship between attitude toward fluoridation and perception of fluoridation propaganda. In one study,[20] perceptions of a communication on fluoridation of the community water supply were studied. The respondents in the study, women residents of the community, were asked how favorable toward fluoridation they perceived the communication to be. Their responses were related to the attitudes they held about adding fluorides to the water supply. Women who were highly favorable toward fluoridation perceived the message in the communication to be more highly in favor of fluoridation than did other respondents. Those women opposed to fluoridation saw the article as less favorable toward fluoridation than did respondents who held positive attitudes toward the issue. The interpretation given these results was that the communication was perceived by the respondents to minimize the discrepancy between attitude and message and thus reduce any disruptive effects of the message on attitudes.

A subsequent study using the same communication about fluoridation compared the perceptions of public health school nurses with those women in the previously mentioned study who resembled the nurses in attitudes toward fluoridation. The nurses perceived the communication to be significantly less favorable toward fluoridation than did the subsample of women residents of the community. This difference in perception is likely attributable to differences in cognitive and social support between the nurse and nonnurse groups, with the nurses feeling less pressure to perceive the communication as similar to their own view of fluoridation.

These studies suggest that information from health agents or agencies may be interpreted in a variety of ways, depending upon the attitudes of the recipients. Differences in perception will likely be reduced when information is extreme, clear, and definite. From the standpoint of attitude change, however, extreme, definite stands taken by health actors may not be most conducive to change. Sherif and Hovland[21] have suggested that moderate arguments inducing gradual change may facilitate successful persuasion with involving issues, as health matters seem to be.

Attitudes and feelings affect logical or rational thinking. McGuire[22] found that degrees of truth associated with sets of beliefs were distorted in the direction of wishful thinking. If a person held a given set of events to be desirable, he tended to consider it more true; if he held the set of events to be less desirable, he tended to think it was less true. At the very least this study and others imply that rationality yields ground to strong feelings in arriving at conclusions based on one's cognitions.

An early study by Levine and Murphy[23] illustrates the role of attitudes in learning and forgetting of controversial material. This study found that learning and retention were better for persons whose own beliefs agreed with the material to be learned. A more recent study by Jones and Kohler[24] shows that better learning occurred when subjects in the experiment were asked to learn plausible arguments supporting their own views and implausible arguments opposing those views. With both kinds of arguments—plausible arguments favoring one's own stand and implausible arguments opposing it—one is acquiring supporting or consonant information.

These studies have implications for evaluation of health programs. When a health program is to be evaluated through research, what are some of the pitfalls strewn in the path of evaluation by program personnel? Such personnel are likely to have most abundant information on the workings of the program, but what of involvement in it and the implications of this involvement? Under circumstances of high involvement selective interpretation may be paramount.

These and similar studies also suggest that information disseminated by health actors may undergo unanticipated modification as it is interpreted by segments of the public or other professionals. Future theory and research should focus upon the kind of distortion likely to occur, its extent, the circumstances that modify differences in perception or other processes, and implications for behavior.

Attitudes and Action

While attitudes and beliefs influence behavior, it should be recognized that in any context attitudes toward the focal object are only a portion of the factors coming to bear on the individual. Social pressures from other individuals, legal constraints, and other factors will exert important influences upon action.

Some studies of prejudice and action toward minority groups have shown a lack of correspondence between attitudes and action. In a classic study, LaPierre[25] traveled through the United States with a Chinese couple, eating at many restaurants and staying at many hotels and motels. LaPierre and his friends were not refused services at any of the places they stopped. At a later time he sent a questionnaire to each of these establishments and asked if they would accommodate Chinese customers. Approximately one-half of the establishments returned the questionnaire, and nearly all of these places (about 92 per cent) indicated that they would not serve Chinese. This expression of policy is clearly counter to the behavior previously exhibited. Subsequent studies have shown prejudiced attitudes without consonant prejudiced actions.[26] Other studies have shown a correspondence between ethnic attitudes and action.[27] As previously stated, we can expect that many factors determine behavior, with no small part played by the social setting of the behavior. An understanding of the contribution of attitudes toward behavior requires a thorough analysis of the many factors in the situation.

There is strong research evidence to suggest that behavior, in its part, molds attitudes. Festinger's[28] theory of cognitive dissonance addresses itself to, among other things, the question of the correspondence between attitudes and behavior after the behavior has occurred. Under some circumstances, if an individual behaves in a way that is discrepant with his beliefs, the beliefs may change so as to be more consonant with his actions. If I am induced by means short of compliance to eat food that I dislike, I may adopt a more favorable attitude toward the food because of the fact that I have eaten it. According to this theory the element bringing about a more favorable attitude is not familiarity or the like, but rather the perceived discrepancy between my previous beliefs and my actions. Such discrepancy is said to be uncomfortable and therefore motivating. The theory does not specify that the only way of reducing this dissonance is to bring attitudes into line with action, but that this is one way of achieving dissonance reduction. The amount of dissonance will importantly determine the potential for attitude change. How much dissonance is to be expected should vary with, among other things, the extent to which the action was forced upon the actor or freely chosen, with greater dissonance associated with the latter.

The effect of compliant behavior per se upon attitudes is not known.

We can speculate, however, that compliance may lead to more enduring changes in attitude through the control of behavior and behavior supports. Allport has said of legislation and prejudice that personal prejudice cannot be legislated, but that "outward action . . . has an eventual effect upon inner habits of thought and feeling."[29] With some health issues legislation has proved of moot worth insofar as attitude changes are concerned (for example, fluoridation); with others (for example, the polio immunization law for school children in California), more time and investigation will tell the story.

Persuasion and Attitude Change

During the past several decades there has been a growing concern with the importance of initiative and continued cooperation on the part of the public with health actors in the pursuit of health care. In chronic diseases, for example, there is need of early detection and long-term treatment, both generally requiring a degree of initiative on the part of individuals. Health promotion, broadly conceived, requires changes in attitudes, beliefs, and actions in areas of personal hygiene and sanitation, as well as such actions as use of medical services for diagnosis and care. In view of these concerns great importance attaches to an understanding of the process of persuasion and behavior change.

To be effective, persuasion must be appropriate to the motivational supports for the target attitudes. We have said earlier that these supports, or bases, may be knowledge, social adjustment, or defense of the ego. Because ego-defensive mechanisms are based upon personality conflict within the individual, attitudes formed on this basis are difficult to change, and will almost certainly not be susceptible to change solely through information about the object of the attitude.[30] At the present time we do not have knowledge of the extent to which attitudes related to health are based upon ego-defensive processes. We can speculate that ego-defensive attitudes are important in attitudes toward individuals or groups of people. If true, this would imply substantial relevance for the practice of public health.

Attitudes formed largely through social adjustment should be most susceptible to changes in the reference group norms or in the attitudes of the significant other who serves as a referent, changes in the role relationship to the group or individual, and the like. Under these circumstances the attitude to be changed grows out of identification with a group or other person and serves this relationship rather than being based on the merits of the object per se. Information about characteristics or attributes of the object will be of little value in achieving change. Another kind of information is required, for example, information that conveys an altered set of beliefs or policy stand on the part of the referent. As the view to be changed in these situations may often be ascribable to group standards of one kind or another, the clarity of the group standard and the degree of identification on the part of the individual with the group are important considerations.[31]

It is only in the case of attitudes based primarily upon knowledge about the object per se that information specifically about the object will be most useful in evoking attitude change. In such cases information alone may go far in achieving the desired results, but we can expect few health attitudes to arise and persist solely on the basis of information.

It is essential to recognize that a single attitude may be the result of several motivational factors rather than a single one. Nonetheless, one motivational force may serve as the major basis of any given attitude and therefore be the most important with which to deal.

Most studies of communication and attitude change rest on the premise that attitudes play an influential role in determining behavior. As Krech and associates have stated, "By knowing the attitudes of people it is possible to do something about the prediction and control of their behavior."[32] While not questioning the truth of this assertion, we should note that attempts to bring about behavior change rather than attitude change may be more appropriate for public health and other applied problems under some circumstances and for some problems confronting some people. Experience with attempts to fluoridate community water supplies without first achieving appropriate attitude change, however, emphasizes the important role attitudes and beliefs can have in health action.[33] The question of the validity of attitude change as a means to desired changes in behavior is one to receive much future attention. Any view of man as a striving organism directed at least in part by his attempts to understand or adapt to the world around him must take attitudes and beliefs into account. The point of view presented here suggests that attitudes and beliefs play a prominent role in experience and behavior.

NOTES TO CHAPTER 19

1. Murphy, Gardner, Lois Murphy, and Theodore M. Newcomb, *Experimental Social Psychology,* Harper and Bros., New York, 1937; Allport, Gordon W., "Attitudes" in Murchison, Carl A., editor, *A Handbook of Social Psychology,* Clark University Press, Worcester, 1935; Thomas, William I., and Florian Znaniecki, *The Polish Peasant in Europe and America: Monograph of an Immigrant Group,* R. C. Badger Co., Boston, 1918, vol. 1; 2d ed. published by Alfred A. Knopf, Inc., New York, 1927.

2. Sherif, Muzafer, and Hadley Cantril, "The Psychology of Attitudes," Part I, *Psychological Review,* vol. 52, no. 6, 1945, pp. 295–319; Rosenberg, Milton J., and associates, *Attitude Organization and Change,* Yale University Press, New Haven, 1960.

3. Festinger, Leon, *A Theory of Cognitive Dissonance,* Stanford University Press, Stanford, 1957; Brehm, Jack W., and Arthur R. Cohen, *Explorations in Cognitive Dissonance,* John Wiley and Sons, New York, 1962.

4. Smith, M. Brewster, Jerome S. Bruner, and Robert W. White, *Opinions and Personality.* John Wiley and Sons, New York, 1956.

5. *Ibid.;* see also Katz, Daniel, and E. Stotland, "A Preliminary Statement to a Theory of Attitude Structure and Change" in Koch, Sigmund, editor, *Psychology: A Study of a Science,* McGraw-Hill Book Co., 1959, vol. 3; Krech, David, Richard S. Crutchfield, and Egerton L. Ballachey, *Individual in Society,* McGraw-Hill Book Co., New York, 1962.

6. Smith, M. Brewster, and associates, *op. cit.*

7. *Ibid.*

8. Rokeach, Milton, *The Open and Closed Mind.* Basic Books, New York, 1960.

9. Smith, M. Brewster, and associates, *op. cit.,* p. 33.

10. Thurstone, Louis L., "Attitudes Can Be Measured," *American Journal of Sociology,* vol. 33, 1928, pp. 529–554.

11. Selltiz, Claire, and associates, *Research Methods in Social Relations,* rev. ed. Henry Holt and Co., New York, 1959; Krech, David, Richard S. Crutchfield, and Egerton L. Ballachey, *op. cit.;* Edwards, Allen E., *Techniques of Attitude Scale Construction,* Appleton-Century-Crofts, Inc., New York, 1957.

12. Becker, Howard S., and associates, *Boys in White.* University of Chicago Press, Chicago, 1961.

13. Rokeach, Milton, *op. cit.*

14. Simmel, Arnold, "A Signpost for Research on Fluoridation Conflicts: The Concept of Relative Deprivation," *Journal of Social Issues,* vol. 17, no. 4, 1961, pp. 26–36.

15. Srole, Leo, "Social Integration and Certain Corollaries: An Exploratory Study," *American Sociological Review,* vol. 21, 1956, pp. 709–716; McDill, Edward L., "Anomie, Authoritarianism, Prejudice, and Socio-Economic Status: An Attempt at Clarification," *Social Forces,* vol. 39, 1961, pp. 239–245.

16. Lipset, Seymour M., *Political Man.* Doubleday and Co., Garden City, N.Y., 1960.

17. Smith, M. Brewster, and associates, *op. cit.*

18. Lieberman, Seymour, "The Effects of Changes in Roles on the Attitudes of Role Occupants," *Human Relations,* vol. 9, 1956, pp. 385–402.

19. Berelson, Bernard, Paul F. Lazarsfeld, and William N. McPhee, *Voting.* University of Chicago Press, Chicago, 1954.

20. Dillehay, Ronald C., "Internal and External Anchoring Effects in Judgment of a Persuasive Communication." Paper read at American Psychological Association meetings, Philadelphia, August, 1963.

21. Sherif, Muzafer, and Carl I. Hovland, *Social Judgment.* Yale University Press, New Haven, 1961.

22. McGuire, William, "Cognitive Consistency and Attitude Change," *Journal of Abnormal and Social Psychology,* vol. 60, 1960, pp. 345–353.

23. Levine, Jerome M., and Gardner Murphy, "The Learning and Forgetting of Controversial Material," *Journal of Abnormal and Social Psychology,* vol. 37, 1943, pp. 507–517. Reprinted in Maccoby, Eleanor E., Theodore M. Newcomb, and Eugene L. Hartley, editors, *Readings in Social Psychology,* 3d ed., Henry Holt and Co., New York, 1958, pp. 94–101.

24. Jones, Edward E., and Rika Kohler, "The Effects of Plausibility on the Learning of Controversial Statements," *Journal of Abnormal and Social Psychology,* vol. 57, 1958, pp. 315–320.

25. LaPierre, Richard T., "Attitudes vs. Actions," *Social Forces,* vol. 13, 1934, pp. 230–237.

26. Harding, John, and associates, "Prejudice and Ethnic Relations" in Lindzey, Gardner, editor, *Handbook of Social Psychology.* Addison-Wesley Publishing Co., Reading, Mass., 1954, vol. 2, pp. 1021–1026.

27. DeFleur, Melvin L., and F. R. Westie, "Verbal Attitudes and Overt Acts: An Experiment on the Salience of Attitudes," *American Sociological Review,* vol. 23, 1958, pp. 667–673; Wilner, Daniel M., Rosabelle P. Walkley, and Stuart W. Cook, "Residential Proximity and Intergroup Relations in Public Housing Projects," *Journal of Social Issues,* vol. 8, 1952, pp. 45–69.

28. Festinger, Leon, *op. cit.*

29. Allport, Gordon W., *The Nature of Prejudice.* Doubleday and Co., Garden City, N.Y., 1958, p. 442.

30. Wagman, Morton, "Attitude Change and the Authoritarian Personality," *Journal of Psychology,* vol. 40, 1955, pp. 3–24; Katz, Daniel, Irving Sarnoff, and Charles McClintock, "Ego-Defense and Attitude Change," *Human Relations,* vol. 9, 1956, pp. 27–46; McClintock, Charles, "Personality Syndromes and Attitude Change," *Journal of Personality,* vol. 26, 1958, pp. 479–493.

31. Converse, Philip, and Angus Campbell, "Political Standards in Secondary Groups" in Cartwright, Dorwin, and Alvin Zander, editors, *Group Dynamics.* 2d ed. Row, Peterson, and Co., Evanston, Ill., 1960.

32. Krech, David, Richard S. Crutchfield, and Egerton L. Ballachey, *op. cit.,* p. 139.

33. McNeil, Donald R., *The Fight for Fluoridation.* Oxford University Press, New York, 1957.

Part Six

The Process of Socialization

Part Six

The Process of Socialization

SOCIAL FACTORS determine both the nature of the child's family of birth and the social habitat within which he will spend his formative years. The child's first position as a member of society is not of his own choosing. He may arrive as a wanted or unwanted new member, as a joy or burden to other members. The group may be one that eagerly tenders love, affection, support, attention, and opportunity, or one that responds coldly, indifferently, or with hostility, rejecting his overtures for social transaction.

The behaviors of members of this group during the child's formative years serve as models to him in acquiring ways of expressing pain, pleasure, and affection, manners of acceptance or withdrawal, expressions of warmth or distance in interpersonal relationships. From family members he may also learn the form and tone of request, invitation, inquiry, or command; orientations to work and to play; and other modes of response for use in social life.

The child's first exposure to the symbolic life of his society is received in an unselected setting. His possibilities for creative growth are in good part influenced by the discriminating and critical sensitivities, values, and interests of those about him. Their skill in language, music, art, and other forms of cultural attainment, the range and quality of their knowledge, the awareness they have of the social graces and manners of society—all these things, together with the effectiveness of the means they employ in imparting such things to the child, will facilitate his social progress. His breadth and depth of knowledge and range of abilities to cope with future opportunities may be fostered or retarded in accord with the range and quality of opportunities he has in childhood to experience material as well as intrinsic aspects of environment, things to eat, to wear, to read, to view, to hear, to play with, examine, test, think about, and discuss.

While major attention will be given here to socialization processes

313

as they apply in child development and social change, one should recognize that the same processes are at work whenever a new member joins a social group. In recent years agencies of both industry and government have come to recognize the significance of the effective introduction of new members to professional teams. Many unique orientation programs have been initiated to facilitate this process.

Integrating new employees into an organization becomes particularly important in situations, such as those common to public health, where a high degree of autonomy exists at different levels of the organization or in field assignments. This is true also when, again as in public health, members are often expected to substitute for one another as team members or to present to others the philosophy, goals, and approaches of the team in the absence of colleagues. The integration of new members under such circumstances requires some means of helping them to understand and to experience role demands and requirements of other team members. It may also involve the transformations of attitudes, the acquisition of new knowledge, the practice of specific skills.

Undergoing professional training and acquiring a professional self with its rights, obligations, role demands, and role enactments also may be referred to as a socialization process. In the process of acquiring this professional self, the neophyte must become socialized into the philosophy, values, ethics, and practices of the profession, and acquire the skills, knowledge, and attitudes necessary to his new position and roles.

Chapter 20

Acquiring Social Behaviors

MANY THEORIES have been advanced regarding the way man's social environment becomes integrated into his personal life and actions. As yet, however, behavioral science research has not advanced to the point that it can tell us in what way, under what circumstances, and at what age children acquire the modes of thought and action that mark them as integrated members of society. Nor is it known how changes occur under the impact of later experience or the impact of opposing values. Nor do we fully understand the difficulties one faces in acquiring the major values and norms of a society if one is born into one of its unaccepted outgroups.[1]

Socialization is the term used to refer to the processes whereby a child or other new member of society becomes a social being according to the values, standards, and norms of the society. It refers to the processes through which the child "acquires sensitivity to social stimuli (especially the pressures and obligations of group life) and learns to get along with, and to behave like, others in his group or culture."[2] Through this process the individual, "born with behavioral potentialities of enormous range, is led to develop actual behavior within a much narrower range—the range that is customary and acceptable for him according to the standards of his group."[3] In some way social environment becomes more than "what is out there." Just as there is a constant but selective flow in the exchange of elements between physiological man and his biological-physical setting, there is a transactional bind of man to society and culture. The meanings man acquires through these transactions guide his responses to social as well as other things. He acts toward other persons or things in terms of these assigned meanings rather than in accord with matters as they may exist objectively or as they exist for others.

The child is not a passive recipient of the ubiquitous pressures of social environment. He is not "molded" by these early exposures to

315

his social heritage in systematic, regular, and unvarying fashion. He does not accept as his own all ideas, values, beliefs, attitudes, knowings, and norms of his elders. Rather, the child is born with a unique pattern of biological structure, capacities, and potentialities. His social transactions are guided by personal as well as group meanings he assigns to things about him, to the actions of others, to his own responses. While major attention in research seems to have been given to conformity pressures and their effects, deviance from group norms is found in most studies.

EARLY SOCIALIZING AGENTS

A socializing agent is a person who introduces an individual to the ways of a group and assumes primary responsibility for his socialization as an active member of society. Within our society, parents, particularly mothers, usually assume primary responsibility for socializing the child, although other members of the family, such as older children, grandparents, uncles, or aunts, also contribute to his socialization and may, at times, be primary agents. Families with means may assign this responsibility to a nurse, governess, or other employee. In other societies this position of primary socializing agent may be held by a relative or neighbor.

The newborn infant cannot cope effectively with his new world. He lacks the means to obtain the food, warmth, water, and shelter which were formerly provided without personal effort. He cannot express how he feels nor can he tell others what he is doing. He is probably unable at first even to identify the boundaries of his personal being from the world about him. He perhaps lacks a sense of self and personal identity and, accordingly, a self-image to observe, judge, and guide. He is dependent on others for satisfaction of physical need and would not survive this period of helplessness without attentive adult care. His physical, emotional, and psychological well-being all seem to hinge on the nature of adult care provided.

Identification and Imitation

It is the mother or mother substitute who warms him and cuddles him after birth and who starts the feeding process. The infant responds quickly to human contact and to the offer of food. But since his perceptual and responsive behavior is still diffused and general, he probably lacks full awareness of what is happening and may not sharply differentiate the food received from the person who offers it. Her warmness and firmness of support, her gentleness of touch and her softness of voice are integral parts of the feeding experience.

While affective and comforting behavior on the part of the mother contributes to her infant's security, it also facilitates early and strong identification of the infant with his mother, and fosters the learning of these things associated with these secure and satisfying experiences. The mother who provides support, comfort, affection, attention, and food may at first seem to the infant to be an extension of himself. At the same time, the mother may regard her child as part of herself, as something of which she remains a part. The process of mother-child identification is thus fostered. The mother becomes a significant person to the child as he grows, and a primary model for him to observe in developing his own social behavior.

As means of communication with the child are developed, they are used to instill within him an awareness of socially approved behavior. In this way the child learns to accept and value those things that are accepted and valued by significant persons about him, to reject those that are rejected by the group, to disregard those of no apparent significance. He learns to love what others love, to fear what others fear, and to act as they act, even though in so doing his behavior may depart from the hopes and expectations they have of him, for he learns to behave as they behave rather than as they may wish him to behave. He learns to identify with those figures of primary importance to him and to imitate them, and acquires new behaviors by participating with them in activities they approve.

Reward and Punishment

The child learns to retain those behaviors for which he is rewarded by expressions of love, affection, and approval, and conversely, to discard those for which he is punished by disapproval, as he interprets it. His behavior tends to be guided by what *he perceives or judges* to be reward or punishment rather than what the socializing agent *intends* as reward or punishment. Some rewards may be seen as punishing and some punishments may be seen as rewarding. As the child seeks to communicate with those about him, their merely paying attention may be a maximum form of reward, even though such attention may at times be intended to be punishment. Attention paid to undesirable social behavior may be more rewarding than silent approval without attention being paid to desirable social behavior.

One's own orientations to life, as expressed in his own actions, tend to be more effectively communicated than other orientations he may seek to impart. The child thus tends to acquire the aspirations, expectations, concerns, fears, values, and attitudes held by his socializing agents rather than others they may consider more desirable or ideal for him.

It is from his socializing agents that the child first acquires values, beliefs, attitudes, and behaviors of significance to his health or to the health of his community. From them he learns what things in his environment are important and unimportant, what is urgent, and what may be delayed, what is of immediate concern, and what must be considered for the future. Socializing agents, therefore, hold positions in which they may significantly influence the future physical, emotional, mental, and social well-being of the individual and of his society, often without intending to do so.

PERSONAL IDENTITY, SELF, AND SELF-IMAGE

The child begins early to acquire an understanding of his own position relative to other members of his group, to learn what his own responsibilities are in that position, what others expect of him, what he can expect of them and of himself. Thus he develops a sense of personal identity and a self-image. He begins to view himself as a unique individual with characteristics that identify him as a particular person. He starts to expect things of himself, to place demands upon himself, and in particular to demand of himself conformity to standards he develops for judging his own behavior. His sense of identity as a responsible person in a particular position relative to others helps him find personal and group meaning in his own behavior relative to other persons, things, or ideas, and to gain personal direction in an initially confusing world.

Dealing with Oneself

There is wide acceptance today of the viewpoint of William James,[4] George Mead,[5] and others—that man acquires a self which he regards and treats as a self. He holds this image of himself as an acting member of society, an integral part of his group with a position, role, responsibilities, and some sense of direction or purpose. One might view this self-image he holds as a sort of transactional bridge that unites him and the society of which he is part as he observes, directs, and guides this self along the pathways of society.

Blumer illustrates some of the ways man treats himself as a social unit.

> The key feature in Mead's analysis is that the human being has a self. This idea should not be cast aside as esoteric or glossed over as something that is obvious and hence not worthy of attention. In declaring that the human being has a self, Mead had in mind chiefly that the human being can be the object of his own actions. He can act toward himself as he might act toward others. Each of us is familiar with actions of this sort in which the human being gets angry with himself, rebuffs himself, takes pride in himself, argues with himself, tries to bolster his own courage, tells himself that he should "do this" or not "do that," sets goals for himself, makes compromises with himself, and plans what he is going to do. That the human being acts toward himself in these and countless other ways is a matter of easy empirical observation. To recognize that the human being can act toward himself is no mystical conjuration.

> Mead regards this ability of the human being to act toward himself as the central mechanism with which the human being faces and deals with his world. This mechanism enables the human being to make indication to himself of things in his surroundings and thus to guide his actions by what he notes.[6]

Observing Responses of Others to Oneself

How the child is identified by his socializing agents, playmates, and significant others—as male or female, tall or short, weak or strong, graceful or awkward, cheerful or morose, quick or dull, independent or dependent—helps him develop his own sense of identity and self-image. The reactions of others to his actions, moods, manners, dress, and appearances guide him in determining what he wants his self-image to be, and how he perceives himself as being most effectively presented to others.

By observing how others act, and through identification, imitation, and adaptation trying out behaviors he observes, the child learns what actions persons significant to him like or dislike. Their responses to him tell him how he should appear and act to be accepted, loved, and esteemed. Thus he learns how to present himself and express himself effectively to particular audiences and in specific situations. Goffman has aptly stated, "The role of expression is conveying impressions of self."[7]

INDIRECT NATURE OF SOCIAL LEARNINGS

Neither the mother nor the child is likely to realize the extent to which social learning is going on during the formative years of infancy and childhood. The child develops and refines his capacities for discriminating; he learns to recognize and use the symbols of value held by the group, to acquire behaviors in tune with those persons about him, and to discard behaviors that are not in accord with social norms. Social values are attached to all things and actions he acquires, whether cognitive, affective, or overt, for the separation of social motive and value from action during this period is quite impossible. Yet all this may go on without the child's being aware that he is acquiring his culturally derived values, norms, and symbols, and without the communicator's having any conscious intent to communicate these things. In fact, the mother, who has acquired these values, norms, and symbols under similar circumstances, may not be aware that she has acquired them, and that they are part of her social life and that she is passing them on to her offspring.

Indirect Sources of Attitudes

A most revealing objective study of the role of the family in the development of children's attitudes was carried out by Horowitz, whose research concerned the attitudes of white children toward Negroes in America.[8] The conclusions of his research are of great significance to public health workers seeking improvement in health attitudes, beliefs, and practices.

> Attitudes toward Negroes are now chiefly determined not by contact with Negroes but by contact with the prevalent attitude toward Negroes. In their attitude toward Negroes white boys in an all white school in New York were not significantly different from whites in a mixed school. New York children differed very little from Southern children. But, white children raised in a housing project in which the occupants and the recreation program were generally characterized by a political orientation which included opposition to discrimination, showed no bias on the tests.[9]

These and other studies suggest that the child's attitude toward Negroes "seems to have its origins with the child's parents. Apparently parents give direct instruction in these attitudes and cannot recall having done so."[10]

Findings from studies such as this help us understand why children as they grow older may be quite unable to tell why they love certain foods and regard others that they may not have tasted as repugnant, why they fear physicians or dentists whom they have never visited, why they identify drafts as the cause of colds, or personal sin as responsible for disease. Among things learned indirectly during these formative years may also be the tendency on the part of some to equate physical strength and endurance with good health and to distrust evidence of illness obtained through the use of x-rays, blood tests, or urinalyses—methods which yield evidences of conditions that may not be subjectively sensed.

Learning "Must" Behaviors

Some researchers contend that many primary personality characteristics are acquired in the process of learning food habits, elimination control, and similar rules of human conduct, for there are likely to be strong social demands for learning such behavior early in life. In the process of teaching the child to control himself, the mother draws heavily on her own value system for illustration and explanation. Through this process she unconsciously imparts values to the child. At times, she may impart values she does not personally recognize, values that she does not realize are important to her because she has learned them under similar conditions.

These teachings and learnings often take place during infancy, before the child has acquired an extended symbolic life, before his concepts of self and self-image are developed. Under these conditions of learning, the child tends to acquire imperatives for action—"one must do this," "one must not do that," "do this," "don't do that"—without either learning or understanding the purposes of these actions. Once acquired, actions based on such imperatives may be most difficult to influence, for if the individual violates such imperatives he may be burdened with feelings of guilt and anxiety.[11]

In reviewing evidence regarding the manner in which one acquires a conscience and learns to employ it in self-guidance and in making social judgments, Allport proposes:

> The theory I am here suggesting holds that the must-consciousness precedes the ought-consciousness, but that in the course of transformation three important changes occur. 1. External sanctions give way to internal—a change adequately accounted for by the processes of identification and introjection familiar in Freudian and behavioral theory.

2. Experiences of prohibition, fear, and "must" give way to experiences of preference, self-respect, and "ought." This shift becomes possible in proportion as the self-image and value-systems of the individual develop. 3. Specific habits of obedience give way to generic self-guidance, that is to say, to broad schemata of values that confer direction upon conduct.

If early prohibitions and parent identifications were the only source of conscience there would certainly be a fading of conscience in time. It is the generic self-guidance that keeps conscience alive and applicable to new experience. The generic conscience tells us in effect, "If you do this, it will build your style of being; if that, it will tear down your style of being." In proportion as the generic conscience becomes the monitor of growth, emphasis shifts from tribalism to individuality, from opportunistic to oriented becoming. Fear becomes ought as propriate development begins to outweigh opportunistic.[12]

Learning Rules versus Learning "Whys"

Even after the child grows old enough to be able to understand and reason, a mother may lean heavily on the "rules" in seeking to influence behavior. Then she imparts to the child the idea that rules in themselves are important. She may say, "You have to do it this way." "Don't do that!" without explanation. Or "We never do that." She is using phrases which suggest that rules in themselves need to be obeyed without question and without evaluation. While commands cannot always be explained, and commands are an important part of training, an excess of unexplained directions as the child grows places a greater value upon rules for their own sake and a lesser value on understanding why such rules exist.

If the mother, on the other hand, seeks to impart explanation or understanding as well as direction, the child is more likely to learn to evaluate his own actions in terms of consequences other than the breaking of a rule. In this way he may learn to understand why some rules are good and why others may need to be changed or disregarded under certain circumstances. "Let's do it this way so we don't get hurt" suggests the reason for the rule. "Let's do it this way so we don't hurt Johnny's feelings" again suggests the reason for the rule and places a value on the importance of being sensitive to the feelings of others.

One might expect, on the basis of theory, at least, that these two approaches to socialization would differ in their long-term effects on the child. One approach fosters blind acceptance and obedience, the other fosters questioning and understanding.

The child who has not considered the whys of his own behavior has not learned the meaning of values other than the value of rules. Such a child is disadvantaged in his attempts to understand others, their rights and responsibilities, their definitions of role, and the role demands placed upon them. He has difficulty taking the roles of others, understanding their expectations of him, and communicating his expectations of them. He does not understand why others do not feel the same pressures for abiding by rules and why they may even question the validity of established ways of doing things. He is likely to have greater difficulty in living happily with children whose values differ from his own and whose rules of conduct differ accordingly.

The child who learns to think in terms of reasons for particular choices of action, on the other hand, tends to become better able to make decisions in terms of objective or value alternatives. He also learns to seek purpose and meaning in the activities of others, to interpret their behavior in terms of intentions, hopes, concerns, and expectations. Such a child goes through a process of examining, judging, modifying, reorganizing, strengthening, or changing his values and standards in accordance with the conclusions he reaches in testing them out in life situations. Thus he develops for himself a core set of values and standards for evaluating new situations in terms of their potentials for action.

These values and standards become enduring guidelines for the child in all his social relationships. To the extent that he understands their basis in terms of experience, he will be better able to apply them wisely and meaningfully in new situations as they may arise. Such values as these, acquired early in life, help to explain why one man will not steal for any reason, another may steal to save his own life, another may steal only to save the life of someone else.

AN EXPERIMENTAL STUDY OF SOCIALIZATION

While research on human development has made enormous gains during the past century, experimental evidence is still limited. We lean heavily on observation, description, and theory for understanding how the child acquires a sense of love, affection, and trust for other human beings; how he acquires a sense of fear, concern, or doubt regarding other persons. Some children, more than others, learn to attach importance to the feelings and wishes of other persons. Children differ widely in the development of social understanding and in their patterns of social response.

Harlow reminds us that we still know little about the fundamental processes underlying the development of mother love and infant love.[13] This issue was raised in striking manner by Bowlby in his wartime studies in Britain.[14] In the absence of experimental studies we have depended upon observation, intuition, and introspection in developing the theoretical explanation of the process, yet it seems clear that the initial love responses of the infant are to the mother or some mother surrogate. These intimate attachments form the basis for other affectional responses.

The Contact Comfort Hypothesis

Harlow's own ingenious experiments with infant macaque monkeys shed new light on the age-old question concerning the significance of breast feeding as opposed to bottle feeding for the emotional security of infants. Macaque monkeys were chosen for these experiments because they are more mature than human infants at birth and grow more rapidly, so that precise measurements of behavior may be made within the first few days after birth. While this is true, "the basic responses relating to affection, including nursing, contact, clinging, and even visual and auditory exploration, exhibit no fundamental differences in the two species. Even the development of perception, fear, frustration, and learning capability follows very similar sequences in rhesus monkeys and human children."[15]

In preliminary observations it had been noticed that laboratory-reared babies showed a strong attachment for cloth pads, clung to these pads, and engaged in violent temper tantrums when they were moved. "We had also discovered during some allied observational studies that a baby monkey raised on a bare wire-mesh cage floor survives with difficulty, if at all, during the first five days of life. If a wire-mesh cone is introduced, the baby does better; and if the cone is covered with terry cloth, husky, healthy, happy babies evolve. It takes more than a baby and a box to make a normal monkey. We were impressed by the possibility that, above and beyond the bubbling fountain of breast or bottle, contact comfort might be a very important variable in the development of the infant's affection for the mother."[16]

The Experiment

To test his hypothesis, Harlow created two surrogate mother monkeys, alike in form. One, however, was made of wire mesh and the other of a block of wood covered with sponge rubber and terry cloth to provide contact comfort to the baby monkeys. The surrogate mothers were each provided with a single breast located in the upper thorax. Both were heated by radiant heat provided by a light bulb. As Harlow describes the cloth mother, she "was a mother, soft, warm, and tender, a mother with infinite patience, a mother available twenty-four hours a day, a mother that never scolded her infant and never struck or bit her baby in anger."[17]

In Harlow's initial experiment, a cloth mother and a wire mother were placed in different cubicles attached to the infant's living cage:

> For four newborn monkeys the cloth mother lactated and the wire mother did not; and, for the other four, this condition was reversed. In either condition the infant received all its milk through the mother surrogate as soon as it was able to maintain itself in this way, a capability achieved within two or three days except in the case of very immature infants. Supplementary feedings were given until the milk intake from the mother surrogate was adequate. Thus, the experiment was designed as a test of the relative importance of the variables of contact comfort and nursing comfort. During the first 14 days of life the monkey's cage floor was covered with a heating pad wrapped in a folded gauze diaper, and thereafter the cage floor was bare. The infants were always free to leave the heating pad or cage floor to contact either mother, and the time spent on the surrogate mothers was automatically recorded.[18]

Experimental Findings and Conclusions

Records of the time spent on the cloth and wire mothers under the two conditions of feeding clearly reveal contact comfort to be a most significant variable in the development of affectional responses. In comparison to contact comfort, lactation proved to be a variable of negligible importance.

Harlow concludes:

> We were not surprised to discover that contact comfort was an important basic affectional or love variable, but we did not expect it to overshadow so completely the variable of nursing; indeed, the disparity is so great as to suggest that the primary function of nursing as an affectional variable is that of insuring frequent and intimate body contact of the infant with the mother. Certainly, man cannot live by milk alone. Love is an emotion that does not need to be bottle- or spoon-fed, and we may be sure that there is nothing to be gained by giving lip service to love.[19]

In subsequent studies, Harlow found that the infant monkey sought the cloth surrogate in times of distress, disturbance, or danger. The experience of nursing seems to have no relation to the source of support. When the cloth surrogate mother was present in an unfamiliar situation, the infant monkey explored the area with greater assurance than when the surrogate cloth monkey was not present.

Harlow's studies suggest that the mother gains the affection, love, and confidence of the child through providing the satisfying contact, warmth, and physical and emotional support during the initial period after birth rather than because she is the initial source of food. This suggests that the affectionately held bottle fed baby acquires a stronger source of security in the mother than does the baby who is breast fed by a "wire" mother who fails to give him adequate opportunities for physical contact, warmth, and support.

When Harlow's baby monkeys were put in unfamiliar or strange situations alone and without the presence of the surrogate mother, they tended to freeze in a crouched position and in other ways demonstrated severe emotional reactions. When the cloth surrogate mother was present in the same situation, the infants quickly began to use her as a source of security and began to explore and manipulate the strange toys about them. The cloth mother became a symbol of security and base of operations for them and they began to try out the new things, bringing them close to the security base. Having a base of security from which to operate, they were able to learn new things, to increase the range of their opportunities for learning and to acquire greater experience in discriminating between objects. They learned to explore, to judge, to test, to evaluate. Through play experience they learned new ways to cope with future unknown environments.

Harlow's studies demonstrate what mothers have known, that the infant needs the security of his mother as a base of operations in exploring the new world about him and in learning to discriminate between things to fear or things to conquer. The mother who holds her child safely while viewing lightning or listening to the thunder is helping him to gain a naturalistic acceptance of this phenomenon. If his initial experiences in this situation occur under conditions of security, lasting fears are less likely to develop. The lightning and thunder become sources of curiosity rather than sources of fright.

THE LEARNING OF SOCIAL ROLES

The first 47 monkeys Harlow raised in wire cages and in isolation matured into seriously neurotic adults, unable to develop normal social and sexual relations with other monkeys. "We have seen them sitting in their cages strangely mute, staring fixedly into space, relatively indifferent to people and to other monkeys. Some clutch their heads in both hands and rock back and forth—the autistic behavior pattern that we have seen in babies raised on wire surrogates. Others, when approached or even left alone, go into violent frenzies of rage, grasping and tearing at their legs with such fury that they sometimes require medical care."[20]

While monkeys with cloth mothers fared somewhat better than those with wire mothers, neither were able to adapt to adult social and sexual life. However, those with cloth mothers, who were given an opportunity to form normal infant-infant affectional relations, developed normal sexual responses.

Very few of the female monkeys raised in isolation ever became pregnant, even though left for long periods with patient and experienced males. When these few did become mothers, they tended to behave toward their offspring in unmotherly ways. They seemed unable to perform affectional roles with their infants that they themselves had not experienced as infants.

Thus while the experiments Harlow reports were not designed to study the development of role behavior, they nevertheless illustrate in dramatic fashion the significance of role models in the development of social behavior. His monkeys raised in isolation became adults without having learned to perform even those sexual and maternal role behaviors necessary for survival of their group, and as adults could only be taught these roles with great difficulty. Harlow's findings concern monkey mother love, rather than human mother love, but potential significance for understanding human social growth ought not to be overlooked.

Children also need models and affectional relations in developing their social roles. To acquire identity as a social being with social obligations and rights requires learning to take the roles of others, to interpret their intentions and expectations, and to adapt in reciprocal manner to their social responses. To the extent that Harlow's findings apply with respect to human children, the child who lacks appropriate social models to observe and playmates with whom to try out, test, evaluate, and judge the adequacy of behaviors observed for his own use, may be most seriously deprived in self and social development.

In our culture we tend to place a premium on work and study. We underrate play, the child's work, yet it is through play that the child learns to cope with environment, to test assumptions, to define roles and role demands, to practice role taking, and obtain estimates of the adequacy of his role performance. Through play he learns new things, new relationships, new ideas, and ways of integrating them into a private world of his own:

> For play is not only the child's response to life; it *is* his life, if he is to be a vital, growing, creative individual. . . . it teaches him . . . what the world is—how high is up and what is meant by down; what is soft and what is hard, what solid and what hollow, the meaning of inside and outside, wet and dry, and shape and form.
> Second, it teaches him about himself. He learns what he can do to the world outside, where he is strong and where weak, and how a series of failures can lead to success. While he is playing he strengthens his muscles, improves his perceptions, learns new skills, lets off excess energy, tries out different solutions to his problems, practices the tasks of life, learns how to deal with other people, and, eventually, comes to know the values and symbols of his world.[21]

How else but in play can a child learn the dimensions of the world of time and space, of things and animals and people? How else can he try out for himself and obtain a sense of value satisfaction of the experience? How else can he start to see the world and the things in it in terms of their potential usefulness in future situations?

Play is, indeed, a primary means whereby the child can acquire a set of assumptions regarding what is constant and what changes, what can be trusted and what must be watched, what is safe and what is dangerous. Here, too, he learns to sense value in human experience and to formulate his own standards of value for judging future actions.

SOCIALIZING AGENTS AND SOCIAL CHANGE

Of significance to public health is the extent to which inappropriate or invalid health beliefs, attitudes, and knowledge acquired early in life, often without awareness, may be retained in the face of intensive efforts at reeducation. When such beliefs, attitudes, and knowledge are held by significant socializing agents of society, they may comprise an important impediment to progress as defined by public health standards.

Socializing Agents as Barriers to Progress

In a study of the impact of education on nonscientific beliefs in Ethiopia, Lord brings this issue sharply into focus. Her study concerned the responses to 132 true-false questions regarding beliefs held about scientific matters. Included in her sample were students, nurses, graduate nurses, first-aid workers, and teachers, many of whom had significant roles in health education and social change.

Teachers included in the sample were drawn from among those with five or more years of formal education, capable of using the English language as the medium of instruction. Among this group of teachers, 34 nonscientific beliefs were held by 50 per cent or more teachers. Of this group of nonscientific beliefs, 16 were related to disease, its cause, prevention, and cure. "In other words, in a country where the life expectancy is estimated to be between 30 and 35 years, the largest number of false, or nonscientific beliefs, held by native teachers has to do with the problem of diseases, their cause, prevention, and cure."[22]

Lord's study indicates that while progress in scientific education is being made, the intellectual knowledge acquired is not always sufficient to change beliefs held since childhood. In this respect Lord's findings are consistent with evidence from research in the United States. Persons may hold scientific knowledge regarding health, but act on the basis of early acquired beliefs that run counter to their newly acquired knowledge.[23]

Unchallenged Assumptions

Some nonscientific health beliefs, attitudes, and knowledge may be so widely held in a society and so easily inculcated into the belief systems of its members that few members of the society may be sufficiently aware of their presence to challenge them. Margaret Mead tells us that:

> . . . In examining history—from the simplest primitive people of whom we have any record to the most sophisticated members of modern societies, with full access to all our knowledge of the way in which culture is learned—we find those who treat at least certain parts of their cultural behavior, in which they are known to differ from members of other societies, other classes, the other sex, or even other families, as completely innate and not subject to modification.
>
> But such a belief obviously forms an effective barrier against any attempt at reflective change. It may be all-embracing, so that a people feel that everything they do is innate and not subject to change, or it may refer only to parts of life—language may be regarded as more primary than material things, beliefs than objects, religion than eco-

nomics, etc. Or it may be limited in other ways; distinctions may be made between those persons who look most like the group that claims some innate cultural possession—such as a "sense of social justice" sometimes claimed by Eastern European Jews, or an innate sense of fair play sometimes claimed for the English, or clear headedness for the French—and those individuals who either actually do deviate in physique or appear to do so because of other deviant attitudes affecting their posture, etc., who may then be regarded as non-Jewish or un-English, or un-French, in some subtle and unspecified way.[24]

Socializing agents are therefore persons of great significance to public health workers concerned with enduring health improvement in health knowledge, beliefs, attitudes, and practices. As "gatekeepers" to the minds of new members of the society, they may help them acquire attitudes and beliefs about food, about the cause, prevention, and cure of disease, about health practices, and about physicians, dentists, nurses, and other health personnel which can directly influence the success or failure of major health program efforts. Beliefs, values, superstitions, ideas, and attitudes which may be detrimental to a growing society may be held and passed on by a socializing agent without his awareness. Under such conditions, progress may be difficult.

Stabilizing Influences

On the other hand, it must be recognized that socializing agents serve as important stabilizing agents for the society by helping to maintain a constant belief and value system. They help to hold the culture intact against the influence of outside forces. Thus they perform a unifying function that helps to protect the group from rapid changes that may spell social disaster. As new belief systems are acquired by the socializing agent, these, too, will be retained and passed on in spite of outside pressures or further change.

Dictatorial governments seeking to change the basic cultural values and beliefs in a population quickly and drastically have resorted to extreme measures in order to control the period of early socialization. In addition to using mass education approaches, they have sought to separate children from their parents at early ages in order to minimize the role of the mother and father as socializing agents. The revolutionary changes in values, beliefs, and attitudes that have been reported from the U.S.S.R. tend to attest to the effectiveness of these methods. Yet even the introduction of such drastic measures backed by force does not appear to have been completely successful.

Implications for Change

Some of the most difficult problems of achieving lasting change in health-related values, beliefs, attitudes, and behaviors occur in societies or groups where responsibility for socialization rests with some member of the group who holds beliefs deeply anchored in the past; for example, in families where the primary responsibility for taking care of the infant is turned over to the grandmother or grandfather. Their values, beliefs, and attitudes may be out of keeping with those of the social group into which the child will grow. Not only does such practice retard social change; it results in serious adjustment problems for the child involved.

A similar situation occurs where responsibility for child care is turned over to a maid or other domestic who comes from a cultural group with values and beliefs inconsistent with those of the social group into which the child will grow. It is not unusual that the person selected for child care is chosen on the basis of such criteria as ability to cook or do housework rather than the ability to teach. There may be little recognition of the handicap this imposes on the child.

There is considerable evidence that some families are better prepared than others for assuming responsibility for a type of socialization oriented toward the future growth of the group. They are better able to provide the emotional and intellectual setting that offers the richest opportunities for learning. Children whose socializing agents do not expose them to opportunities to learn the basic elements required to function effectively in the social group may be seriously limited in their possibilities for social and personal growth.

Education for Child Rearing

Programs for parent education serve a significant role in our society in preparing parents for their responsibilities as socializing agents. Many different agencies engage in such programs. While they often differ in their value orientations, they tend to hold certain purposes in common. In his evaluation of parent education, Brim describes these programs as follows:

> The primary objective of those parent education programs generally acknowledged as successful and outstanding in quality is to make the parent more conscious of his role performance, to make him more autonomous and creative, to improve his independent judgment, to increase the rationality of the parent's role performance. One can fairly say that the effort of such programs is to improve the decision processes

of parents, both in the parent's choice of ends in child rearing and in his selection of actual child-training practices. This objective is sought by providing the parent with information both on children and on parents, and by providing educational settings in which parents are able to discuss, or individually to think through, and hence to formulate with conscious deliberateness, the ends they will seek and the means they will employ. The recurrent question one must face in the pursuit of this aim is the degree to which it is possible to increase the conscious and rational aspects of role performance by the modern American parent.[25]

Brim concludes that we lack conclusive evidence regarding the effectiveness of such programs. This is a most difficult area in which to conduct good experimental studies, and findings have not been consistent. It is hoped that well-designed studies now under way will provide useful guidelines.

NOTES TO CHAPTER 20

1. Dukes, William F., "Psychological Studies of Values," *Psychological Bulletin,* vol. 52, January, 1955, pp. 24–50.

2. English, Horace B., and Ava C. English, *A Comprehensive Dictionary of Psychological and Psychoanalytical Terms.* Longmans, Green, and Co., New York, 1958.

3. Child, Irwin L., "Socialization" in Lindzey, Gardner, editor, *The Handbook of Social Psychology.* Addison-Wesley Publishing Co., Reading, Mass., 1954, vol. 2, p. 655.

4. James, William, *Principles of Psychology.* Henry Holt and Co., New York, 1890.

5. Mead, George, *Mind, Self, and Society.* University of Chicago Press, Chicago, 1934.

6. Blumer, Herbert, "Society as Symbolic Interaction" in Rose, Arnold, editor, *Human Behavior and Social Processes: An Interactionist Approach.* Houghton Mifflin Co., Boston, 1962, p. 181.

7. Goffman, Erving, *The Presentation of Self in Everyday Life.* Doubleday and Co., Garden City, N.Y., 1959, p. 248.

8. Horowitz, Eugene L., "The Development of Attitude Toward the Negro," *Archives of Psychology,* New York, no. 194, 1936.

9. Hartley, Eugene L., and Ruth E. Hartley, *Fundamentals of Social Psychology.* Alfred A. Knopf, Inc., New York, 1952, p. 705.

10. Horowitz, Eugene L., and Ruth E. Horowitz, "Development of Social Attitudes in Children," *Sociometry,* vol. 1, 1938, p. 336.

11. Smith, M. Brewster, "Personal Values in the Study of Lives" in White, Robert, editor, *The Study of Lives.* Atherton Press, New York, 1963, p. 338.

12. Allport, Gordon W., *Becoming.* Yale University Press, New Haven, 1955, pp. 73–74.

13. Harlow, Harry F., "The Nature of Love," *American Psychologist,* vol. 13, December, 1958, p. 673.

14. Bowlby, John, "Maternal Care and Mental Health." *W. H. O. Technical Monograph Series,* no. 2, Geneva, 1951. Bowlby reviews previous studies in this field as well as reporting his own work.

15. Harlow, Harry F., *op. cit.,* p. 674.

16. *Ibid.,* p. 675.

17. *Ibid.,* pp. 675–676.

18. *Ibid.,* p. 676.

19. *Ibid.,* p. 677.

20. Harlow, Harry F., "The Heterosexual Affectional System in Monkeys," *American Psychologist,* vol. 17, January, 1962, p. 6.

21. Hartley, Ruth E., and Robert M. Goldenson, *The Complete Book of Children's Play.* Thomas Y. Crowell Co., New York, 1957, p. 1.

22. Lord, Edith, "The Impact of Education on Nonscientific Beliefs in Ethiopia," *Journal of Social Psychology,* vol. 47, 1958, p. 344.

23. Hochbaum, Godfrey M., *Public Participation in Medical Screening Programs: A Socio-psychological Study.* Public Health Service, U.S. Dept. of Health, Education, and Welfare, Publication 572, Government Printing Office, Washington, 1958.

24. Mead, Margaret, "Changing Culture: Some Observations in Primitive Societies" in Lerner, Daniel, editor, *The Human Meaning of the Social Sciences.* Meridian Books, The World Publishing Co., Cleveland and New York, 1959, pp. 286–287. Copyright © by The World Publishing Co.

25. Brim, Orville G., Jr., *Education for Child Rearing,* Russell Sage Foundation, New York, 1959, pp. 10–11. See also Sears, Robert R., Eleanor E. Maccoby, and Harry Levin, *Patterns of Child Rearing,* Row, Peterson, and Co., Evanston, Ill., 1957.

Chapter 21

Perceptual Development and Deprivation

THE NEWBORN INFANT is dependent on members of his family for food, warmth, shelter, and for the satisfaction of many other physical, physiological, and emotional needs. Less recognized, but of equal importance, is his dependence on others for sensory stimulation that is essential if his sensory organs are to mature and acquire the degree of discriminating ability necessary to make meaning out of his environment. How quickly and how well he learns to identify and define the abstract ideas to which he is exposed depends in part on the quality of his native capacities for sensing and perceiving and understanding. It also depends, however, upon the richness of opportunity available to him for learning.

Perceiving seems like such an effortless business for the adult that it is almost impossible to conceptualize the complexity of the task for the infant. Even though each of us passed through this difficult stage as part of growing up, it was at a time when we lacked the experience to retain even the slightest conscious memory traces to turn back to as adults. Adult learnings, even though they involve strange symbols, abstract concepts, and complex relationships, seem almost petty when compared to the task the infant goes through in obtaining an understanding of his new world. How much more complex it must be to have to learn that the world does contain things, symbols, ideas, concepts—to have to learn how to recognize these things and what they mean—than to extend an adult base of knowledge by exploring an unfamiliar environment, culture, or language, however complex it may seem.

THE UNSTABLE WORLD OF INFANCY

Adult worlds tend to become organized worlds, relatively stable from day unto day, so much so that Gardner Murphy warns us that the learning process is often relatively irreversible. Thus to understand human nature one must consider "the consolidation of *ways of perceiving and thinking under the pressure of wants;* the tendency to perceive, to think, and to standardize culturally the ways in which members of the group must perceive and think."[1]

We need to be aware that when we discuss the perceptions of the newborn child we do not bring into his situation the patterns of assumptions that help us make order and stability out of our own confused worlds. What remains unstable in a world already organized is bound to be different from what remains unstable in a world that is just beginning to be explored. In the world of perception as in other things we need to be careful not to judge the child and his development against adult standards.

It will be recalled that the difficulties in understanding the newborn child stem in good part from our inability to communicate with him so that we may see the world from his point of view. We must observe his world from the outside and conjecture on the basis of whatever research evidence we can acquire as to the manner of his psychological behavior. In doing so, we need to beware lest we impute meanings that are not present; impart purposes that do not exist, or intentions and expectancies that he could not as yet have acquired. How differently might we react to the newborn child if we could but momentarily glimpse the world from his point of view—from his center of behavior.

One researcher tells us that writers describing the process of socialization during the child's early years "usually agree that during the first months of an infant's life there are few demands made upon him. The infant leads an irresponsible kind of life where his every whim is gratified and where he need do nothing in return—except grow and develop as a normal healthy baby. He cries, and sooner or later he is fed, he sleeps when he is sleepy, evacuates at will, and is indulged and waited upon by loving relatives who make him the center of the household. As a result the child's first concept of himself is not that of a helpless infant, but rather of an omnipotent being whose mother and others are at his beck and call."[2]

Such a point of view seems grossly inconsistent with present evidence concerning the challenges that face the newborn child. Although some of his sense organs have served him prior to birth, they are now being put into use to provide him with information of a strange new world that is still essentially meaningless to him. "Evidence indicates that the perceptual world and purposeful behavior of the infant develop together, each expanding, limiting, and affecting the other as the child matures and carves out a world for himself in the process of experiencing—doing and doing-experiencing which constitute living."[3]

What difficulties the infant must have in gaining a sense of what is stable or constant in a new and ever-changing environment! What difficulties he must undergo in learning to identify and interpret changes of personal significance!

In a critical review of the current status of research on cognitive learning in infancy and childhood, Fowler observes:

> At birth, the infant, virtually lacking any knowledge at all, must spend an "apprentice" phase acquiring the most elementary foundation discriminations and generalizations on the nature of the physical and social world. These primary concepts are perhaps the most difficult and slowest to come by. This is because the infant possesses no general frames of reference to serve as guides or conceptual leverages for learning.[4]

DISCOVERING THE WORLD

The infant's first patterned experiences after birth probably relate to the chill or warmth of his surroundings, to the touch and pressures of the arms that support him and of the clothing in which he is wrapped, to a diffused pattern of worldly noises, to the odors of the strange air into which he is born, and to the taste and smell of liquids he is offered. When his eyes open, he may find a confusion of lights and shadows cast by the slats of his crib, the face and body of his mother, the ceiling, wall, and furniture, and a host of other unknowns which command equal attention.

The crib lines seem to move back and forth as he wiggles. They become large and small; sometimes they are light and sometimes in shadow; sometimes they are near and sometimes they are far. Many different types of forms come from them to his retina. From all this confusion of size, shape, and form he must learn to identify them as stable and consistent things in his environment.

His mother's face looms large above him when she is close. It becomes smaller as she moves away. At times it is in light, at other times in shadow. It, too, takes different forms as she moves her head from side to side or he moves his—yet in a relatively brief period of time he learns to identify it as a familiar face. He learns to place a common meaning on a wide range of stimulus patterns that come to him through the process of perception. The bottle may be large when nearby, small as it goes farther away, and at first may appear to be a part of his mother. It, too, takes different forms and shapes as it is moved around and yet from the confusion of patterns he acquires an identification of the bottle as a single separate item of his environment, one which has meaning and value for him. He learns also to recognize the head of his mother as part of her body, to see one, and know the other is present, and thus acquires gradually an image which, varying as it does in pattern, is stable and constant.

Even though the infant has learned to hear before birth he must still acquire a sense of constancy regarding a wide range of sounds, all of which mean his mother's voice. The sound may be loud or soft, near or far, in the form of a shout or the form of a whisper. It may come as a cooing to him as he is held or it may comfort him from a distance if she is working in the kitchen. It may reach his ears in an almost infinite variety of forms, yet from this mass of confusion in sound he learns to recognize something that is familiar and also to associate this familiar sound with the familiar visual image.

Frank notes that during the early years of life the world of the child is organized to an extraordinary degree around things that can be felt, things we can "feel through our skins."[5] One has learned before birth to accept and to adapt to certain of the pressures and movements of his mother. When uncomfortable in the uterus he has perhaps changed his position to remove undesired pressures. Now in the new world he learns to accept and ignore the pressure of his clothes and of his bed, and to seek other pressures that are satisfying. Over a period of time he starts to recognize by touch his own body parts and those of his mother.

In the kinesthetic area also he learns to sense differences in movement that bring his hands or feet in particular positions. Long before he has learned to control his muscles he had learned to open and close his hands at will and to turn his head as he chooses.

While learning to give meaning to these various patterns of perception, the child also acquires a recognition of the relationship between perceptions received through different sources. He learns to harmonize in some general way the information coming to him from various sources by means of several sense receptors and, in some way as yet unknown, to choose between conflicting patterns of stimulation.[6] From repeated patterns or sequential patterns of perception he gains slowly a sense of cause-and-effect relationships and from this evolves a sense of continuity in things.

As a child starts to create a stable environment out of his sensory impressions he learns to ignore those items in his environment that are stable and dependable. He cannot perceive everything at once, but must choose among the range of his perceptions those that have significance and meaning to his developing purposes. His pattern of social motives then plays a greater role in directing his search for meaning. Much that is constant becomes consciously ignored and he may move freely without paying attention to so many things at once. As James Harvey Robinson has noted, "We could not remember anything unless we forgot almost everything."[7] In learning to forget as well as in learning to perceive purposefully, the child becomes a social being.

ACQUIRING CONCEPTS

Most of the studies of perception in children tend to be modeled after adult experiments. They have been carried out at ages when the child can respond and provide verbal information regarding the object exposed to him. On the whole they tend to find children's perceptions somewhat more subject to error than those of adults. Reports tend to become more complete and accurate throughout childhood and as the child approaches maturity.[8]

One of the most creative and insightful child psychologists, Jean Piaget, has carried out many studies which suggest that even though the child is capable of recognizing differences in things at a very early age, he behaves almost to the end of the first year as though objects really disappeared when they momentarily move out of his field of perception. He acts as though they ceased to exist. Piaget suggested that the world of the child "is not made up of permanent objects with autonomous trajectories, but of moving perceptive pictures which return periodically into nonexistence and come back again as the functional result of the proper action." He uses a very simple experiment to demonstrate this. "One has only to give a five or six months old baby his bottle with the nipple away from him, and turn it around slowly before his very eyes. If the child can see a bit of the rubber nipple at the other end of the bottle, he immediately turns the object around, but if he doesn't see the nipple, he doesn't even attempt to turn it, but sucks the wrong end!"

". . . as the activity of the baby develops and the causal, temporal, and spatial sequences which this activity creates become more complex, objects are detached more and more from the action itself, and the body of the subject becomes one element among others in an ordered ensemble. Thus a total reversal of perspective takes place, which marks the beginning of the objectification of the external world, and of the idea of its permanence."[9]

When the child grows older and acquires language and a fuller understanding of the permanence of concrete objects, he still has the problem of learning concepts of matter, weight, movement, number, and other ideas that are normal components of adult life. The conservation of matter when physically changed is a concept most difficult to acquire and even older children may have difficulty accepting the idea that sugar dissolved in water still exists in solution.

ACQUIRING LANGUAGE

Learning to understand spoken words and to respond to them through speech is one of the most remarkable achievements of the child. His progress in human and social relations throughout life depends on how well he is able to acquire these communicating abilities, for the ability to communicate through the use of symbols not only distinguishes man from animals but also differentiates those who can and those who cannot progress in social relations and intellectual pursuits. Abilities in communication serve as a ladder to progress throughout society.

How early and how well a child learns to understand and to talk depends, of course, on the capacities he has for discriminating sounds and for expressing different sounds. It depends also on his ability to make a wide range of complex sounds and to discriminate with the native capacities that he has between the wide range of sounds available to him. He must learn to discriminate words from among the various sounds available in his auditory environment and to assign meanings given those words by adult members of his group. He learns also to associate the words he hears with the words he utters and to recognize nuances between the various words he uses. Discrimination and sensitivity to choice of words are stepping stones toward acquisition of a rich and effective means of expression.

The child learns to read long after he has acquired verbal abilities. Progress in learning to read is greatly hampered if he has not first learned to speak and to understand spoken words. Conversely, if he has acquired a large spoken vocabulary and has learned the significance of relationships between words, progress in acquiring reading abilities is greatly facilitated. The transfer of learning between these two communicating processes is very heavy.

The process of learning to discriminate words and to respond with words is a give-and-take process carried out with other children or with adults in his group. His mother's nods or smiles give him assurance of success. Her patient repeating of sounds guides his attempts, for he wants to be approved. More important, perhaps, her attention to him as he tries to converse lets him know the importance she places on learning the sounds. It gives him a sense of the significance of learning to communicate. Such a "feedback" process greatly facilitates his learning new things. The nonverbal means of communication acquired early in life stand him in good stead in helping him to progress in acquiring new means of coping with environment.

EXPERIMENTAL STUDIES OF CHILDREN

Innate capacities for hearing, discriminating, and vocalizing lie at the basis of this verbal activity. The child with organic or neurological difficulties may be unable to achieve the ability to speak at all. But speaking is more than vocalization, for any child learning to speak requires maturation of the organs and neuromuscular mechanisms involved, and also requires experience within a social environment that provides a variety of meaningful sounds to be learned. This social setting also serves as a testing ground in the child's efforts to acquire the new skill.

Studies by Welch as reported in Landreth's *Psychology of Early Childhood* suggest that discriminating abilities can be developed more rapidly when the infant is provided opportunities to use materials that offer a wide range of visual, tactual, and auditory stimulation. The infant learns the properties of different kinds of materials by testing them out, matching them, comparing them, relating them. Meanwhile, he leans on others for guidance in his behavior, guidance provided by indications of approval or disapproval. Opportunities to test out ideas related to his own interests within the pattern of his own understandings help him also acquire a wider range of ideas or concepts to use in daily living.[10] As Piaget has shown, some of the abstract ideas of our society are most difficult to learn. Opportunities to "experiment" fosters the acquisition of abstract ideas and creative abilities.[11]

Long before children start to use words, they try out different kinds of vowels and consonants, different types of sounds, which form the basis for adult speech. Irwin has developed a reliable method of recording and analyzing these speech attempts of infants and young children. His research suggests that the social environment within which the child grows plays a significant role in the development of speech. Differences between children of laboring parents and children of professional business and clerical parents start to appear during the first three or four months of life, both in terms of number of types of sounds used and the frequency with which they are used. By the age of fifteen months, these differences are quite striking. Brodbeck and Irwin found that these differences are even more striking between children raised in orphanages and children raised in the family setting.[12]

Landreth has cited a number of studies which suggest that occupational level of parents plays a significant role also with respect to the speed with which sentences and phrases are acquired by the child. Children in upper socioeconomic circumstances tend to acquire earlier the ability to use sentence conversational units and tend to maintain this advantage with time during the first four years.[13]

McCarthy found that children whose parents are in the professions tended to make more informative statements and ask more questions than the children of unskilled workers.[14] There is some evidence that this may be related to expectation of receiving adequate answers.[15] Those who grow up in a world in which concrete things are a central focus of attention tend to learn more about concrete things, and to acquire specific abilities given importance in their groups. Those raised in an environment that fosters the use of abstract ideas tend to acquire more ability in dealing with abstractions. Accordingly, as has been found in studies employing intelligence tests, the discriminating abilities of children reared in different socioeconomic environments will vary to some extent in accord with these differing backgrounds. These differences are sometimes reflected in their responses to different types of intelligence test items.[16]

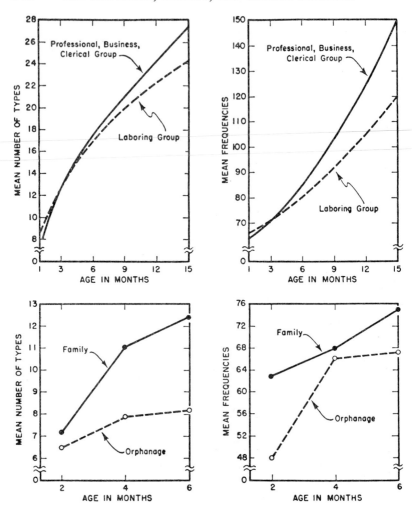

FIGURE 12. Mean Frequencies of Vocalizing and Mean Numbers of Types of Sounds in the Vocalizing of Infants of Laboring and Professional Parents and of Infants in Homes and Institutions.

Reproduced from Irwin, O. C., "Infant Speech," *Journal of Speech and Hearing Disorders,* 1948, vol. 13, pp. 224–225 and 320–326, and from Brodbeck, A. J., and O. C. Irwin, "The Speech Behavior of Infants Without Families" *Child Development,* 1946, vol. 17, pp. 145–156.

SOURCE: Landreth, Catherine, *The Psychology of Early Childhood.* Alfred A. Knopf, Inc., New York, 1958, Figure 48, p. 129. Reproduced with permission of the authors and publishers.

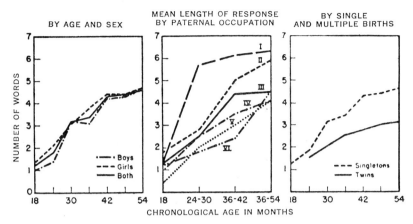

FIGURE 13. Mean Length of Response by Chronological Age, by Sex, by Paternal Occupation, and by Single and Multiple Births.

Reproduced from McCarthy, D., *The Language Development of the Preschool Child, Institute of Child Welfare Monographs,* ser. no. 4, 1930, University of Minnesota Press, and from Day, E. J., "The Development of Language in Twins," *Child Development,* vol. 3, 1932, pp. 179–199.

SOURCE: Landreth, Catherine, *The Psychology of Early Childhood.* Alfred A. Knopf, Inc., New York, 1958, Figure 51, p. 139. Reproduced with permission of the authors and publishers.

Other Experience and Intelligence

In an evaluative review of studies of maternal deprivation, Yarrow notes considerable variation in research findings. A history of institutionalization sometimes, but not always, leads to mental retardation, depending upon the type of experience provided. Factors of significance, in addition to constitution of the child, include the amount and type of individualized stimulation provided, the age of the child when institutionalized, and the length of stay.[17] A number of studies support the conclusion that intelligence as measured by tests can be influenced by varying environments, and that experimental approaches which provide special environmental stimulation for retarded children may lead to significant improvement in their intellectual functioning.[18]

Follow-up Studies

During the 1930's Wellman, Skeels, and their associates at the Iowa Child Welfare Research Station, State University of Iowa, initiated studies of retarded children who were placed in situations that offered various degrees of attention and affection. Their preliminary reports, which have been much disputed by other researchers, suggested that substantial changes in intelligence could be effected by varying environmental conditions. Of particular concern to reviewers at that time was the short follow-up period over which observations were made.[19]

The National Institute of Mental Health is presently completing a second follow-up study to determine the adult status of children who were subjects in three of the most interesting demonstrations. The subjects now range in age from twenty-five to thirty-five years. Harold Skeels, reporting on the present status of this research, advises that it may be possible to find and interview almost 100 per cent of the subjects participating in these early studies even though many are now married and living in places far from Ames, Iowa. All of one hundred adopted children and their foster parents who participated in one of the early studies have been located sixteen years after the follow-up.

> Preliminary indications are that these adopted children as adults are achieving at levels consistently higher than would have been predicted from the intellectual, educational, or socioeconomic level of the biological parents, and equal to the expectancy for children living in the homes of natural parents capable of providing environmental impacts similar to those which have been provided by the adoptive parents.[20]

Of particular interest here are the findings regarding the effects of differential stimulation on two small groups of mentally retarded children. All subjects have been located and interviewed after a lapse of twenty-one years since the first follow-up study was completed. Skeels reports that:

> It will be recalled that in the original study, the 13 children in the experimental group, all mentally retarded at the beginning of the study, experienced the effects of early intervention which consisted of a radical shift from one institutional environment to another, which provided a much higher degree of one-to-one mother surrogate-child emotional relationships, and superior stimulation. This was followed by placement in adoptive homes for 11 of the children.
>
> The contrast group of 12 children, initially at a higher level of intelligence, were exposed to a relatively non-stimulating orphanage environment over a prolonged period of time. In the initial study, children in the experimental group showed a remarkable increase in rate of mental growth, whereas the children in the contrast group showed progressive mental retardation.

In the adult follow-up study the two groups continued to be remarkably divergent. All 13 children in the experimental group are self-supporting, and none is a ward of any institution, public or private. 11 of the 13 children are married, and 9 of these have children."

In the contrast group of 12 children, 1 died in adolescence following continued residence in a State institution for the mentally retarded; 5 or 40% are still wards of State institutions; 1 is in a mental hospital; and the others are in institutions for the mentally retarded. Of those no longer wards of State institutions, only 2 have married, and 1 of these is divorced. Out of 4 females in the contrast group, 3 were sterilized in late adolescence to preclude the possibility of procreation in the event that they were placed out on work placements at older ages.

In education disparity between the two groups is great. For the experimental group the median grade completed is 12th grade, whereas the median for the contrast group is less than 3rd grade completed. In the experimental group 4 have gone on for one or more years of college work, with one of the boys having received a B.A. degree from a university. Occupationally the range is from professional and semi-professional to semi-skilled laborers or domestics. In the contrast group 50% of them are unemployed and those that are, with the exception of one case, are characterized as "hewers of wood and drawers of water."[21]

A preliminary estimate of the relative costs of care under the two conditions studied suggests that children kept in institutions were a cost to the state of more than ten times that of children placed in foster homes, and that these costs will continue for many years hence.

Skeels concludes that:

> From the above, and substantiated by many other supporting studies in the past 20 years, it would seem that we have adequate knowledge to implement certain programs of intervention which can be applied to counteract the devastating effects of poverty, socio-cultural deprivation, maternal deprivation, or a combination of these circumstances. Serious consideration must be given to expenditures in relation to prevention, rather than a limitation to tremendous costs of a curative nature. This, of course, does not preclude the need for further research and exploratory studies to determine the optimum modes of intervention and the most appropriate ages for initiating such procedures.[22]

One ought not interpret these findings as implying that all mental retardation can be influenced so dramatically by environmental change. Innate and prenatal factors, birth injuries, and even specific kinds of infant experience may lead to types of mental retardation which our present scientific approaches have not proved capable of reversing.

While sociocultural deprivation and inadequate affectional and emotional support often accompany maternal separation, they are not necessarily associated with maternal separation. In some instances the separation of mother and child may be beneficial to both. In a cogent review of evidence concerning some of the salutary effects of maternal separation, Seiden notes that under some circumstances separation is necessary to protect the child from the mother, or mother from the child, and to provide proper care. Such separation may yield therapeutic consequences. He notes that:

> . . . maternal separation cannot be regarded as a singular concept to be studied and understood from a purely structural approach. Instead, investigation must concentrate upon the dynamic qualities present in the interaction of mother and child. It becomes a meaningless question to ask whether separation is good or bad. What must be explored are the relevant intermediate variables. As a minimal requirement, the following areas call for careful examination in future research: 1. Quality of previous maternal care, 2. Maturity of the child (a) chronological, (b) emotional, (c) physical (health status), 3. Emotional maturity of mother, 4. Nature of the mother-child relationship, 5. Quality of substitute care to be provided, 6. Length of separation, 7. Choice of the child regarding separation.[23]

EXPERIMENTS WITH DOGS

We are limited in our attempts to understand the significance of a rich or poor environment for the child in developing psychological maturation because it is not possible to experiment freely with children. One cannot systematically rear children in barren environments for the purpose of determining what the permanent effects from such an upbringing will be in terms of their perceptual, emotional, and social behavior. For studies of this nature we must lean on animal research.

During the past decade several exciting research studies concerned with the influence of a barren environment on the intelligence, activity, and emotional and social behavior of dogs have been conducted in the psychological laboratories of McGill University. Two psychologists, William Thompson and Ronald Melzack, carried out one such experiment with Scottish terriers under controlled conditions established at the age of four weeks, as soon as they were weaned. Several litters of Scotties were divided into two groups—one to be raised normally as controls, the other to be raised under the experimental conditions. Members of the experimental group of dogs were confined alone in cages with opaque sides and tops so they could not see outside. The feeding and cleaning arrangements were such that the dogs never saw their keepers. The animals lived in this blank, isolated environment until they were between seven and ten months old.

"After their release these dogs were exceptionally active and playful, showing a puppy-like exuberance that belied their physical maturity. This behavior was almost opposite to what one might have expected, because it is commonly supposed that early separation from contacts with others has a depressing effect."[24] Their behavior in a new environment under observation was far more active and exploratory than that of normal dogs who soon became bored and quietly relaxed in the same situation. Such findings were consistent for eleven restricted dogs and seven control dogs. In many ways, their behavior was markedly immature.

In one experiment the dogs were subjected to the pursuit of a toy car which gave them an electric shock when touched. Normal dogs quickly learned to avoid being hit and retreated calmly and deliberately. Restricted animals behaved wildly and aimlessly. On an average, they took 25 shocks each to learn to avoid the car and even then became excited when they saw the car. In several situations the restricted dogs demonstrated unintelligent behavior under observation. One banged his head into a pipe by the wall more than 30 times in a single hour. Their reactions to other emotion-producing stimuli were far less mature than those of the control dogs.

In a series of tests with 18 different maze problems the dogs were scored according to the number of errors made to reach the food at the end of the maze. The restricted Scotties' performance was substantially inferior to their litter mates. On the average they made 50 per cent more errors on the series of problems. Even dogs which had been out of isolation several years scored lower than their contemporaries which had not been restricted. The effects of early confinement were lasting.

A sociability test involved measuring the amount of attention paid to two other dogs in separate cages in the same room when the subject was free to roam around the room. The normal Scotties were considerably more sociable than those raised under restricted conditions. The latter paid little attention to the dogs during the first session and in subsequent sessions also tended to be less attentive to the visitors. This lack of interest in companionship also persisted for years.

From this series of studies Thompson and Melzack conclude:

The experiments we have described clearly indicate that a rich and stimulating environment in early life is an important condition for normal development. Restriction of experience during this crucial period can result in enduring retardation of an animal in various psychological traits. It must be emphasized that our studies of Scotties have little specific bearing on human beings, for the environmental situations are drastically different. But the experiments bring out clearly that any animal needs varied sensory stimulation in order to develop normally, just as it needs food and drink. This is a fact that has frequently been neglected by psychologists. It has long been assumed, either explicitly or implicitly, that all behavior is governed by a basic need to minimize tensions and disturbances in order to preserve the stability of the organism. This is evidently not so. Organisms like to be disturbed (as by an exciting novel, climbing a mountain and so on). And indeed they cannot live normally and fully if they are not. Especially during the early, plastic period of life, they must have a good deal of stimulation in their environment. If they do not, they may remain forever immature.[25]

THE EPIDEMIOLOGY OF READING DISABILITIES

There has been a growing awareness among researchers of a relationship between reading ability and social adjustment of children in school. Adolescents who have been identified as having chronic antisocial behavior have been observed to have reading difficulty in certain situations and there has been some speculation also that other mental health problems may be significantly related to the inability to read. It seems reasonable that inability to acquire skills such as language skills, which are basic to success in our society, will lead to the expression of frustration, aggression, and conflict with others more successful.

Awareness of this possible close relationship between reading ability and mental illness and mental health has led the National Institute of Mental Health to initiate a long-range study of the epidemiology of reading disabilities. This study is being conducted in its Mental Health Study Section in Langley Park, Maryland. In this study the authors state:

> The origins of reading disability, undoubtedly complex and multiple, are of major concern. . . . Our major professional orientation is toward patterns of interaction within families as they shape and reflect attitudes toward learning, and we are interested in these patterns as products of cultural, social, and economic forces in communities. . . .
> We are also interested in the consequences of reading disability for

the mental health of individuals. Reading is a basic and highly valued communication skill and a disability in this area, whatever its origins, limits an individual's capacities in many areas. It almost certainly is damaging to his self-esteem and reduces his opportunities for social interaction. . . . As with so many chronic disorders, its consequences reduce the probability of its correction and may, in fact, lead to its entrenchment and even enhancement. We are interested in exploring and documenting this apparent destructive potential.[26]

This long-range study of the National Institute of Mental Health has already started to yield significant findings. Early findings indicate that reading retardation is a serious problem among children in the county under study. During 1955–1956, 19 per cent of the children in the third grade were 1.3 years retarded; 16 per cent of those in the fifth grade were 2.3 years retarded. Significantly more boys than girls had reading difficulty. An analysis in terms of intellectual abilities of those with reading difficulty indicated that the problem is not one of intelligence. "It would therefore appear that the larger percentage of children with reading difficulties were of at least normal intelligence."[27]

Some progress has been made thus far in studying reading disability as related to the ecology of the county, a possible technique since all the school districts in the county are administered by the same Board of Education and the philosophy, standards, and supervision are essentially uniform. Data have also been available on the quality of housing in the area so that analysis could be made in these terms also.

Findings from such analyses are as follows:

Briefly summarized, the school districts with the higher reading level, as a group, were rated at least one quartile better than those with the lower reading level in quality of housing, population density, and rate of social assistance and juvenile court cases. There was no difference observed in community facilities. The latter, incidentally, were considered only for their presence or absence, not their quality.[28]

In its continuing studies the NIMH group is following up the 1954 sixth-grade students through high school, at the same time seeking to have a clearer understanding of the neighborhood and family relationships from which they grew. Several studies of clinical groups supported the hypothesis that there was a close relationship between emotional problems and reading difficulty. The question still remains, of course, as to which comes first, or whether they are not so intimately related from the beginning that separation of the language difficulties from the emotional difficulties will be difficult, if not impossible.

Attention on studies such as this and the application of their findings to the school program has been focused on the early identification of the mentally disturbed, in the hope that improvements can be initiated before serious emotional problems develop. Thus attention has been paid to the positive health implications of such findings. To the extent that such opportunity for acquiring skills during childhood is limited by the quality of the environment available to the child, the opportunities for self-fulfillment or potentiality are limited.

It may be hypothesized, at least, that herein lies one of the major opportunities for developing positive mental health programs.

IMPLICATIONS FOR PUBLIC HEALTH–MENTAL HEALTH

While one cannot safely generalize from such studies of animals to human behavior, it should be noted that the findings of Brodbeck and Irwin, McCarthy, and Welch reported above are consistent in general with the findings from the studies. Children reared in limited social environments do tend to be deprived of adequate opportunities for learning means of dealing with the broader environment into which they grow.

A wealth of evidence derived from both clinical and experimental studies suggests that some of the most lasting patterns of reaction of an individual are acquired in early life. Deprivation in affectionate support during infancy and childhood can leave lasting effects on the personality of a child just as food deprivation leaves its mark on the physical development of the child. During those years the child learns to feel secure or anxious, confident or uncertain, accepted or rejected, self-respecting or unworthy, eager for experience, or withdrawn.[29]

There is growing evidence that the child may also be deprived of the opportunities for acquiring, developing, and gaining confidence in the use of the means for coping with environment. He may not have an equal chance, as he grows, to learn the language skills necessary for progress in the society in which he moves. He may even be unable, for lack of opportunity, to acquire sensitivity to the importance of ideas and their relationships or skill in use of ideas and the symbols which represent ideas. Good oral and written communication skills are essential for effectively coping with the problems of modern life.

Children who lack language skills at the time of entrance to school, for example, will find their progress seriously blocked.

Children with serious physical defects, in our society, may be more easily identified than those with handicaps of a psychological nature. If a child lacks physiological means for full sensory experience, he is early identified as a handicapped child who needs support and help so that he does not become frustrated by his inability to do the things that other children do. It is recognized that frustration over a long period of time leads to serious emotional difficulties so that adaptation to a normal society is difficult.

The child who lacks the opportunity to develop language skills and skill in the use of ideas is not readily identified during infancy, yet he may be equally frustrated in his efforts to cope with his growing environment. He may not understand why he has more difficulty learning to read or to use numbers. Feelings of shame, guilt, or anxiety may be reinforced by the behavior of his parents or peers who mock his unsuccessful efforts. Even though a deficiency may be overcome through unusual effort or circumstance, such a child does not have the opportunity to develop the level of positive health of which he was initially capable.

One might reasonably ask if our society is sufficiently aware of the possibilities for stimulating creativity, critical ability, and intellectual growth through the influence of infant environment. Can positive mental health be fostered by providing sufficient opportunities for intellectual growth so that future opportunities for goal achievement are not frustrated? Are there unrecognized opportunities for fostering the development of intellectual as well as emotional means of coping with environment?

NOTES TO CHAPTER 21

1. Murphy, Gardner, *Human Potentialities*. Basic Books, New York, 1958, p. 52.

2. Stendler, Cecilia B., "Critical Periods in Socialization and Overdependency," *Child Development*, vol. 23, March, 1952, pp. 3–12. Reprinted in Hartley, Eugene L., and Ruth E. Hartley, editors, *Outside Readings in Psychology*. 2d ed. Thomas Y. Crowell Co., New York, 1957.

3. Cantril, Hadley, and Charles H. Bumstead, *Reflections on the Human Venture*. New York University Press, New York, 1960, p. 46.

4. Fowler, William, "Cognitive Learning in Infancy and Early Childhood," *Psychological Bulletin*, vol. 59, no. 2, 1962, p. 144.

5. Frank, Lawrence K., "Tactile Communication," *Genetic Psychology Monographs*, vol. 56, 1957, pp. 209–255.

6. Hilgard, Ernest R., "The Role of Learning in Perception" in Blake, Robert R., and Glenn V. Ramsey, editors, *Perception: An Approach to Personality*. Ronald Press Co., New York, 1951, p. 106.

7. Robinson, James H., *The Mind in the Making*. Harper and Bros., New York, 1921, p. 36.

8. Dennis, Wayne, "Cultural and Developmental Factors in Perception" in Blake, Robert R., and Glenn V. Ramsey, editors, *op. cit.*, p. 158.

9. Piaget, Jean, "Principal Factors Determining Intellectual Evolution from Childhood to Adult Life" in Piaget, Jean, *Factors Determining Human Behavior*. Harvard Tercentenary Publications. Harvard University Press, Cambridge, Mass., 1937, pp. 47–48. For a review of Piaget's theory and studies, and an excellent bibliography relating to his works, see Flavell, John H., *The Developmental Psychology of Jean Piaget*, The University Series in Psychology, D. Van Nostrand Co., Princeton, N.J., 1963.

10. Landreth, Catherine, *The Psychology of Early Childhood*. Alfred A. Knopf, Inc., New York, 1958, pp. 268–275. The following papers are cited: Welch, Livingston, "The Development of the Discrimination of Form and Area, *Journal of Psychology*, vol. 7, 1939, pp. 37–54; *Idem*, "The Development of Size Discrimination Between the Ages of 12 and 40 Months," *Journal of Genetic Psychology*, vol. 55, 1939, pp. 243–268; *Idem*, "The Span of Generalization Below the Two-Year Level," *Journal of Genetic Psychology*, vol. 55, 1939, pp. 269–297; *Idem*, "A Preliminary Investigation of Some Aspects of the Hierarchical Development of Concepts," *Journal of General Psychology*, vol. 22, 1940, pp. 359–378; *Idem*, "The Genetic Development of the Associated Structures of Abstract Thinking," *Journal of Genetic Psychology*, vol. 56, 1940, pp. 175–206; Welch, Livingston, and L. Long, "The Higher Structural Phases of Concept Formation in Children," *Journal of Psychology*, vol. 9, 1940, pp. 59–95; *Idem*, "A Further Investigation of the Higher Structural Phases of Concept Formation," *Journal of Psychology*, vol. 10, 1940, pp. 211–220.

11. Piaget, Jean, *Judgment and Reasoning in the Child*. Harcourt, Brace and Co., New York, 1928.

12. Brodbeck, Arthur J., and Orvis C. Irwin, "The Speech Behavior of Infants Without Families," *Child Development*, vol. 17, September, 1946, pp. 145–156; Irwin, Orvis C., "Research on Speech Sounds for the First Six Months of Life," *Psychological Bulletin*, vol. 38, 1941, pp. 277–285; *Idem*, "The Profile as a Visual Device for Indicating Central Tendencies in Speech Data," *Child Development*, vol. 12, 1941, pp. 111–120; *Idem*, "Development of Speech During Infancy: Curve of Phonemic Frequencies," *Journal of Experimental Psychology*, vol. 37, 1947, pp. 187–193; *Idem*, "Infant Speech: Development of Vowel Sounds," *Journal of Speech and Hearing Disorders*, vol. 13, 1948, pp. 31–34. For a discussion of the aforementioned studies, see Landreth, Catherine, *op. cit.*, pp. 127–128.

13. Landreth, Catherine, *op. cit.*, p. 138; cf. McCarthy, Dorothea A., "The Language Development of the Preschool Child," *Institute of Child Welfare Monographs*, ser. no. 4. University of Minnesota Press, Minneapolis, 1930.

14. McCarthy, Dorothea A., *op. cit.*

15. Landreth, Catherine, *op. cit.*, p. 147.

16. Fowler, William, *op. cit.*, pp. 116–152.

17. Yarrow, Leon J., "Maternal Deprivation: Toward an Empirical and Conceptual Re-Evaluation," *Psychological Bulletin,* vol. 58, no. 6, 1961, pp. 459–490.

18. *Ibid.;* Hunt, Joseph McV., *Intelligence and Experience,* Ronald Press Co., New York, 1961.

19. Skeels, Harold M., and Harold B. Dye, "A Study of the Effects of Differential Stimulation on Mentally Retarded Children," *Proceedings,* American Association on Mental Deficiency, vol. 44, no. 1, 1939, pp. 114–136; Skeels, Harold M., and Irene Harms, "Children with Inferior Social Histories: Their Mental Development in Adoptive Homes," *Journal of Genetic Psychology,* vol. 72, 1948, pp. 283–294; Skodak, Marie, and Harold M. Skeels, "A Final Follow-up Study of 100 Adopted Children," *Journal of Genetic Psychology,* vol. 75, 1949, pp. 85–125.

20. Skeels, Harold M., "An Interim Brief on the NIMH-Iowa Follow-up Studies Relative to Mental Retardation, Dependency and Maternal Deprivation." Informal memorandum, March 31, 1964, mimeographed. Referred to here is the study by Marie Skodak and Harold M. Skeels, *op. cit.* A book is in preparation on the second follow-up study, and will be published under the title *Adopted Children Grow Up.*

21. Skeels, Harold M., *op. cit.* Reference is to the study by Harold M. Skeels, and Harold B. Dye, *op. cit.* The follow-up study of this will be published under the title *Where Are They Now? Long-Term Effects of Differential Stimulation on Mentally Retarded Children.*

22. Skeels, Harold M., *op. cit.* Reference is to the study by Harold M. Skeels, and Irene Harms, *op. cit.* The follow-up study will be published under the title *The Escape from Social Deprivation.*

23. Seiden, Richard H., "Salutary Effects of Maternal Separation." Unpublished paper presented at the Eighth Annual Meeting of the Kroeber Anthropological Society, Berkeley, California, April 25, 1964.

24. Thompson, William R., and Ronald Melzack, "Early Environment," *Scientific American,* vol. 194, January, 1956, p. 38.

25. *Ibid.,* p. 42.

26. Miller, Alan D., Joseph B. Margolin, and Stanley F. Yolles, "Epidemiology of Reading Disabilities: Some Methodologic Considerations and Early Findings," *American Journal of Public Health,* vol. 47, October, 1957, p. 1251. The study mentioned here is that by Helen H. Zolkas, "What Research Says About Emotional Factors in Retardation in Reading," *Elementary School Journal,* vol. 51, May, 1951, pp. 512–518.

27. Miller, Alan D., Joseph B. Margolin, and Stanley F. Yolles, *op. cit.,* p. 1253.

28. *Ibid.,* p. 1254.

29. Mussen, Paul H., John J. Conger, and Jerome Kagan, *Child Development and Personality.* 2d ed. Harper and Row, Publishers, New York, 1963, chaps. 6 and 7.

Human Learning and Health Action

Part Seven

Human Learning and Health Action

THE AGENCIES of public health have a primary responsibility for initiating changes in society for the betterment of the public's health. The central mission of the Bureau of State Services, one of the major arms of the Public Health Service, has been described as providing "a bridge between the many sources of knowledge and the still more numerous agencies for its application."[1] Such a mission cannot be accomplished by the gathering and distribution of information alone but requires broad public health education. The information must be applied by individuals and by groups, and the application in most instances involves learning, with learning defined as improvement as judged by public health values and standards.

"To be effective," as Mountin long ago suggested, "education must extend beyond the mere dissemination of technically correct information designed for general application; also consideration must be given to motivating factors that shape human conduct."[2]

A quarter-century has passed since Mountin made this observation. During this period public health education has undergone a significant metamorphosis in its approaches. An initial interest in communication techniques and media has evolved into a behavioral science orientation concerned with application of principles of human learning and social change. Fuller consideration than previously is now given to "motivating factors that shape human conduct."

Achievement of the broad and challenging mission of public health requires the effective application of many principles of human behavior. Great skill in the handling of interpersonal and group relationships is demanded of anyone responsible for introducing new and what may be considered strange ideas into stable and resistant sociocultural settings, particularly when one is not satisfied merely to gain leadership and popular acceptance and support for the ideas, but, in addition, desires that they be integrated into the social practices of

357

daily life. This may require an understanding of the dynamic characteristics of the group, its values, purposes, and mores, its patterns of power, influence, and social control, the sources and nature of support for its membership, the structuring of positions, and the integration of social roles, the modes of behavior and limits of group variation, the group aspirations, expectations, hopes, fears, and attitudes that may relate to social implications identified with the proposed change.

Differential learning is largely responsible for the diversities in individual and group behavior that characterize man. Indeed, so much of man's behavior is learned behavior that an understanding of the way learning takes place is central to any theory of human behavior. Study of learning processes, and of the conditions that foster or impede learning, has therefore attracted many of our most eminent and productive scientists. Among their studies are found some of the most elegant models of experimental design, control, and analysis. Their research has had a significant influence on the development of behavioral science theories and has contributed in far-reaching ways to the improvement of educational practices.

Since scientists who study the learning process tend to be guided by their philosophies of life and of science, by their own conceptions regarding the nature of man, and by their notions concerning human motivation and its role in learning, it is not surprising that one finds many theories of learning, rather than a single one, guiding their research efforts. There is little agreement among them regarding the acceptability of any single all-purpose theory of human learning. At times, in fact, differences in theory and in terminology seem to cloud considerable agreement on facts and principles that are fairly well supported by research evidence.

NOTES TO INTRODUCTION TO PART SEVEN

1. Christensen, Aaron W., "Communication Challenge in the Behavioral Sciences (Community Health)." *Surgeon General's Conference on Health Communications, November 5–8, 1962.* Public Health Service, U.S. Dept. of Health, Education, and Welfare, Publication 998, Government Printing Office, Washington, 1963, p. 83.

2. Mountin, Joseph W., "Selection of Items for a Public Health Program," *West Virginia Medical Journal,* June, 1940. Reprinted in Mountin, Joseph W., *Selected Papers.* Thomas Parran, Harry S. Mustard, and Dean A. Clark (Editorial Committee), Joseph W. Mountin Memorial Committee, n.p. 1956, p. 18.

Chapter 22

Learning Theories and Health Action

IN RECENT YEARS public health leaders have shown an increased interest in theories and principles of learning. These principles are frequently mentioned in the literature of public health, and any discussion of change in health behavior is certain to invoke reference to authoritative sources concerning the way learning comes about.

Some attention has already been given to processes involved in the development of a private world and in the learning of motives and incentives, values, beliefs, attitudes, norms, and roles. Of equal importance to public health practice is the application of learning principles to the acquisition of health skills and knowledge and to the initiation of health action and social change. What meaning does the concept of learning have in this context? What is the range of research applicable to these issues? How does learning differ from other effects of experience? By what standards may we judge that learning has or has not occurred? Should theories of learning other than those held by the research scientists be considered?

EXPERIMENTAL STUDIES OF LEARNING PROCESSES

In order to have a broader understanding of the issues related to theories of learning, it may be profitable first to consider a number of typical experimental approaches to the study of learning. These examples have been chosen from among many discussed in greater detail in current psychological textbooks, to which the reader is referred.[1] They illustrate the range of study under way and highlight the difficulties involved in developing a common theory of learning.

Classical Conditioning

The term "classical conditioning" is used to refer to the simple stimulus-response type of research on learning employed by Pavlov. It will be recalled that Pavlov developed a procedure whereby it was

359

possible for him to measure the saliva secretion of a dog under controlled experimental conditions. He noted that the dog salivated in response to the sight or smell of food, and called this natural or native response an *unconditioned response* (salivating) to the *unconditioned stimulus* (food) because training was not necessary to elicit this natural response. He noted also that the dog reacted to a bell by pricking up its ears, but not by salivating. However, when the bell was sounded regularly prior to offering food, the dog began to salivate at the sound of the bell in anticipation of the food, and eventually learned to do so even if food were not present. This unnatural response of salivating in response to the sound of a bell he referred to as conditioning, and called the salivating response a *conditional response* to the *conditioned stimulus* (the bell).

In this early experiment, and in subsequent ones, it has been learned that such conditioning is most efficiently developed when the conditioned stimulus (bell) briefly precedes the unconditioned stimulus (food), and that such classical conditioning procedures can be applied to a wide range of responses with human, as well as animal, subjects. Examples of responses of human subjects that can be conditioned include the withdrawal to fear, sweat gland activity, the knee jerk, dilation of the pupillary muscles, blinking of the eyelid, and the like.

Once a conditioned response has been established, stimuli similar to the original conditioned stimulus may also elicit the conditioned response. This phenomenon is known as *generalization*. A child may be conditioned to respond with fear to a cat by sounding a frightening noise when the cat is presented. The child's fear of cats may then become *generalized* so that the child reacts with fear toward other furry animals or to other furry things.

By presenting an animal with two similar but different conditioned stimuli, such as two slightly different tones in varying order, and rewarding responses to only one of these two stimuli, one can train animals to make fine discriminations. If too great a demand is placed upon the animal in making such perceptual discriminations, the animal will develop an experimental neurosis and be unable to function effectively. Such techniques of conditioning have helped us learn much about perceptual capacities of animals and have also yielded insights concerning their manner of functioning under conditions of stress.

If a conditioned stimulus is repeated many times without reinforcement (reward), it will eventually lose its power to elicit a conditioned response unless, of course, other satisfiers serve as rewards in that situation. One might say that *extinction* of the conditioned response occurs. Thus the child who becomes afraid of cats through conditioning may lose this fear over time if he is frequently in the presence of a cat and provided the negative unconditioned stimulus (the frightening sound) is not repeated. After this fear response has been extinguished, it may still spontaneously return at some later time, but eventually the fear response will become fully extinguished.

In evaluating the significance of the conditioned response as a simple form of learning, Krech and Crutchfield conclude:

> The conditioned response, relatively simple as it is, resembles other forms of learning in many ways. It is adaptive; it generalizes to new stimulus situations; it disappears when no longer reinforced. On the other hand there are clear points of difference between the conditioned response and other forms of learning. Perhaps the most significant derives from the relative lack of awareness and control which is characteristic of conditioning. Moreover, intent or motivation plays a much more decisive role in the performance of other kinds of learned behavior than it does in conditioning.[2]

Rote Learning or Memorizing

Rote learning or memorizing is one of our chief means of adapting to new situations, of acquiring new words and concepts, of learning new skills. Krech and Crutchfield observe that "most of the experimental work *in the entire field of learning* has been devoted to the study of rote learning of verbal material."[3] In these studies attention has focused upon the conditions that influence the acquisition of items, their retention and recall, and the transfer effects of what has been learned upon subsequent learning.

Ebbinghaus, who carried out some of the most creative research of this area of study, invented the "nonsense syllable," created by placing a vowel between two consonants, such as BIK or BOK, as a tool for studying the processes of learning, memory, and recall. He hoped in this way to escape the effects of past verbal habits or vocabulary in the study of verbal behavior. Using himself as his sample, he memorized more than 1,200 lists of nonsense syllables, recorded the time required to learn each list, the memory loss over time, and then the time required to relearn these lists after various time intervals. By plotting the average percentage of nonsense syllables retained over varying intervals of time, he developed a "curve of forgetting." Ebbinghaus's pioneer work on rote learning and memory, which was published in 1885, is regarded as a classic in the area of research on verbal learning, even though studies have since shown that many of the "nonsense syllables" he used in his studies had some meaning through their associations with meaningful words.[4]

Ebbinghaus found that forgetting takes place so rapidly in this kind of learning situation that less than half the content learned can be recalled at the end of an hour and only about one-third by the end of one day. After that, the curve gradually flattens out over the next several days. Other research has since confirmed the general pattern of this curve for forgetting nonsense material. When the material learned has meaning, people tend to learn more quickly and forget more slowly. Since motivations play a significant role in both learning and forgetting, however, different types of curves of learning and forgetting are found when material has different significance for the learner, or when the material learned is controversial in nature.[5]

It may be of interest to students that the least amount of forgetting occurs during periods of sleep or inactivity, whereas participating in activities after learning leads to a significant loss in retention. The student might thus profit by going to sleep immediately after studying and then rising in time for a brief review before recitation or examination.

Students of learning still employ the techniques similar to those Ebbinghaus used for measuring the amount of learning acquired and retained, although many other approaches have also been developed. Objective measures, such as his, have permitted study of verbal learning of different types under varying conditions, with different content, and have also permitted study of the influence of boredom, emotional state, motivation, and of the personal characteristics of the learner. Such research has yielded evidence that learning is facilitated by rewarding success, by distributing practice, by the use of recitation or other types of active practice, and by grouping or organizing material in meaningful ways. Feedback of knowledge of the results of efforts to learn facilitates the correction of errors and fosters efficient learning.

Trial and Error Learning

Edward L. Thorndike, near the end of the past century, began a series of studies of animals and humans to learn how they solved problems. His "trial and error" learning experiments have had a significant impact on both psychology and education. On the basis of his observations of problem-solving under experimental conditions, he developed several "laws" concerning the learning process that still command the attention of research students of psychology and education.

Thorndike devised, as his experimental situation, a number of puzzle boxes that could be opened by pulling a string, pressing a lever, or turning a knob. A cat placed in one of these boxes would try to escape to reach food, water, or freedom. It would scramble about, push and claw different parts of the box, and eventually would release the lock through such varied trial and error behavior. Thorndike noted that the cat, on being returned to the box a number of times, would learn to discard unsuccessful actions and repeat those that were associated with success. Through the process of eliminating failures and repeating successes, his attempts at escape became more effective. After a series of such experiences, the cat placed in the puzzle box learned to go directly to the "latch" or "key" to the solution and obtain his escape from some "annoyer" or receive his reward or "satisfier."

On the basis of his experimentations and observations with animals, and also with humans performing puzzle experiments, Thorndike formulated three "laws of learning" concerned with *readiness, exercise,* and *effect,* laws that have had a significant impact on the thinking and studies of many other researchers. He held that conditions for learning must be present, that practice of successful experience strengthens learning, and that those behaviors that lead to satisfying effects (rewards) tend to be acquired, whereas those leading to discomforting or annoying effects (punishments) tend to be avoided. Thorndike thus viewed learning as a motivated process in which those behaviors that were reinforced by some kind of reward are retained, and those resulting in punishment are discarded unless, of course, the punishment itself should be regarded by the acting subject as satisfying in some way.[6]

The white rat has replaced Thorndike's cat as the favorite subject for researchers. His fecundity and rapid growth, ease of handling, feeding, and care, intelligence, and adaptability commend him to this work.

The simple maze, much as drawn in children's puzzle books where they trace their way through a pattern to reach the castle, but made with passageways for animals to run through, has proved to be a most useful tool for studying trial and error learning. The T-maze, most frequently employed in this research, is formed by making a series of T-like passageways connected in an order so that the animal must choose between right and left turns. Each correct turn leads him closer to the goal of water, food, attention, escape, or other reinforcement. If he makes the wrong turn, he must reverse tracks and try again. Barriers may be introduced en route so that his frustration responses can be observed. A valuable feature of this maze is the unique experience it tests. A minimum of transfer from previous experience is likely to interfere with the research. Furthermore, this type of maze permits objective measures of progress because both time and errors can be recorded.

Although the behavior of the white rat in the T-maze under varied experimental conditions and with rigid controls has been the primary focus of study of many of our outstanding learning theorists, other animals, such as planaria, worms, fish, chickens, guinea pigs, cats, monkeys, and apes have also been used as subjects. Findings from such animal research have contributed significantly to the improvement of both theory and methods employed in the study of human subjects. Principles derived from these studies have been put into practice in all sorts of educational settings.

Instrumental or Operant Conditioning

Operant conditioning is less well known outside the field of psychology than is classical conditioning. These two approaches differ in several important ways. In operant conditioning, the animal or person is permitted considerable freedom of movement. The animal may roam around in its cage rather than being strapped in a particular position as in Pavlov's experiment. The response, which is conditioned through some type of reward or reinforcement, is a response made by the subject in the course of searching for food, water, freedom, or while exploring the environment. Any response, even scratching, bending, turning, or gesturing may be reinforced through operant conditioning. Thus in operant conditioning, the response conditioned is initiated by the subject rather than elicited by the experimenter as in the case of classical conditioning. Operant conditioning is so named because the animal acts upon or "operates" upon its environment in order to achieve some effect or reward. The act or response that is rewarded is called an *operant;* the reward (food, water, and the like) is referred to as a *reinforcer.* Thorndike's "trial and error" learning experiments were early illustrations of the operant conditioning approach, although the terms currently employed are those used by Skinner and his followers.

Skinner, in his experiments with operant conditioning, has taught pigeons to twirl, nod, peck a round disk, peck a particular playing card, turn in a counter-clockwise manner, and perform other superstitious-appearing behaviors by rewarding chance actions. In one such experiment, a pigeon is taught to peck on a round disk in order to get food. The pigeon may begin by pecking some remote part of the experimental box. Each time the pigeon pecks any part of the box closer to the disk, a reward is given. Thus the movement of the pigeon is guided toward the disk until the round disk is pecked. The pecking behavior continues as long as reinforcement continues, and for some time after rewards stop. Intermittent reinforcement at variously spaced intervals has been found to be more effective than continuous reinforcement in teaching the pigeon to continue the pecking after rewards (reinforcements) are withdrawn. Thus discontinuance or extinction of the behavior occurs more slowly when reinforcement is irregular.[7]

It has been suggested that the rituals we perform for changing our luck are similar to the superstitious-appearing behaviors of pigeons trained through operant conditioning. The irregular rewards of the gambler playing the slot machine lead him to continue a losing game in much the same way as the conditioned animal for whom rewards are irregularly provided.

Research has demonstrated that reinforcement procedures can shape the behaviors of human, as well as animal, subjects. In one study Greenspoon asked two groups of students to say as many words as possible until stopped. With one group of students the experimenter said "Mmm-hmm" whenever a plural word was mentioned. With the matched group no such reinforcement was employed. During a period of twenty-five minutes members of the reinforced group used more than twice as many plural words as the matched group, yet only one subject in the experiment realized that the experimenter was guiding his responses.[8]

The principles of operant conditioning have provided the basis for teaching machines which are now receiving widespread attention. Positive or negative reinforcement of responses, immediately applied by providing the student with "feedback" regarding correct or incorrect choices, guide the student in learning new words, skills, or even concepts. The immediate feedback mechanisms built into these machines also help to keep the student interested while guiding his responses.

The first essential to the development of such programed teaching of new knowledge, skills, attitudes, or practices is the formulation of clear and precise goals to be learned. One must then make a systematic analysis of the components or parts of the task to be learned, being careful to specify in detail the steps required to reach the goal. This analysis needs to include identifying all barriers or problems that could interfere with goal achievement, whether these barriers are, in fact, present, or perceived to be present by the student. The actions required to overcome these barriers need then to be specified. The final programing involves the arranging, in precise sequential order, of all the steps, large and small, that the student will need to take in order to attain the defined goal. Reinforcement techniques can then be employed to shape the student's path to the ultimate goal. Needless to say, such programing techniques are more readily applicable to the teaching of language or mathematics than to the teaching of values, morals, and interpersonal conduct.[9]

Other Research Examples

Psychologists are currently studying the learning processes of human subjects in many laboratory, school, institutional, industrial, social, and governmental settings. This research is directed toward formulating more adequate learning theories and principles, and toward identifying factors that facilitate or retard learning under varying experimental conditions. A variety of theoretical approaches have been employed in designing these studies. Since even modest gains in knowledge regarding the learning processes can lead to enormous savings in teaching and learning time, effort, and money, this research deserves far more attention than can be given within this context, and public health officials are urged to consult other sources.

Some examples of areas in which experimental studies have been carried out with human subjects include the learning of scientific, mathematical, social, and ethical concepts by children and adults; the attainment of efficiency in reading, writing, arithmetic, and other school subjects; the learning of skills, such as typewriting, playing the piano, driving an automobile, attending a telephone switchboard, sorting materials, and operating machines; the acquisition of attitudes toward new or different foods, toward other ethnic or minority groups, authority figures, and the like; the learning of new roles and functions and new social or job relationships; and the solution of puzzles and problems under laboratory, classroom, work, and field conditions.

PROBLEMS OF DEFINITION AND GENERALIZATION

Scientists who conduct experimental studies of the learning process have been plagued by many issues related to definition and measurement. They have found it essential to be systematic in their formulations and have developed their operational definitions with caution and precision. Care has been taken in experimental research to distinguish learning from such native biological tendencies as instincts, tropisms, and reflexes. Systematic controls have been employed to differentiate the effects of learning from the effects of growth and development, fatigue and illness, varying emotional and motivational states, the influence of conditions of observation and measurement, and a complex of other conditions related to internal or external environment.

While authorities vary considerably in their theoretical definitions of learning and in their descriptions regarding basic conditions or underlying processes necessary for learning to occur, they tend to be in closer agreement regarding factual or operational definitions of learning—the empirical or observed events relating to learning. Kimble states that "As regards the factual definitions, there has always been general agreement among authorities on the subject that *learning refers to a more or less permanent change in behavior which occurs as a result of practice.* In such a statement, both the dependent variable (changes in behavior) and the independent variable (practice) are reasonably objective. The term *learning* itself has the status of an intervening, unobserved variable linking these two sets of observables."[10]

Yet learning may occur without observable changes in behavior being present, or learning may not necessarily be contributing to change in the expected manner when behavior changes are observed. As Kimble suggests, learning should be viewed as a change in "behavior potentiality" that may not be immediately reflected in action.[11] Furthermore, the practice or experience needs to be supported or reinforced by some kind of accompanying event which might be referred to as a reward or gain for appropriate behavior, or as punishment or failure for inappropriate behavior.

Since learning cannot be observed directly, but must be inferred from behavior, objective criteria of achievement are employed to determine whether or not learning occurs under conditions of experimentation. When conclusions of studies are generalized to broader areas of human conduct, these specific definitions and criteria of measurement need to be kept in mind. The translation of research findings to community action programs requires the consideration of issues of interpretation and value of considerable significance.

Learning and Maturation

In the discussion of socialization, attention was given to the problem of differentiating maturation and learning processes. This problem is of major concern to those who seek to develop and test theories of learning.

The nature of the learning process may be different during infancy and during maturity. Hence a different theory may be necessary for predicting and understanding the behavior of infants from that required for predicting and understanding the behavior of adults. A theory of learning that leans heavily on conditioning may be adequate for explaining and understanding the earliest learnings of the infant; the adult who is learning a new skill or idea, however, draws heavily on a body of past learnings. In the latter situation some type of association theory or insight theory may be more useful for predicting learning behavior.[12]

Different principles of learning may be involved in learning to suck, or to see, learning to crawl and to walk, learning to use language, and to play with others. In each instance, also, a certain state of maturation must be present for learning to occur, although the presence of such a state of maturation is not alone sufficient to assure that learning will occur.

Such a viewpoint is consistent with our current knowledge of the course of human development and patterns of human response. Each individual goes through certain critical steps in growth that are optimal periods for acquiring direction in his social, intellectual, and emotional development. In a timely summary of the current status of research in this exciting area, Scott invites attention to three such critical periods of growth during which unusual sensitivity is present regarding particular aspects of environment. At such times there is present a high receptivity for particular types of learning:

> Thus, the neonatal period is chiefly characterized by the process of neonatal nutrition—nursing in mammals and parental feeding in many birds. The transition period is characterized by the process of transition to adult methods of nutrition and locomotion and the appearance of adult patterns of social behavior, at least in immature form. The period of socialization is the period in which primary social bonds are formed. If we consider processes alone, it is apparent that they are not completely dependent on each other and that they can therefore be arranged in different orders. It is also apparent that certain of these processes persist beyond the periods characterized by them. For example, a mammal usually retains throughout life the ability to suck which characterizes the neonatal period, although in most cases this ability is little used.[13]

Even though no single theory of learning may be adequate for interpreting and predicting man's learning behavior under all these conditions of growth and experience, considerable progress has been made in both theory and research. There are serious limits, however, to what man can do in his attempts to study man in order to understand his own behavior. Rigorous controlled experimentation is seldom possible over long periods of time. Control of some of the most significant variables would require the violation of value orientations held dear by the scientist himself, as well as by the subjects of his research.

Learning and Experience

Learning has been defined as "a highly general term for the relatively enduring change, in response to a task-demand, that is induced directly by experience; or the process or processes whereby such change is brought about."[14]

As a growing child gains experience in coping with environment, many changes occur in the patterns of his behavior. The vague, general tensions of infancy become transformed into motives, concerns, wants, and aspirations. General emotional feelings become refined into delicate shades of sentiment, love, and affection, or into awesome states of fear, fright, or anger. Early massive efforts to cope with environment have given way to specific patterns of behavior varying in terms of the possibilities for action in any given situation. Uncertainties regarding himself and the world of which he is a part become replaced by systems of value and belief, and by a sense of surety in following the mores of the group in which he lives.

One might say that the child is at once internalizing the culture of his group and acquiring an individualized pattern of wants, tastes, interests, concerns, and hopes that are in tune with the requirements of his group. He is also developing unique ways of dealing with problems that concern him and ways of mastering himself or his environment in order to attain his aspirations.

These changes taking place are usually described as learnings that have occurred during growth and development. The child has acquired general and specific patterns of emotional behavior and reaction, and has begun to internalize the values and mores of the sociocultural setting into which he was born.

Some psychologists reasonably ask whether it is meaningful to apply the term "learning" to describe so broad and inclusive a range of behavioral change which has not been systematically guided in accord with designated goals. They feel that such a definition is too general to be of very much use in either theory or practice. Accordingly, they have been obliged to develop precise definitions more suited to their purposes.

While this problem of differentiating learning from other experience in situations comparable to the one described above may appear to be an interesting issue for fraternal dispute among psychologists, it is also a matter of significance for health workers who seek to interpret and to apply the findings of their research. Illustrated here is the importance of knowing precisely what a researcher or consultant means when he suggests principles of learning for public health application, or conditions likely to affect an increase in public health knowledge and understanding. Is he referring to learning as a process that involves predetermined and predefined goals toward which learning may be guided and against which achievement may be measured, as in the manner of programed learning? Or is he referring to learning as a process that involves self-direction, evaluation, and decision?

Learning as Improvement

English, in a delightful paper, "Learning—'They Ain't No Such Animal,'" performed a valuable service in calling to attention the confusion that arises from the use of the definition of learning as experience, without at the same time recognizing that the change expected as a result of the experience is change of a particular kind or in a specific direction.

> All psychophysical or organic activity leads inevitably to a change in performance. You can call this change learning if you like, but to segregate the aspect of change from the totality of organic activity is an abstraction. When we perceive, when we think, when we emote, we certainly change in our capacity for later behavior; but the laws or explanatory principles are those of perceiving or thinking, or emoting.
> . . . I would not on that account abandon all talk of learning, but I would restore to the term its original meaning. Try as we will, we cannot for long avoid bringing in the notion of learning as "improvement." Now that means that we leave the field of science for the field of psycho-technology, and that is where the concept of learning belongs.[15]

It is useful to distinguish between how people acquire knowledge, attitudes, values, skills, and other behaviors, and how people can be taught these things. The former involves basic theories of behavior; the latter concerns theories of education and influence. Basic theories of behavior cannot always be directly translated into programs of action. When we outline learning principles to apply in practical public health action programs we are, as English suggests, more concerned with principles of psychotechnology than with basic scientific theories.

Scientific students of learning have tended to reject the position taken by English that all learning be treated as a practical rubric which is only of limited value as a scientific construct. The study of learning continues to grow as a major and productive area of scientific research. Yet scientists working in this area find themselves continually faced with the issues English so cogently called to attention in 1951; the inadequacies of definitions in use, a tendency to stretch the construct of learning in interpreting widely diverse behaviors, the dangers of overgeneralization of findings from research on limited problems, and many inconsistencies among the theories of learning currently held.

Perhaps most scientific students of the learning process would, however, agree with English that when we speak about practical learning principles, the notion of learning suggests improvement. Learning is usually treated in research as *"a process in which a change in performance or behavior results from training, practice, or observation."*[16] As such a definition implies, the researcher is concerned with change in a particular direction, or satisfaction of some particular criterion of success or achievement. A value judgment is therefore made concerning the kinds or types of change which are to be considered improvement.

Lewin, for example, observed that *learning* implies in the broad sense " 'doing something better than before,' is a 'practical' term referring to a variety of processes which the psychologist will have to group and treat according to their psychological nature." He suggests, further, that "within what is called learning, we have to distinguish at least the following types of changes: (1) learning as a change in cognitive structure (knowledge), (2) learning as a change in motivation (learning to like or to dislike), (3) learning as a change in group belongingness or ideology (this is an important aspect of growing into a culture), (4) learning in the meaning of voluntary control of the body musculature (this is one important aspect of acquiring skills, such as speech and self control)."[17]

The term "learning" when used in this way clearly refers to change in an intended or desired way. Any "principles of learning" that apply under such conditions are principles relating to influencing planned change—change in accord with the intentions, desires, or values of some individual or group including, of course, oneself or one's own group. To speak of such principles of learning is to speak of principles involved in changing behavior in accord with some predetermined intentions, which involves a consideration of numerous philosophical, sociological, cultural, and administrative factors not usually included within the framework of the systematic theories of learning now currently held.

LEARNING AND SOCIAL VALUES

When learning is regarded as improvement or achievement resulting from experience, the decision as to whether or not learning occurs becomes a value decision. One of the most significant philosophical issues that must be faced by educators, community leaders, public health officials, and others who are concerned with public education in its many forms, relates to the choice of standards whereby achievement or success in learning can be judged.

All humans, everywhere, are continually changing through growth and experience, and through decay. They can and do change regardless of age, socioeconomic or ethnic background, or cultural setting. They are continually changing day by day throughout life, for every experience, whether it involves emotions, motivations, cognition, or overt actions leaves traces of effect upon the individual which tend to influence future responses. Whether or not such changes are to be regarded as learnings depends upon the definition of learning employed, and particularly the standards of value chosen to judge whether progress has taken place.

The decision on whether or not learning occurs in a particular situation thus becomes a decision of human values. The decision implies a value placed on a particular kind of change resulting from experience. The question then is not whether change occurs—it always occurs, although the experience encountered may lead the individual to cling more tightly to former practices. Rather, the question becomes whether the individual changes in a way that we or someone else wants him to change; whether the individual learns what we or someone else thinks is good for him to learn.

This places an enormous moral burden on anyone who would influence social change through any form of education. In assuming that learning a particular attitude or action is desirable for an individual to learn, the change agent is, in effect, assuming that his values are superior to the values of the individual he is attempting to influence. He assumes that his values are better than those the individual presently holds, that an improvement in terms of his own scale of values will lead to profit for the individual subject to influence, and that this gain for the individual will be greater than any losses in value satisfaction that an individual may incur.

Serious problems are posed for those concerned with initiating programs involving other cultural groups. As Brock Chisholm has observed:

> It is not easy for any of us to see clearly and truly anything which lies in areas in relation to which our culture or subculture takes firm attitudes. These cultural or group certainties, taboos, faiths, or anxieties, color and distort our observations without our recognition, and perhaps our main problem in attempting any study is to see through the shadows thrown by our own prejudices about what is "right" or "proper" or "good" or "safe" or "moral" or "democratic" or "Christian" or some other classification of possible answers. It is clearly impossible too for any of us to look at world problems from all points of view, that is, from the points of view of all kinds of people in the world. A Norwegian fisherman, a Chinese laborer, an American bond dealer, a South African native miner, a Swiss watchmaker, a Korean farmer, a French artist, a Russian engineer, and everyone else everywhere, all are vitally

affected by such problems as are suggested above, and valid solutions must eventually prove useful and acceptable for all kinds of people everywhere, though of course people's attitudes, and what is acceptable to them, may change.[18]

The Value of Resistance

It is perhaps fortunate that we do not as yet have a consistent, valid set of principles which, if applied in a specific, rigorous manner with individuals and groups, will assure that they will learn and will change their behavior in a manner desired by the innovator. The stubborn response of man to efforts by others to change his behavior for better or for worse without his understanding, consent, and cooperation is a most potent force in assuring his protection against unwanted direction or control. This characteristic stubbornness helps him to be free.

"Changing peoples' customs," notes Spicer in his introduction to *Human Problems in Technological Change,* "is an even more delicate responsibility than surgery."

Whenever the administrator of a technological program "seeks to alter a people's way of life, he is dealing not with one individual but with the well-being and happiness of generations of men and women. If his skill is poor and his judgment bad, he can destroy cooperative human relations and create hatreds that will affect uncountable numbers of people. If, on the other hand, his skill is equal to the task, the possibility is open for creating cooperation where it did not exist and for bettering the lives of generations."[19]

The issue Spicer raises deserves serious consideration by those who would view education as a science based on valid principles ordered within a unified theoretical framework. The characteristic stubbornness of man in reacting to unwanted pressures, together with the infinite variability of his response patterns, poses problems that require the effective educator to be artful or professional in his approach, constantly adapting his techniques to the unique requirements of the situation. Like members of the medical, engineering, or administrative professions, he must draw heavily on many sciences and technologies in developing his principles. This does not imply, of course, that one may not at once be scientist and educator, or make scientific studies on the process or principles involved in education.

Textbook Weaknesses

Those who teach principles of education in formal settings, or who prepare textbooks on learning, at times fail to emphasize that they are dealing with learning as improvement and to draw attention to the broad implications of this fact for understanding change in behavior. Unless this is emphasized, the student may not recognize that change is always occurring and that the principles apply only to changes which are "improvements." It would seem a most serious omission, for example, to devote entire texts to the principles of learning as measured by performance standards without reference to the role of values in determining these standards, and to the implications this may have for understanding the reasons for failure to learn as judged by such standards.

It is not surprising that persons leave such courses of study with strong beliefs that there is scientific evidence that some people can learn and others cannot, nor is it surprising that they identify particular phases of life as periods during which people learn and other phases as those in which people do not or cannot learn. That part of life which is identified with the classroom becomes recognized as a part identified with learning, yet only a small part of one's life is within the classroom. A large sphere of learning outside the classroom may be scarcely recognized. Likewise, in giving attention to learning in terms of improvement, there may be a tendency to assume that learning as change either occurs or does not occur. Other changes that occur, changes even counter to the intentions of the educator, but consistent with the intent of the learner, may be completely ignored. From the standpoint of other value standards these, too, are learnings.

Earl Kelley has provided a most valuable service in shaking us up by drawing attention to some of the assumptions that have tended to guide many of our approaches to education. In his provocative *Education for What Is Real* he outlines assumptions, such as those touched upon above, which "have been with us so long and are so firmly grounded in tradition that they have virtually become axioms to us. They are hard for us to dig out because they are so deeply embedded. We have believed them so long that we scarcely know we believe them."[20] His list of assumptions which have questionable validity, together with his discussion of alternatives, is much too long to be included here, yet it deserves the attention of public health, as well as formal school educators.

Other Theories of Learning

There are many theories of learning other than those held by scientists. Each person who seeks to influence someone else acts in accord with some theory of learning, usually without realizing that he is doing so. His efforts are guided by his expectations concerning what is likely to be effective.

Whatever theory of learning is held by a member of a sociocultural group needs to be understood and kept uppermost in mind by anyone who would stimulate change within that group. If the group does not think, for example, that certain things can be learned, a first step to progress for change may be one of achieving change in that assumption. If the group believes that learning occurs only in particular situations, these situations need to be considered in developing an effective educational approach.

Margaret Mead has emphasized the importance of considering cultural theories of learning in planning cultural change.

> Human societies differ very sharply in whether they believe that "you can't teach an old dog new tricks," or that new skills can be learned at any age. The assumption that childhood is a time for learning and adulthood the period for which the learning was done is deeply ingrained in our own society and is, indeed, a feature of most civilizations with a weighty classical tradition that, by its very nature, is regarded as something which, once learned, is a permanent and unchangeable possession. A kind of partial counterpart to such a view of learning is found in highly mobile societies, or societies dependent upon adult immigration and new adaptations, such as the United States and Australia, but in this case the emphasis may shift from a belief that all important skills are learned in childhood to a decrease in the complexity of skills demanded from adults. The skilled task becomes just a job; an adult becomes not a person with great possibilities of transformation within a new situation, but a person who can hold many lightly differentiated jobs.[21]

In initiating a health education program in any community, therefore, it becomes essential to consider the type of learning theory held by leaders in the community and their followers. The theory of learning held may influence decisions about choice of leadership, choice of content, and the like.

CONCLUSION

One should not, therefore, expect to find a consistent, fully satisfactory set of learning principles applicable to all learning situations. Rather, there exist many principles not always consistent with one another that must be adapted to any specific situation at hand. Generalizations that can be safely made on the basis of our present knowledge tend to be broad and inclusive. To be meaningful in terms of action, they need to be made specific in terms of the problem at hand; they must take into account the conditions under which learning takes place, and the kinds of behavior to be learned.

Science has not yet progressed to the point where we can safely describe the learning process of the unborn fetus in the same terms or using the same constructs as we might use in describing the learning process of an educated adult exploring a new science. Perhaps one should never expect consistency to develop between the principles of the scientist who seeks to conceptualize a problem of learning on a physiological basis and the principles of a scientist who attempts his conceptualization within a social situation.

This is not to imply that general principles of learning are not useful to the public health educator or others concerned with community change; rather, any principles thus developed or presented must be drawn from a wide range of knowledge regarding behavior change. To be of maximum use, they need to be specifically tailored to the unique situation in which they are to be employed, together with the change desired.

The public health official who draws upon learning principles for guidance in planning programs of change will find it imperative to distinguish clearly the purposes he has in mind in order to make maximum use of guidelines available. Some learning principles may be of great value in planning for the learning of knowledge, attitudes, or skills when the knowledge, attitudes, or skills to be taught are known to the program director and he and his colleagues decide upon the intended outcomes. Quite a different pattern of learning principles may apply when such outcomes are not known in advance, and the program has as its purpose the fostering of new ideas and orientations and the formulation of goals by the group itself. Under these circumstances one may seek to avoid imposing his values and intentions upon the group, and may instead give support to an emergent evolution in the development of the group. The principles applicable in fostering such unplanned or unprogramed learnings are quite different from those applicable in planned or programed learning situations.

NOTES TO CHAPTER 22

1. For excellent elementary reviews of learning theories and principles, with examples of studies, see: Mednick, Sarnoff A., with the collaboration of Howard R. Pollio, *Learning,* Foundations of Modern Psychology Series, edited by Rich-

ard S. Lazarus, Prentice-Hall, Inc., Englewood Cliffs, N.J., 1964; Munn, Norman L., *Psychology: The Fundamentals of Human Adjustment,* 4th ed., Houghton Mifflin Co., Boston, 1961, especially pp. 371–478; Krech, David, and Richard S. Crutchfield, *Elements of Psychology,* Alfred A. Knopf, Inc., New York, 1961, pp. 401–456. The study by Munn, and that by Krech and Crutchfield, both offer excellent bibliographical references to original studies. For a brief review of learning theory and personality, see Lazarus, Richard S., *Adjustment and Personality,* McGraw-Hill Series in Psychology, McGraw-Hill Book Co., New York, 1961; and Idem, *Personality and Adjustment,* Prentice-Hall, Inc., Englewood Cliffs, N.J., 1963. *Selected Readings on the Learning Process* by Theodore L. Harris and Wilson E. Schwahn (Oxford University Press, New York, 1961) contains reports of experimental studies of learning. For a critical comparative review of current theories of learning see: Koch, Sigmund, editor, *Psychology: A Study of a Science,* Study I, Conceptual and Systematic, vol. 2, General Systematic Formulations, Learning, and Special Processes, McGraw-Hill Book Co., New York, 1963; Kimble, Gregory A., reviser, *Hilgard and Marquis' Conditioning and Learning.* Century Psychology Series, 2d ed., Appleton-Century-Crofts, Inc., New York, 1961; Estes, William K., and collaborators, *Modern Learning Theory: A Critical Analysis of Five Examples,* The Century Psychology Series, edited by Richard M. Elliott, Appleton-Century-Crofts, Inc., New York, 1954; Young, Paul T., *Motivation and Emotion,* John Wiley and Sons, New York, 1961; Hilgard, Ernest R., *Theories of Learning,* Appleton-Century-Crofts, Inc., New York, 1956; Mowrer, O. H., *Learning Theory and Behavior,* John Wiley and Sons, New York, 1960 (see particularly the bibliography, pp. 495–534). The studies cited in this note are widely quoted in psychological literature.

2. Krech, David, and Richard S. Crutchfield, *op. cit.,* pp. 408–409.

3. *Ibid.,* p. 410.

4. Ebbinghaus, Hermann, *Memory: A Contribution to Experimental Psychology.* Translated by H. A. Ruger and C. E. Bussenius. Columbia University Press, New York, 1913.

5. Levine, Jerome M., and Gardner Murphy, "The Learning and Forgetting of Controversial Material," *Journal of Abnormal and Social Psychology,* vol. 38, 1943, pp. 507–517. Reprinted in Maccoby, Eleanor E., Theodore M. Newcomb, and Eugene L. Hartley, editors, *Readings in Social Psychology.* 3d ed. Henry Holt and Co., New York, 1958, p. 94.

6. Thorndike, Edward L., *Human Learning,* Century Co., New York, 1931; Idem, *Animal Intelligence: Experimental Studies,* Macmillan Co., New York, 1911.

7. Skinner, B. F., *The Behavior of Organisms,* Appleton-Century Co., New York, 1938; Idem, *Science and Human Behavior,* Macmillan Co., New York, 1953. These two publications provide the best outline of Skinner's theoretical orientation and describe various experiments undertaken.

8. Greenspoon, Joel, "The Reinforcing Frequency of Two Spoken Sounds on the Frequency of Two Responses," *American Journal of Psychiatry,* vol. 68, September, 1955, pp. 409–416.

9. Mosel, James N., "The Learning Process," *Journal of Medical Education,* vol. 39, May, 1964, pp. 485–496. An excellent discussion of principles of learning as applied to medical education. The serious student of research and theory relating to programed instruction is referred to DeCecco, John P., editor, *Edu-*

cational Technology: Readings in Programmed Instruction, Holt, Rinehart, and Winston, New York, 1964; Hughes, J. L., editor, *Programed Learning: A Critical Evaluation,* Educational Methods, Chicago, 1963; Fry, Edward B., *Teaching Machines and Programmed Instruction: An Introduction,* McGraw-Hill Book Co., New York, 1963; Lumsdaine, A. A., and Robert Glaser, editors, *Teaching Machines and Programmed Learning: A Source Book,* Dept. of Audio-Visual Instruction, National Education Association, Washington, 1960.

10. Kimble, Gregory A., *op. cit.,* p. 2.

11. *Ibid.,* pp. 4–5.

12. Hebb, Donald O., *The Organization of Behavior: A Neuropsychological Theory.* John Wiley and Sons, New York, 1949, pp. 108–109; 116–117.

13. Scott, John P., "Critical Periods in Behavioral Development," *Science,* vol. 138, November 30, 1962, p. 950.

14. English, Horace B., and Ava C. English, *A Comprehensive Dictionary of Psychological and Psychoanalytical Terms.* Longmans, Green, and Co., New York, 1958, p. 2.

15. English, Horace B., "Learning—'They Ain't No Such Animal,'" *Journal of Educational Psychology,* vol. 43, 1952, pp. 321–330. Reprinted in Hartley, Eugene L., and Ruth E. Hartley, editors, *Outside Readings in Psychology.* Thomas Y. Crowell Co., New York, 1957, p. 121.

16. Landreth, Catherine, *The Psychology of Early Childhood.* Alfred A. Knopf, Inc., New York, 1958, p. 309.

17. Lewin, Kurt, *Field Theory in Social Science: Selected Theoretical Papers,* edited by Dorwin Cartwright. Harper and Bros., New York, 1951, pp. 65–66.

18. Chisholm, Brock, *Can People Learn to Learn? How to Know Each Other.* World Perspectives, edited by Ruth N. Anshen. Harper and Bros., New York, 1958, vol. 18, p. 4.

19. Spicer, Edward H., editor, *Human Problems in Technological Change: A Casebook.* Russell Sage Foundation, New York, 1952, p. 13.

20. Kelley, Earl C., *Education for What Is Real.* Harper and Row, Publishers, New York, 1947.

21. Mead, Margaret, "Changing Culture: Some Observations in Primitive Societies" in Lerner, Daniel, editor, *The Human Meaning of the Social Sciences.* Meridian Books, The World Publishing Co., Cleveland and New York, 1959, p. 300. Copyright by The World Publishing Co.

Chapter 23

Learning Components of
Public Health Programs

MANY OF THE PUBLIC HEALTH and personal health practices that agencies seek to initiate require full understanding, acceptance, and support if they are to result in effective health behavior. Within our democratic pattern of society lasting social changes usually require public understanding, involvement, and commitment. This applies whether we think in terms of broad community programs or of the type of individualized instruction that may be given in the well-baby clinic or nursing home visit.

All changes undertaken for the improvement of the public's health, however, need not involve learning by the general public to the same degree. The initiation of some public health programs is at times undertaken by responsible leadership groups with little more than public acceptance and compliance. Other factors than knowledge and understanding may lead to such acceptance and compliance. One may comply without serious question because traditional action patterns have been established, because members of his group comply and "it's the thing to do," or because the issue is not seen as one of sufficient personal concern or threat to require defensive response. Thus action taken to chlorinate the public water supply may go forward with little public discussion or reaction in a community where initiating action to fluoridate the water supply involves an intensive educational program. Likewise, relatively uninformed groups may accept the program to immunize children in traditional ways but vigorously resist changes that include new immunizations or new methods of application if they are viewed as personally threatening.

TYPICAL LEARNING SITUATIONS IN PUBLIC HEALTH

In discussing the application of learning principles to public health actions, one must first note some of the different types of learning situations in which public health officials are involved. Three quite different learning situations may be observed. In the first situation, a particular predetermined action or series of actions is *required* of members of the staff or public, and the subjects are expected to acquire the information and attitudes necessary in order to perform the required actions. In the second situation, the particular action or actions are *recommended* and the subjects are urged to comply, but they may or may not choose to accept the recommendation. In the third situation, the learning experience is *self-directed,* and the subjects define for themselves the goals to be achieved.

These three types of program situation, as illustrated more fully below, differ significantly in their philosophical orientations, in their purposes, and in their methods and approaches. The criteria for judging success or failure must be defined differently for each. While learning principles are of significance in the achievement of such programs, the manner in which they apply varies according to the type of program and the ultimate responsibility of the public health team relative to its goals.

Few public health programs may be viewed as being purely one or the other of the three types mentioned. One observes combinations of all three types going on at the same time, in the same setting, with the same population, and often closely intermeshed. Difficulties arise when the same public health teacher has responsibility for more than one type of program involving the same group of subjects at the same time.

A sanitarian working with restaurant or other food establishments may be responsible for a directive program regarding some potentially dangerous food poisoning issue, and may need to employ legal powers to achieve compliance. The fact that he is known to be backed by such powers may of itself be sufficient to achieve compliance. At the same time and with the same population, the sanitarian may be responsible for recommending and employing persuasion to achieve improvements in environmental sanitation and food handling. It is not surprising to learn that he has difficulty separating his directive and persuasive roles under these conditions, and that there may be ambiguity in the minds of his subjects regarding his role.

The reader must judge for himself what the teaching goals are for his own programs, and what the extent and limits of his responsibilities are regarding their achievement. He must also judge for himself how these goals may be operationally defined, and by what criteria the program may be judged as successful or unsuccessful. How learning principles apply to his particular programs will depend upon these determinations. It is hoped that the illustrations offered in this section will be of help in identifying the way learning principles can be applied in his special areas of responsibility.

Programs with Required Outcomes

Some public health programs are planned to achieve specific predetermined changes in knowledge, attitude, or behavior within a defined population group. For such programs the administrator or aides responsible, together with their colleagues and advisers, decide for that population what information is to be learned, the attitudes to be acquired, and specific action to be taken under various conditions. By selection or appointment, they hold the power of deciding how members of the designated population shall behave under specific conditions.

An emergency program, such as one for the control of a highly contagious disease when public safety is threatened, may fit such a program pattern. Immunization may be required for the public good; individuals who acquire the disease must be quarantined or isolated in some way to protect other members of the society. The health officer responsible for the public's safety may decide what actions need to be taken, and by whom. Members of the public may be given no choice as to whether or not they choose to follow instructions; they have delegated to the health officer the responsibility for making this decision.

Public health officials hesitate to employ such directive or police powers as they may hold when dealing with problems of communicable diseases, certain aspects of food sanitation, water pollution, air pollution, and the like. They prefer, insofar as possible, to gain public health ends by means of education rather than by direction. In many programs such as these, however, the program goals are defined by the public health team, and the appropriate actions to be taken are determined by them rather than by the acting individuals. In programs where the public health team determines the specific actions required for program success, the primary measure of effect becomes action performed in the indicated manner. A programed type of approach to planning and achieving the educational and action goals may be appropriate under these conditions.

Mosel, writing for the health professions, has outlined the process to follow in developing a programed approach to teaching such specific content and skills where the goals of the teaching program can be precisely and validly defined. He emphasizes the importance of making an empirical study and analysis of the content to be learned, the problems faced by the learner, and the process most suitable for teaching the specific content or task. The task or content to be learned must first be broken down into distinct steps, and these steps ordered into an appropriate teaching sequence. A distinction is made in this analysis between basic axioms or "kernels" and the range of ways in which these kernels may be "transformed" in application. As in other learning situations, active involvement together with early, systematic "feedback" of knowledge to the student facilitates speed and quality of learning.[1]

Such a programed approach to learning may also be appropriate in teaching members of the staff specific content or skills where the information and tasks to be acquired are predetermined and not subject to question or change by the "students." Examples might include training laboratory technicians to carry out a series of analyses, teaching clerical workers to code content in accord with an established coding system, or training file clerks to adhere to a planned outline of procedure. In each of these situations, successful performance requires rigorous adherence to a set of rules or regulations. A major problem for the teacher is determining how the material or series of tasks can best be organized to facilitate easy and efficient learning. An empirical study and analysis of the task performance will help to eliminate unnecessary steps, to assure that steps are taken in the most efficient manner, and that errors, when they occur, will be spotted.

Programs with Recommended Outcomes

A completely different type of learning and decision-making pattern obtains when the public health program has as its purpose the informing, alerting, and advising of the public, and providing the conditions necessary for citizens to make their own evaluation and judgments regarding the worth of some health action. In such a program, the health officer and his staff are responsible for making available to the public all the information necessary for arriving at a sound decision, and for providing the public, directly or through its representatives, the opportunity to make the decision. The public health officials cannot require compliance with their recommendations. Success in this type of program may be measured by how well the public becomes informed about significant alternatives, and how fully it participates in making the decision regarding health action.

Evidence that the proposed recommendations have been accepted by the public becomes a measure of the success of the persuasive efforts of the public health team rather than a measure of its formally assigned responsibilities. Actions on the part of the public indicate the degree to which the public health judgments of value are accepted by the public.

A large proportion of our public health activities fall within this general pattern, in that the actions to be taken are recommended rather than required. Included are programs concerned with personal health, hygiene, and sanitation; periodic health examinations and corrections; immunizations under conditions other than those of an emergency nature; maternal, infant, and child care; education regarding the hazards of smoking, alcoholism, obesity, and malnutrition; many features of environmental sanitation, and the like.

In initiating and conducting programs of this type within our society, the public health team primarily employs education, recommendation, and persuasion rather than direction. The health worker may advise, urge, plead, or cajole his audience into following healthful regimens, but he cannot demand or order the changes in behavior desired except in unusual circumstances.

This program pattern may be illustrated in terms of a proposal to fluoridate the community water supply when responsibility for the decision to be made rests with the citizens of the community or their designated representatives. The public health team may strongly feel that the action they recommend will be good for the community and its members, and may put great effort into reaching a favorable decision. If the citizens of the community reject such a proposal after being informed, alerted, and duly involved, the public health team may feel they have failed. Whether the proposal wins or loses, the program must be judged successful from the standpoint of formal responsibility if the decision is made by an alert, informed, and participating citizenry acting on the basis of its own judgments of value.

On the other hand, it is clear that in rejecting this proposal, the citizens of the community have chosen to disagree with the value judgment and value priority assigned to the program by the public health team. Thus the program effort must be judged to be unsuccessful insofar as the persuasive efforts of the public health team are concerned.

It seems essential, in considering learning principles, to keep clear this distinction between the educational and persuasive responsibilities of public health. All educated people do not hold the same values and value priorities. An educational effort may be highly successful without leading to the acceptance of a recommended value decision. The public health team have a responsibility for placing their value judgments before the citizens for evaluation and consideration for adoption in competition with other social values. It remains the responsibility of an informed public to decide what priority health values should have as related to other social values.

The following evaluative study of a local nutrition educational project well illustrates the complexity of the relationship between knowledge, attitudes, values, and other personal and social factors involved in a community educational program. The study draws attention to the importance of making a clear distinction between the educational and persuasive responsibilities of a local health unit in planning and in measuring program effects. It illustrates also the difficulties of developing a programed teaching approach in areas where all conditions of learning and characteristics of the population have not been first empirically studied.

Shimberg and Harris conducted a systematic evaluation of a nutrition education program concerned with the use of nonfat dry milk by members of a low income rural population. They found the educational program to be effective in teaching most of the facts the program was designed to teach, and that these facts were generally retained two months later. Yet the program failed to induce any of the women interviewed to purchase the nonfat milk during the intervening two months.

Many factors were involved, some of which were not anticipated: adequate information about the low cost and special advantages of this milk may not have been retained; attitudes toward the milk, particularly regarding its taste, tended to be negative or neutral rather than positive; there was unawareness by many of the minimum recommended daily requirements, especially for adults.

In reviewing their findings, the authors conclude:

> The implication of this discussion is that in planning an education program, consideration must be given not only to the content of the program but also to the relationship between the content and the group

needs as they are perceived by those for whom the program is intended. In reviewing the development of the experimental nonfat milk program, it would seem that while the content aspect was planned in considerable detail, the relationship between the content and the motivational aspect was not thoroughly explored. This may be gathered from several of the assumptions about the motivations of the group which were implicit in the program and which might have been tested prior to developing this education program: (a) that people already had adequate knowledge about milk and accepted it as part of their diet; (b) that people were not drinking milk primarily because they could not afford it; and (c) that there were no important psychological barriers or experiential factors which might keep members of the group from accepting nonfat milk as a substitute for regular milk.

To test such assumptions, evidence should have been obtained about the people and their cultural setting. Adequate exploratory fact finding would have revealed whether the foregoing assumptions were justified. To the extent that they were not justified, the program content, procedures, and points of emphasis might have been modified to take account of the situation as it existed. If it had been found, as some of the data suggest, that the members of the group did not regard milk as an important part of the adult diet, the program might have placed greater stress on the importance of milk rather than on the use of a cheaper form of milk. If explorations revealed that the group had had unsatisfactory or unpleasant experiences with the use of nonfat dry milk, it might have been possible to point out that, as a result of research, the present product tastes better and is packaged so that it will not spoil as readily as it did formerly. If dislike for the taste of the milk was found to be an important factor, emphasis might have been placed on ways to use the milk in cooking, in making cream sauces and ice cream, and in preparing flavored beverages.[2]

The failure of the public to act on some new program or proposal such as this cannot safely be interpreted as reflecting lack of knowledge or understanding alone. Basic value conflicts may lead to the rejection of a program when the social values of the group are judged more significant than the public health values. There may be disagreement as to the meaning of the facts, or of the implications of the action for the particular group concerned. Some alternative action may be preferred to the one recommended; other demands may command higher priority; the methods of action proposed or the persons designated as responsible may not have public acceptance; and so forth.

Thus although learning may play a significant role in program development, the use of program goal achievements as criteria against which to judge the extent of public learnings may be invalid. One should note also that while programed teaching may hold great promise in community educational programs, intensive research would need to be conducted to identify the situational and personal factors influencing learning and acceptance before a valid approach to educational programing would be possible.

Self-Directed Learning Situations

A third type of learning and decision-making pattern obtains in those situations in which representative community groups are encouraged and provided assistance in conducting their own studies, evaluations, and plans, and making their own program recommendations. The role of the public health team may be one of providing the best possible atmosphere for the self-seeking, exploratory, analysis, and planning activities of the group. This includes, of course, providing expert information, assistance, guidance, and recommendations for the group to consider. The community group, however, is responsible for final determinations regarding avenues to explore, situations to observe, data to examine, and criteria for judging significance. It is responsible also for setting priorities on alternative possibilities for community action. Under this pattern of conditions, the community group determines what it wants to learn, how it wants to go about the process of learning it, and what outcomes are to be judged evidence of success.

The community self-surveys and the community development programs that have received much attention in recent years illustrate this approach.[3] When such methods are employed in initiating or revitalizing community action programs, the decisions reached by the community leaders may place public health goals in a different order of priority from that the public health team might desire. Even the philosophy of the department may be challenged; major changes in priorities and methods may be proposed. While learning is involved throughout this self-seeking, examining, and judging process, the manner of its involvement is quite different from that present in a formal teaching situation. What takes place, rather, is a self-initiated and self-guided pattern of learning.

LEARNING AS A SUBJECTIVE, IRREGULAR, PERCEPTUAL PROCESS

While one may discuss learning in a logical, systematic way, learning does not always come about in a regular, progressive fashion. The processes of life are less consistent and far more overlapping in their patterns than can be outlined on paper. An individual will rush through some phases and bog down on others; go back and pick up experiences of which he may not have been at first aware; shuffle about at times in thought, emotion, and action as though his behavior lacked meaning and significance. He may not differentiate in his own mind the dynamic steps through which he moves in learning, nor even be aware that he is progressing. Rather, he lives and behaves, and in behaving, changes. Should features of his environment lead him to live, behave, and change in the manner intended by the change agent, whoever he may be, one may judge that learning has occurred.

One should recognize also that learning concerned with the acquisition of health knowledge and attitudes, while it need not precede some health actions, often occurs following the change. New behaviors may be acquired and then, after they are undertaken, new attitudes may be developed and knowledge obtained, if necessary, to justify to oneself or others the new behaviors. Festinger has suggested that an individual feels a pressure within himself to be consistent in his cognitive behavior. Festinger theorizes "that the human organism tries to establish internal harmony, consistency, or congruity among his opinions, attitudes, knowledge and values . . . there is a drive toward consonance among cognitions."[4]

Thus if an individual acquires some new behaviors, obtains a physical examination under the influence of group pressures, for example, he will then seek to justify this in his own mind and to acquire a rationale to explain or support his behavior. The action of obtaining the examination may thus lead him to take initial steps toward acquiring new knowledge and understanding. Should his involvement not be personally viewed as significant enough to warrant justification, such learnings may never take place.

Learning thus involves changes within the subjective life of man's private world, often without his awareness. While one may discuss the learning process as a separate issue, to do so would be academic were one never aware that perception and learning are closely joined: one learns to perceive, and in perceiving defines the situation in which he lives and acts. A potential hazard is no threat to the individual who does not perceive it; incentives have no appeal to the individual who is unaware of their existence; what seems to one individual to be a simple task may be perceived by another as an overburdening challenge.

One must always ask: How does the situation appear to the acting individual? What subjective facts exist for him in this situation? What concerns *him?* What alternatives does he identify? What courses of action hold priorities for him?

LEARNING BEGINS WITH INTEREST OR CONCERN

Learning is a dynamic process. It begins with some desire, urge, or concern, or some less conscious state of tension that leads the individual to be receptive to outside stimulation. In order to learn new things he must first experience some uncertainty or frustration or have some curiosity, perhaps, about the content or issue in which change is desired. If he trusts and is satisfied with his present facts, perceptions, values, and assumptions, he will have no need to seek new knowledge, skills, or attitudes, or to become alert to the potentialities of new ideas or alternatives.

In discussing conceptual tools for solving human problems, Spicer states as his first proposition regarding change "that people do not vary their customary behavior unless they feel some need which existing ways do not satisfy. The response to feeling such a need is to invent or to borrow from some other people a technique or form of organization or belief which is felt to satisfy that need. This in essence is the basic process of cultural change."[5]

The basic principle that learning, like other behavior, is motivated is deceiving in its simplicity. Few would question it, yet a good part of the time we all ignore it. We assume, without inquiry, that others share our own interests, concerns, curiosity, and in proper degree.

Perceptual Curiosity

In recent years a number of ingenious studies have again drawn attention to the significance to learning of what Berlyne refers to as "perceptual curiosity."[6] When alternatives are available, animals as well as men, tend to exert themselves to avoid boredom and to seek stimulation. In reviewing such studies, Berlyne observes:

> For example, mice will learn to jump on to a platform that clicks and sinks slightly (a), rats will learn to press a bar if this leads to an increase in illumination (b), monkeys confined in a box will learn to open a door if this enables them to see what is going on outside (c), and human beings confined in a dark room will learn to press a key that causes colored lights to be projected on the ceiling (d).

In situations of this sort, the response is not preceded by a state that can be construed as "wanting" contact with a particular stimulus object, and stimuli emanating from more or less any stimulus object could have the attributes on which reinforcement of the response depends. We have thus no grounds here for invoking a *curiosity* drive, but it might be thought that a *boredom* drive is operating.[7]

Enforced boredom may, indeed, have serious damaging effects for the individual. In a study under the direction of Hebb, at McGill University, Mayo college students were offered $20 a day to lie on a comfortable bed in a lighted cubicle twenty-four hours a day as long as they cared to stay, taking time only for meals or going to the lavatory. "They wore translucent plastic visors which transmitted diffuse light but prevented pattern vision. Cotton gloves and cardboard cuffs extending beyond the finger tips restricted perception by touch. Their auditory perception was limited by a U-shaped foam rubber pillow on which their heads lay and by a continuous hum of air conditioning equipment which masked small sounds."[8]

On a series of tests given at twelve-hour intervals, the experimental subjects' performance tended to be impaired by the isolation and was poorer than that of the control members. Of greater interest, perhaps, was the influence of boredom on the thought processes of the subjects. After a while the subjects were unable to think continuously about current problems or studies and reached a point where it was an effort to concentrate. Their minds began to wander. Some experienced "blank" periods where they did not seem to be thinking at all. A number had hallucinations of various types. They began to see images. These hallucinations were at first in simple form. Later the subjects seemed to have little control over the content of the hallucinations. One test concerned their reaction to a recording of an argument on the reality of ghosts. This record was played to the subject during his period of isolation. It tended to make subjects susceptible to the argument that such supernatural phenomena existed.

Since some subjects frequently mentioned that things looked curved, large, small, or unreal when they emerged after isolation, systematic tests were made of visual perception. "The most striking finding was that when subjects emerged after several days of isolation, the whole room seemed to be in motion. In addition there was a tendency for surfaces to appear curved, and for subjects to appear to change their size and shape."[9]

Heron concludes: "A changing sensory environment seems essential for human beings. Without it, the brain ceases to function in an adequate way, and abnormalities of behavior develop."[10]

How Much Concern?

While some degree of concern, interest, or curiosity seems essential if learning is to occur, an excess of concern or fear may retard learning. An overly anxious student is not likely to be an efficient worker; a frightened community leader may be too fearful to act in an intelligent and constructive manner.

Hochbaum, in his study of public participation in the mass x-ray program, found that while a high state of psychological readiness, including a personal concern about the tuberculosis problem, facilitated participation, an excessive fear about the dangers of tuberculosis for oneself seemed to inhibit action.

> . . . There were 16 respondents who seemed . . . intensely afraid. None of these 16 had had even one voluntary x-ray during the 8-year period.
> Another 118 respondents showed signs of relatively strong fears in connection with the thought of getting tuberculosis. Their participation in case-finding did not follow any clearly discernible common pattern, although it was smaller than that of the rest of the sample.[11]

These empirical findings are supported by experimental studies of the effects of fear-arousing communications. Students were exposed to a health information program which included slides of tooth deformities and disease to indicate the dangers that may result from bad tooth and gum infection. Other students in a matched group were exposed to a more positive type of informational program regarding tooth care. The use of the fear appeal in this situation proved to be less effective than the more moderate appeal in convincing students to use good dental practices.[12]

A significant theoretical and practical question remains unanswered; How does one judge the proper amount of concern? The line between realistic concern and fear cannot be sharply drawn. Nor is it likely to be the same for all action situations. An important variable to consider is the availability of an opportunity, present and perceived, for the individual to take action appropriate to alleviate the concern aroused. It has been suggested that when an appropriate course of action is immediately available and perceived, a high level of fear may lead to direct action; where no such realistic course of action is perceived, or where the opportunities for action are seen as undesirable, even a low level of concern may lead to blocking.[13]

Role of Education in Arousing Interest

The motives that guide and sustain individual efforts toward tension reduction or satisfaction cannot be imparted from without. Rather, they are peculiar to the individual, part of his mental context acquired through the process of personal and group experience. Interwoven in this personal motive system are the individual's values and beliefs, attitudes, and understandings that help to protect him from undesired external pressures.

The role of education within this dynamic setting thus becomes one of supporting and guiding rather than one of defining and directing. As Whitehead in *The Aims of Education* observed, "Education must essentially be a setting in order of a ferment already stirring in the mind: you cannot educate mind *in vacuo*."[14]

When an individual lacks concern, interest, or curiosity about the new ideas or possibilities for action in the area in which change is being promoted, the task of the educator or innovator of change becomes especially difficult. Before he can hope to lead the individual toward a solution of a health problem, he must first develop the conditions that lead the individual to acquire some perceptual curiosity about the issues involved, to recognize that a health problem exists, and to identify it as one of personal or group concern. The individual must become dissatisfied or frustrated or at least curious regarding his present state of health or health affairs before he is likely to acquire an interest in doing something about it. In some way the individual must be guided into experiences that develop within him a sense of uncertainty or interest and lead him to experience a period of exploration, or groping, or discursive activity, of shaping new questions, of challenging old facts. Until such a state of mental ferment is aroused regarding the health problem or issue, informational or directive efforts and goal definitions or methods of solution are likely to be futile.

An apparent lack of concern, interest, or curiosity regarding potential threats to one's own health or to the community's health ought not to be interpreted as an indifference. Rather, it may reflect a relatively greater curiosity or concern about issues of more immediate importance than the personal or community health issue being promoted.

As many professional workers who deal with the influencing of individuals or groups have learned, asking questions is often an effective means of arousing curiosity, concern, and involvement. Berlyne conducted an interesting experimental study of this matter. He describes the experiment as follows:

> There was an experimental group that received (1) a prequestionnaire of forty-eight questions about invertebrate animals, each followed by two alternative answers between which a choice had to be made, (2) a list of seventy-two statements about invertebrate animals, including answers to all the questions in the prequestionnaire, and (3) a postquestionnaire consisting of the questions of the prequestionnaire in a re-randomized order but without the answers, so that answers had to be supplied by the subjects. A control group underwent exactly the same procedure except that the prequestionnaire was omitted.
>
> The outcome was that the experimental group supplied a mean of 32.4 correct answers in the postquestionnaire, as compared with 27.2 for the control group. The difference was significant and was taken as evidence that questions heighten epistemic curiosity, facilitating the retention of facts that answer the questions when they are subsequently encountered.[15]

In his follow-up study, Berlyne learned that more curiosity was aroused by questions about familiar animals, and in particular those questions that surprised the subject and that seemed to associate the familiar animal with statements that appeared unlikely. All questions are not equally provocative in arousing curiosity. Considerable exploration may be required to develop an approach that creates the desired state of doubt, uncertainty, or epistemic conflict in the minds of those interviewed. Needed are questions that cannot be simply answered with a sense of certainty, but, rather, questions that arouse a series of unknowns of interest, or that cause one to doubt previously held assumptions. Should the subject feel confident in his answer, he will not be likely to search for additional information.[16]

The use of demonstrations or the presentation of issues that directly challenge past experience is at times an effective way of arousing conceptual conflict and curiosity, provided adequate care is taken to avoid the development of defensive responses and the outright rejection of further exposure. The Ames-Cantril rotating trapezoidal window demonstration has been widely used in this way with both student and adult groups for initiating discussion regarding the significance of past experience in perception.[17]

In reviewing various research on means of arousing perceptual conflict and curiosity, Berlyne observes:

The pedagogical implications of all this stress on conceptual conflict may be of some importance. Ever since Herbart, educationists have recommended that new material should be presented in a way which relates it harmoniously to the "apperceptive mass" that the child's previous learning has deposited. This will, no doubt, facilitate the process of assimilation. But it may be that the opposite condition—a head-on clash between new material and prior experience—is best able to motivate intellectual inquiry and accomplishment in the first instance.[18]

Illustration from Public Health Nursing

The importance of interest or concern in the learning of improved health practices is well illustrated by Derryberry in his intensive study of nursing home visits, conducted a quarter of a century ago. His observations have significance for all health professions.

> Paradoxical as it may seem, few individuals are sufficiently interested in their health to do anything particular about it unless there are symptoms to nag or scare them into doing something. Most persons will agree that a well-balanced diet, regular visits to the dentist, periodic health examinations, etc., are excellent habits that should be practiced by everyone; but as for them, they are getting along all right. This point applies as much to the doctors and nurses who know what they should do and don't do it as it does to the layman.
>
> In sickness a person feels the absence of that health which he took for granted. He looks upon health now objectively as a condition which he would like to make his. He wants it back, and he wants the nurse and the doctor to tell him what to do, what to take, what to avoid, and so on.
>
> A convalescent patient is a ripe subject for health instruction. He is interested in the whys and wherefores of the condition which unbalanced him and in what he can do in the future to prevent its recurrence. Hence, teaching at that stage has an excellent chance of yielding profitable returns. Of course, the nurse cannot restrict herself to convalescent patients, but, at least, the enhanced opportunities for teaching in such situations should be recognized, and utilized to the greatest possible extent.
>
> The spreading of the principles of health, to which the public health movement has pledged itself, involves the whys and wherefores of disease and disability, and the necessity of guarding oneself against them. This message is often directed toward persons who are well at the moment and not unduly concerned, and unless the patient, or person interviewed, can be stirred with the desire to learn what the nurse is there to teach, her visit will amount to little more than a lifeless interchange of words from which the person interviewed receives little or no impression other than that a member of a health agency has come and is gone.
>
> Perhaps a partial home visit from among our collection will illustrate this failure to arouse the interest of the patient. On a first visit to the

home of a patient diagnosed as tuberculous in the hospital, the nurse collects a long history, grudgingly given by the patient's older sister, and then asks:

NURSE: After she left for the hospital, was her room and bed thoroughly disinfected?

MISS A: No.

NURSE: Is anybody sleeping in her bed now?

MISS A: No, my brother has his own room and my mother and I sleep together.

NURSE: Her room should be disinfected with Lysol or some disinfectant. Everything in her room should be wiped off with this disinfectant. Take a brush broom and go through all the mattress, the tufts and all, with this disinfectant.

MISS A: We are going to have the whole place painted anyway.

NURSE: Of course, the things in the room should be disinfected before the painter comes in. You people, have you been examined at all?

MISS A: No.

NURSE: We feel it is important that you be examined. (Then after giving the address and hours of the clinic, the nurse continues.) Will you be down to the clinic then some day in the future?

MISS A: Well, I won't say for sure. I don't know. I will speak to them about it and see what they say.

. . . I do not intend to minimize the difficulties of reaching the mind of one who is not interested at the moment, and is bound up in his own affairs as most of us are. The stimulation of interest in those being taught is baffling enough to teachers in our schools where the contacts with the students are longer and there is more opportunity to learn their interests and turn them to the account of instruction. The problem is far more complex when, as in nursing, the contacts are intermittent and there is little time to determine the interests of the clients and to use these interests as a basis for teaching. Nevertheless, interest in learning is a highly important factor in the situation and cannot be neglected.[19]

Public health leaders scarcely need to be reminded of the frustrations they have experienced in trying to develop new programs in areas of low public concern. The history of public health is replete with illustrations of communities failing to respond to excellently planned and executed directives for human betterment. The scientific documentation in support of such directives may be lost on an uninterested or unconcerned audience—an audience preoccupied with other things.

Psychological Readiness in Tuberculosis Case-Finding

The case-finding study by Hochbaum has helped to identify some of the factors related to whether, and when, people participate voluntarily in case-finding programs. It focuses particularly on the role of a state of readiness in voluntary x-ray behavior, but the principles found to apply here have been demonstrated also to be of significance to other case-finding efforts.[20]

Primary attention in the study was focused toward identifying psychological factors related to voluntary x-ray behavior. But psychological factors are not the only determinants of behavior. They do not exist in a vacuum. To produce behavior, they combine and interact with situational conditions, including social and physical factors.

Personal interviews were conducted with 1,201 adults selected by random sample techniques from the population over twenty-five years old in Boston, Cleveland, and Detroit. These communities were selected for study since they had been the focus of case-finding efforts.

It was hypothesized that a person must be psychologically ready to act and conditions must be auspicious before he will take action. The state of readiness that is required before a person voluntarily submits to a screening examination has many components, which include knowledge, previous experience, feelings, and emotions. In this study the psychological state of readiness was defined as composed primarily of three components:

1. A belief on the part of the individual that he, personally, might contract tuberculosis. Seventy-one per cent of the sample held this belief.
2. A belief on the part of the individual that he could have tuberculosis for some time without being aware of any symptoms or signs. Fifty-three per cent of the sample held this belief.
3. A belief on the part of the individual that he would benefit from early detection of tuberculosis. Sixty-three per cent of the sample held this belief.

The term "belief" here refers to more than knowing the facts and believing these facts as applicable in general. It includes, also, accepting the fact as applying to himself. This "self-including" belief characterizes the individual who has a state of readiness to volunteer for x-rays.

Two hundred and fifty-nine respondents were identified as persons who accepted the possibility that they, personally, could contract tuberculosis, who also accepted the fact that they might not be aware of having contracted it—since they could have it without being aware of any symptoms—and who believed that they would benefit from early diagnosis. Eighty-two per cent of respondents who manifested such a state of readiness had had at least one voluntary x-ray without prior symptoms during the seven preceding years, as contrasted with 47 per cent of the total sample. Of 108 individuals who held none of these three beliefs, only 21 per cent had obtained a voluntary x-ray without prior symptoms.

The study also yielded evidence regarding the role of situational factors in health action. X-ray facilities must be available, within the means of the individual, known to him, and available psychologically as well as physically.

Significant cues that help to trigger action include any changes in bodily function observed and interpretation as possibly being symptomatic of tuberculosis or other respiratory condition, and influences exerted by others, supportive or in opposition to obtaining x-rays.

Hochbaum concludes:

> A person must be psychologically ready to act, and conditions must be opportune before he will take any action. The state of readiness required before a person voluntarily submits to any screening examination has many components, which include knowledge, previous experiences, feelings, emotions, and others.
>
> The findings revealed that basic to the state of psychological readiness to obtain x-rays are the individual's belief that he may contract tuberculosis at any time—indeed, that he may actually have the disease at the time of decision—and his belief that early diagnosis of tuberculosis would have beneficial effects for him, should he contract the disease.
>
> At first glance, these beliefs seem to be merely a matter of information. However, knowledge may equip a person to give correct answers to questions but may not in any way influence his behavior.[21]

Illustration from Maternal and Child Health

In a study referred to earlier in this volume of 252 mothers interviewed in the maternity section of a county hospital shortly after being delivered, Gadalla used a number of indirect as well as direct approaches to determine why they obtained, or failed to obtain, prenatal care. His findings which are also relevant here support the conclusion that motivational factors exceed situational factors in their significance for health action.

> The study emphasized the importance of the potential motivation (psychological readiness) of mothers for seeking prenatal care. The higher such motivation or readiness, the higher was the utilization of prenatal care. Their high motivation made them seek prenatal care even

when they had no symptoms of pregnancy illness or complication. It also made them perceive the situational conditions of prenatal care as less inconvenient.

It was shown that situational inconveniences were of secondary importance as barriers to seeking prenatal care. If mothers were motivated and ready to seek care, the situational inconveniences were easily overcome. It was also found that very few mothers did not have access to prenatal care facilities.

The main barrier to seeking prenatal care was the lack of motivation of mothers. They did "not want" prenatal care. Their "not wanting" prenatal care was due to many reasons. For example, some "felt good," and therefore they did not think that they needed prenatal care. Some believed in old wives' tales. Others, especially the multiparas, thought they knew how to manage by themselves. Still others did not like doctors or were afraid of doctors and their pelvic and internal obstetric examinations. The latter were mainly the inexperienced young primiparas.[22]

Lack of Professional Concern

Nor is this apparent lack of concern with public health issues limited to the layman. The public health physician frequently has difficulty gaining official or professional support for actions which he feels to be urgent but which may be viewed with indifference or doubt by other officials or physicians whose worlds of fact and assumption are different from his.

While public health leaders often express concern that other professional groups in the community fail to support new programs, the lack of concern or interest may, at times, be found among leaders in their own group. This is well illustrated in a study by Gustafson (1963) designed to compare the interests, attitudes, and judgments of public health and private physicians regarding the extent of problems of chronic illness and the possibilities of effective action. He found that some public health, as well as private, physicians lacked conviction regarding the significance and extent of the problem, the availability of methods of control or rehabilitation, and the value of community action for solution.[23]

A major barrier to change may sometimes be the member of one's own group who is a passive or mild supporter of change. Such a person may not be fully convinced of the need for action and may lack any ego-involvement in the possible effects desired. He may, in fact, view the development as a possible threat to his own position of leadership but may not have the personal strength or integrity to express his concern and opposition openly and frankly. Rather, he may seek to delay the new and potentially threatening development by passive resistance until he feels emotionally and intellectually prepared to take a leadership role in the change process.

EXPLORATORY BEHAVIOR AS PART OF LEARNING

When an individual, through his explorations, begins to identify what he believes to be the source of his concerns or the reasons for his frustrations, he reaches a state of readiness for action. He seeks ways of doing something about his problems by defining the issues involved and examining the resources at his command. At this point he is better prepared than previously to consider and evaluate alternative possibilities for action, viewing them in terms of the significance they may have to him in his efforts to protect, extend, or enhance his self-image or ego image. This may involve finding ways of alleviating negative pressures or conditions and examining future possibilities. Thus both the "stick" and "carrot" aspects of motivation may be operative.

Man is not a passive adapter to his sensory and perceptual environment. He does not respond in constant fashion to stimulus situations at hand; rather, he takes the initiative in orienting himself to new situations or in changing the stimulus field through exploratory activities. He does seem to possess, as Berlyne suggests, a "perceptual curiosity" which leads him to explore, investigate, and examine his environment.[24]

Man "*directs* his attention" in selective ways and thus controls to some degree the nature of sensory and perceptual input and the intensity of his attention to it.[25] In directing his attention he may be guided by a preference for one sense modality over another, choosing whether to look or to listen when a conflict is present between what can be seen and what can be heard. At times he may prefer the familiar over the unknown, and at other times choose to attend the novel, exciting, or surprising. His motivational and affective state, together with his perceptual set or frame of reference, plays a significant role in attention.

Krech and Crutchfield have summarized in lucid fashion the qualities of the stimuli that help to gain attention:

> The *attention-demanding* properties of stimuli have been extensively studied by the experimentalist in the laboratory and by the applied prac-

titioner in advertising, in dress design, etc. The important stimulus factors can be summarized as follows: *intensity,* the shriek of the fire siren; *repetition,* the television commercial; *isolation,* the single word of advertising on the white magazine page; *movement and change,* the wigwag at the railroad crossing; *novelty,* the extreme design of the latest car model; *incongruity,* the woman smoking a cigar.[26]

Types of Exploratory Responses

Berlyne distinguishes three types of responses which we employ in exploring new situations in addition to being selective in attention.[27] Through exploration one increases his opportunities for receiving information and understanding by adjusting or moving to "get a better look" or by changing the situation to identify new elements or aspects not at first observed.

First, one may make orienting responses to a situation, altering the state of his sense organs, listening or looking intently, possibly focusing attention in a specific manner. We elicit this type of reaction when we say, "Listen!"; "Look at this!"; or "Watch this for me."

Secondly, a person may make a locomotor response, moving or changing his posture to get closer to the stimulus field or to reach a more favorable vantage point for observing and attending. We elicit this response when we say, "Come, see this"; "Go listen"; or "Bend over and you will be able to see it." Field visits often provide a more meaningful learning experience than lectures or pictures, for they permit the student to observe situations at first hand and from various points of view. They also permit him greater freedom to select for himself the subject matter to observe so that he may attend matters that the instructor might not have realized would be of interest or value to him.

Finally, a person may make investigatory responses by manipulating the stimulus field, or by affecting changes in it in order better to observe it, to see how it works, and to understand it. An apprenticeship or an action-observation type of field training experience illustrates this learning situation. When the student serves in an active role with responsibility under expert supervision, he has an opportunity to manipulate or vary some of the conditions present. This helps him find out why some approaches work better than others, what steps need to be considered before initiating a new approach, how various features of the situation relate to one another, what barriers to action need to be taken into account in planning, and so forth.

One should recognize, of course, that nearness to a situation and an opportunity to manipulate conditions does not necessarily yield the best exploratory findings or provide the most fruitful learning experience. One may become too ego-involved in a situation or too committed to a position or course of action to remain independent as an observer. Or one may become so busy with specific aspects of the situation and focus his attention so intently on limited features of the situation that he loses the broad and independent perspective necessary for identifying major factors.

Discursive Beginnings

Early efforts to deal with concerns are likely to be discursive and explorative both in thought and in action. One may confide in others and discuss with them ways of coping with difficulties. If one is fearful of personal disclosure, however, he may examine alternatives in personal reflection and imagination. Or he may make inquiries embedded in devious impersonal references, hoping in this way to gain various points of view and to identify nonthreatening sources of information, support, and guidance. As he seeks adequate definition of his concerns, realistic and meaningful goals, and ways of attaining them, the individual may be quite unaware of the dynamic steps through which he is moving.

While theory might imply a systematic, logical approach to goal definition and action, the rational man demanded by such theory does not seem to exist. Actions cannot neatly be separated from their ends. One acts, and in acting moves toward some goal which he may not have stopped to define. Choosing courses of action and defining goals thus tends to be a diffused, uncertain process accompanied by much mental exploration and reflection, as well as random and experimental activity. The needs-means-ends analysis of the philosopher suits the armchair, the experimental laboratory, or the program-planning session better than it does the thought processes of the tense, uncertain, possibly frightened individual acting under the pressures of a threat to his health.

A person who has personally become aware of the need for new ways to deal with a problem which he feels responsible for helping to solve, will actively seek new ideas and information to aid him in its solution. Awareness of a concern or an interest in change will itself tend to influence the kinds of things he notices and may lead him to detailed sources of information immediately available but previously unnoticed. His tentative choice of means of solution will also guide him on his search.

If his car has stalled several mornings and he thinks the battery he is using may be responsible, he is likely to begin noticing the arguments presented in various battery advertisements. Should he tentatively decide that the car needs mechanical adjustments or overhauling, his attention is likely to be directed toward an evaluation of alternative garage services. If his car has been unsatisfactory in other ways, his attention may be attracted to new or used car advertisements, depending on his subjective judgment of possibilities for action. Any of these, or other alternative searches for information and guidance, may take place, depending upon his subjective definition of the situation and subjective choice of possibilities. Yet the search for solution may go on for some time before he is fully aware that he is paying greater attention to the specific kinds of advertisements and other sources of information about him.

In a similar way, a man who experiences a pain in the pit of his stomach several times after eating may believe the problem to be one of indigestion and may begin to pay greater attention to his menu and eating habits. He may also begin to notice various advertisements of antiacids or similar pain reducers. If he relates these pains to tension-producing experiences which he is unable to control or avoid, he may become more aware of the many types of tension reducers offered in advertisements. If he believes that his heart or lungs are involved, this knowledge may alert him to identifying the various medical resources available, and to consider ways of judging their relative acceptability for himself. However, should he identify these pains as symptomatic of long-term illness or death, and if he and his family are not adequately covered by insurance, he may pay greater attention to information needed in choosing appropriate coverage, and ignore or conceal his symptoms in the hope that he will be able to obtain good coverage before something serious happens. In either instance, he is likely to learn many new things because of his active search for means of dealing with the problem as he defines it.

Approaching Solution from Learner's Point of View

For each of these various situations, the information or actions the individual learns will tend to be those appropriate for the situation as he defines it and in accord with the possibilities for action that he identifies as appropriate. Information or recommendations for action that are not in accord with the way he defines the situation may not be attended or seen as pertaining to his particular problem, may not be recognized and evaluated as useful and applicable. Those who would guide or counsel him under such circumstances need his active participation in order to develop their educational approaches within the framework of his definition of the situation.

The importance of presenting even a simple task from the observer's point of view in a teaching situation is nicely demonstrated by Roshal, who was interested in testing the hypothesis that "the learning of a perceptual motor act through films will be more effective as the film approaches a representation of the learner himself performing the act to be learned."[28] To test this hypothesis he presented a knot-tying task to 28 companies of army recruits. Three knot-tying tests were presented: the bowline, the sheet-bend, and the Spanish bowline. Half the recruits were shown the task in a film which presented it from the observer's point of view as the knots were tied; that is, they saw the knot as though it were tied in front of them by someone on the stage. The other half of the recruits were presented the knots in films showing the process from the performer's point of view; that is, they saw the knots tied as though they were looking over the shoulder of the performer. Immediately after presenting a short version of the knot-tying process, each recruit was given a short piece of rope and asked to tie the knot shown.

The results of Roshal's study clearly indicate that the film was a more effective teaching tool when the knot was presented from the performer's point of view; that is, when the knot was seen as though the observer were looking over the shoulder of the person tying the knot.

Identifying Barriers to Action

The individual's path toward the solution of his concerns or the attainment of his goals is not likely to be straightforward and unimpeded. In his efforts to draw upon available resources and to initiate effective actions, he may encounter or anticipate various barriers that thwart his progress. Such barriers may be real or unreal, objective or subjective, but barriers that he perceives are real to him as he identifies them in his observation or imagination. How he responds to, and deals with, these barriers he encounters or perceives has a great bearing on what he learns from the experience.

Possibilities for action must not only exist, they must be perceived as existing and possible. Unless so perceived, they do not exist for the individual concerned.

For example, a student needing dental or medical care, glasses, or some other costly aid, may avoid taking action for lack of funds. He may not realize that the sources of funds are available for such emergencies and that charity is not necessarily involved. Yet since he may carry within him certain assumptions regarding the possibilities and the threats to his ego suggested by charity, he may be embarrassed to tell anyone he lacks funds to take the corrective action. Thus a barrier to action may exist within his mind even though it is contrary to the real situation at hand. Under such circumstances a way must be found to help him identify the problem and to determine a solution satisfactory to himself without in the process increasing an already high level of frustration.

Learning Through Solving Problems

By identifying a barrier and finding some means of successfully or satisfactorily dealing with it, one learns new ways of acting and stores these new ways aside for future use. His assumptions, beliefs, opinions, and knowledge grow. When he is unable to resolve the frustrations that have arisen, learning may be blocked, or even negative responses may be acquired.

A woman who believes she has symptoms of breast cancer is likely to examine, reflectively, many possibilities for action and their potential implications for the defense of her self-image. She may at once feel an urgent need for expert diagnosis and fear the embarrassment of discussing her problem, even with an expert. The choice of physician may be a serious barrier to action if she is afraid to open so intimate a discussion with anyone. How can she protect herself against the dangers of unwarranted mutilation? Of inadequate diagnosis? Of excessive cost? The sense of futility that may accompany excessive fear is likely to be fostered in a setting where so many barriers to effective action are perceived. How real such barriers may be for the woman concerned, even though she may reside in a community having the most advanced and readily available medical facilities!

Should such a woman muster the courage or gain the support to take the initial steps toward diagnosis, she may find these potential barriers far less imposing than she had anticipated. The sense of progress she experiences will tend to reinforce her positive efforts and provide the encouragement necessary to complete the diagnosis and any necessary course of treatment. On the other hand, a significant rebuff or failure to experience success in her first steps toward action may block further effort.

Effects of Thwarting

The individual who finds his course of action thwarted may reexamine and reevaluate the situation. Alternate possibilities may be tested. Should these alternative efforts fail, he may discard the goal as beyond his reach, or as one not worth the effort. In a future similar situation he will be less likely to attempt to solve his problems. Any one of several courses of action may be taken: he may decide the problem is beyond solution, and learn to live with it; he may rationalize the problem as one of little serious significance and not requiring action; or he may deny, even to himself, that the problem exists. Thus the learnings acquired in his early negative experience may have serious long-term health implications.

The test-retest experience which an individual goes through in the search for solution of a health problem may bring into play a more critical examination of the assumptions, beliefs, and attitudes that he holds. Often basic assumptions regarding knowledge, value, and belief are forced into focus by the frustrations experienced in attempting to act. The experience of being thwarted either as an individual acting alone or as a member of a group may force attention upon many sociocultural and psychological factors relating to change, lead to a reevaluation of these factors from new points of view, and provide the basis for new goal identification and more effective methods of goal attainment.

THORNDIKE'S "LAW OF EFFECT"

Thorndike has shown that responses that lead to a "satisfying state of affairs" are likely to be learned and repeated, whereas responses that lead to a "discomforting or annoying state of affairs" will tend later to be avoided. He called this principle *the law of effect,* a "law" that deserves the most serious study by public health workers who are concerned about the effects of their efforts to influence health actions.[29] Few theoretical formulations have guided so much research on the learning process, and survived the tests of experimentation with so few modifications.

Tolman and his many associates have demonstrated that in the process of performing in a maze, rats learn the effects of error (reaching a blind alley), as well as the effects of success (reaching food or water). Through practice the rat learns the signs or cues to alternative pathways, and in time seems to develop for himself a cognitive map of the learning situation. The cues to blind alleys as well as the cues to rewards are learned.[30]

Incidental or latent learning has been subjected to considerable study by the group of researchers because if some type of reinforcement is essential to learning, what accounts for incidental learnings when no apparent rewards or punishments are present? Animals, as well as men, learn things and remember things in the absence of any apparent reinforcement.[31]

Tolman suggests that a curiosity drive seems to be present which leads rats and men to explore and examine things in the absence of other incentives, and that this curiosity may account for such incidental learnings.[32]

The Timing of Effect

The importance of timeliness of reward or punishment deserves special emphasis. An individual needs to see the relationship between his behavior and its effects if learning is to occur. Learning is in good part a process of discovering the relationship between cause and effect. The more quickly a health-related action is followed by appropriate reward or punishment, and the connection perceived, the more likely is learning to result.

Unfortunately, in most public health situations this condition of learning is most difficult to satisfy. The effects of both personal and community public health actions may occur so long afterwards that the outcomes are not even recognized when they do occur. The action taken may have been forgotten.

Rather than immediate rewards for actions taken to avoid or prevent ill health or unhealthy conditions, one may experience immediate punishment. Personal insults to the body through probings, scrapings, blood tests, or biopsies, or personal insults to the ego incurred during intimate questionings and examinations may be viewed by the individual as immediate punishments that far outweigh, in their significance for him, the possible, uncertain, and ambiguous long-term health gains. With regard to group actions, such as the community fluoridation program, for example, the immediate prospect of an increase in taxation, the immediate "threat" of science, the immediate concern of increasing the power of governmental authority, and so on may far outweigh the promise of fewer cavities years hence for one's children and grandchildren.[33]

Delayed Rewards May Not Be Seen as Effects

When rewards are vague and long delayed, as so often is the case in public health programs, rewards, when they do come, may not even be seen as emanating from earlier decisions. The person who does not become ill because he took some preventive action in earlier years may never appreciate the importance of this previous choice of behavior. Even if he does note the relationship, the reward will likely be received too late to have a significant impact on related health behaviors. Since some illnesses, even those that are contagious like tuberculosis, are selective in their effects, the relationship between health action and health outcome cannot always be defined even by the specialist. The layman needs, therefore, to have great faith in the judgment of others and in the efficacy of science and medicine to offset this lag in direct evidence of effect.

Relating preventive actions to positive health outcomes is even more difficult for chronic illnesses than for those of a contagious nature. Society has not, as yet, accumulated a backlog of successful experience with some chronic illnesses to help even the alert individual to learn from the experiences of others. Learning and appreciating the significance of relationships between health actions and their effects is most difficult with conditions that develop slowly. They are seldom, if ever, linked to a particular cause; they do not always follow a consistent course of development; and they cannot be prevented by a single action. Only as a backlog of effective experimentation and demonstration results in successful experience can one expect widespread learning regarding the value of preventive action to occur.

Possibilities of Early Reinforcement

The rewards for learning appropriate health knowledge, attitudes, and practices need not, of course, be tied only to ultimate outcomes.

Knowing that one has satisfied the expectations of the health expert, as evidenced by a positive response on his part, may be sufficient reward for many people. A key feature of programed learning, so successful for imparting some types of content, is the provision of immediate rewards and punishments—learning at once whether one's responses are correct or incorrect. A New York State health exhibit which provides reenforcement for responses to a health test by ringing a bell took advantage of this feature of the teaching machine. A Public Health Service exhibit on accident prevention provided an opportunity for the observer to experience immediate reward or punishment by permitting him to test for himself, and learn in a dramatic manner, that one cannot distinguish combustible fabrics from fireproofed fabrics by sight and touch alone.[34]

In most instances, perhaps, one does not see the immediate effects of each action, and is unable to judge immediately whether satisfaction or discomfort will occur. In such situations, it has been suggested that one judges effects in terms of his expectations.[35] If learning is to occur, the reinforcement he receives upon acting "must be such as to confirm an expectancy." Tolman's research suggests that one tends to follow the "signs" which he identifies as marking the route to the goal he seeks. If his expectations are confirmed, a new pattern of behavior will be acquired.[36]

"Inappropriate" Behaviors May Relieve Concerns

At times an individual may learn to live with his symptoms rather than take action to remove their cause because the futility of action is communicated to him through his social group. This is particularly likely to occur with respect to slowly developing aches and discomforts for which he perceives no adequate solution. Koos found that many members of the lower socioeconomic group he studied had aches and pains for which they knew no adequate treatment. They tended to accept them as a normal part of life—something everybody had as they grew older.[37] In her study of factors influencing delay in seeking medical care for symptoms of breast cancer, Roberts noted that some women, even though they believe they have developed an abnormal condition, often delay seeking professional help until a change occurs in the symptom. The delay may continue for some time. In the cases under study feelings of urgency were not aroused until a change in the breast was observed (redness, bleeding, or irritation).[38]

It seems reasonable to hypothesize also that some early symptoms of chronic illness go untreated by competent medical practitioners because the persons involved are able to find other seemingly adequate means of alleviating their concerns. A person may have a recurrent headache or backache and find that aspirin, or bufferin, or anacin provides temporary relief. The symptom goes away and the concern is reduced. However, even though the symptoms are allayed, the underlying cause of the illness remains and its course may continue unimpeded. When the temporary treatment no longer is sufficient to limit the discomfort, the illness may have reached an advanced stage.

It should be emphasized that the health action judged by the concerned individual to be appropriate and adequate for dealing with his health problem need not be medically appropriate, yet it may prove effective from the individual's point of view. Quack medicine flourishes on the chance recoveries of persons who take nostrums and "learn by experience" of their effectiveness, and communicate this finding to others. The use of such nostrums, previously experienced as effective, may serve to alleviate tensions and reduce the likelihood of the individual's taking more appropriate action.

It is even possible that some health-related activities encouraged by public health leaders serve the unexpected purpose of alleviating health concerns and lowering readiness for appropriate health action. For example, persons who are encouraged to participate in public health drives for needed funds, or who are enlisted to assist in getting others to participate in case-finding programs may, through their program efforts, take vicarious actions that alleviate personal concern. A personal contribution to a fund drive may serve to release personal tensions. Encouraging others to participate in a cancer detection drive may serve to reduce a person's own anxieties to the point that he does not participate himself. This hypothesis deserves intensive investigation.

"LEARNING BY DOING"

Learning is an active process. It is most likely to take place when the individual actively seeks to acquire insights and understandings for himself. This applies to all phases of the learning process, such as the identification of areas of concern, the choice of means of problemsolving, the formulation of goals, or the evaluation of progress. Unless the individual participates and becomes ego-involved, learnings are less likely to occur. Changes in behavior, observed under conditions where the individual has not been involved, tend to reflect passive acceptance or compliance. The internalization of the experience, so essential to learning, has probably not taken place.[39]

Dewey's philosophy of education which emphasizes the importance of "learning by doing" has had a most significant impact on modern education.[40] As Allport noted, "He more than any other scholar, past or present, has set forth as a psychological problem the common man's need to participate in his own destiny."[41]

Students of education have compiled a mass of evidence regarding the effectiveness of Dewey's problem-solving approaches. What was at the turn of the century called "the new education," seems now here to stay. Many of our leading business and industrial organizations are now applying the principles of participation in the training of their senior management and staff members. There have been efforts to simulate some of the most complex individual and group problems so that significant learnings could be more effectively imparted.[42]

Ego-Involvement in the Task

In applying the broad principle of participation to the learning process, whether in classroom, industry, or community, one must clearly distinguish between mere activity and personal participation. As Allport has emphasized, task-involvement and ego-involvement are quite different things.[43] True personal participation requires ego-involvement on the part of the participant, as well as on the part of the change agent.

When an individual becomes ego-involved in the solution of a problem, he takes an active part in the process of solution, and in doing so learns, whether or not an educator is present. What he learns may not, of course, be appropriate from the educator's point of view, even though solutions gained may satisfy the acting individual.

Involving the individual in health actions, in such a way that he learns from the experience, may require much creative planning on the part of the change agent. The learning experience needs to be developed in participation with the individual (or individuals) affected so that he identifies the issue as one of personal concern, sees possibilities of solution that seem reasonable for him to undertake, and formulates goals that are both desirable and attainable from his point of view. Gaining his participation and involvement in the learning process enhances the possibility that significant and appropriate learnings will take place.

Hoff has drawn attention to the importance of considering such psychological factors in planning rehabilitation programs. He notes that in the past physical impairments and symptoms of patients have tended to dominate planning for recovery, probably because physical signs and symptoms are easier for health personnel to observe and understand. In a study of 59 physically impaired, hospitalized patients who were diagnosed as suffering from strokes, spinal cord lesions, and fractures, Hoff found that ego-strength, flexibility, sociability, and social presence, as measured by psychological tests, were all significantly related to success in rehabilitation. Patients' success in this instance was measured by obtaining independent staff ratings of specific achievements of patients as related to their potentialities for improvement.[44]

Gaining Acceptance of Participation in Learning

The idea of involving others in the planning of his own learning experience, as is implied by the approach, is not, of course, easy for all administrators or educators to accept. As Griffiths suggests:

> First, in our American culture, we have placed a premium on individuals being able to accept responsibility and to carry through independently on an activity. Most of us would certainly not employ an individual who would be dependent on others in a work situation. A premium is rightly placed in our society on this characteristic, for much of what we have to do in our work is of such a nature that progress is made through individual decision and initiative. Paradoxically, this same valued personality trait makes it often difficult for us to involve others effectively.
>
> Second, in working by ourselves, and especially if the outcomes have been successful, we, or our agencies, have gained from others recognition that has given us real satisfaction. To share recognition is not as personally satisfying as being the single recipient.
>
> Third, many of us have been nurtured on the saying that if you want something done right, do it yourself. It is a concept that is essentially based on the lack of confidence in others to make a sound decision. As health workers, we often feel that we understand clearly how a health activity can best be accomplished and that if we involve less trained and experienced persons they will not be wise enough to accept our directions. Distrust in others, sometimes psychologically deep-rooted, is a strong barrier in the effective involvement of others.
>
> Once we can accept the concept that we don't change or educate

people, but that people educate and change themselves, then we will take greater advantage of all the opportunities which arise for truly democratic personal participation. We will discover that programs of staff education, volunteer training, and patient education will be more meaningful to those involved, that boards and committees will function more effectively, and that community programs will have less apathy.[45]

Importance of Participation in Change Processes

Public health educators, adult educators, and agricultural extension agents have been in the forefront of those who have systematically employed means of securing the participation of people in the process of innovating change. Such participation enables them to acquire a sense of concern regarding existing conditions, to develop an awareness of the possibilities of doing something to improve conditions, and to make necessary individual and group adjustments in a manner that lessens damage to existing values, beliefs, and customs.[46]

Those who employ such approaches find that this process of search, in which the individual engages in the learning process, may yield high personal satisfaction. As Cantril has suggested, the process of seeking the solution may be more satisfying than the end goal achieved. He invites attention to the value we place on playing the game, of expressing oneself in creative effort, or of testing oneself in purposive strivings. One may observe, "My, that was fun!" or "I sure enjoyed that game!" and secretly regret that the game is over, no matter who won. Thus the satisfaction derived from purposive activity in seeking solutions may in itself have motivational value and help to spur the individual on to further explorations and further learnings.[47]

SOCIAL AND EMOTIONAL SUPPORT FOR LEARNING

Social learning involves emotion as well as intellect. Learning tends to progress best in an atmosphere of friendly acceptance where emotional support is available from the change agent and from members of one's group, where members of the group can assist in defining the problem, examining alternatives, and reinforcing decisions to change. It requires what the eminent public health and mental health physician Frank Fremont-Smith once called a state of "free floating security."

One who would influence the learnings of others must ever remember that man does not acquire and integrate new behavior in isolation. The love and affection of his intimates, the associations he holds dear, the sanctions he honors, the rules he obeys, the boundaries he respects, the punishments he fears—all these human properties that are at once personal and social bind him to other men in ways that may either foster or restrict his search, discovery, examination, and acceptance of change.

Learning new facts, beliefs, attitudes, or practices may involve discarding those currently held by one's friends and colleagues as well as by oneself. Accepting the new may therefore involve rejecting shared norms and standards, thus endangering the harmony of interpersonal life. Such real or imagined threats to one's ego-extensions and social supports foster uncertainty, frustration, and even fear.

Support from Social Groups

The significance of groups to social change is a topic that extends beyond the present discussion, for social change involves a complex of factors in addition to learning. Yet one would be amiss to discuss learning without mentioning some of the social and group factors that contribute to its occurrence.[48]

One draws upon members of one's family, friends, associates, acquaintances, and even strangers, alone and in groups, for help when under personal stress. Talking out a problem may help one understand himself better. Discussions with others may identify issues of personal and social significance not otherwise recognized, and provide emotions and moral support for dealing with them. Thus the individual may at once gain a more realistic evaluation of the problem at hand and become convinced of the need for action. Others may help him test out the path ahead by identifying potential obstacles and ways of dealing with them. They may identify and evaluate with him the possible outcomes of action or delay, thus deriving with him an estimate of the worthwhileness of doing anything. They may assure their support on emerging issues, thus whetting his appetite for action. In these, and many other ways, the process of reorganizing knowledge, beliefs, attitudes, or practices may be facilitated and fostered by others in one's social environment.

Expectations of Others' Reactions

Learning may be either facilitated or blocked by the expectations an individual has in regard to the appropriateness of discussing problems or issues with others. The new member of a health department staff, for example, may begin the job with many uncertainties as to what to expect of others. He may also have a pattern of expectation regarding what is or is not appropriate in his new role, what he is expected to know already and what he is expected to learn, whom he is free to talk with, what topics are permissible or taboo. Learning to function effectively in the new, still ambiguous role will require much give-and-take discussion with fellow staff members. One's expectations about what ought or ought not be discussed, one's concerns about posing questions in areas believed to be "touchy," one's fears about appearing stupid, naive, or gauche may prevent valuable learning experiences from emerging. The health officer who is aware that such expectations, concerns, and fears may be held by new, and also old, staff members can do much to create that warm, supportive, and inviting atmosphere that fosters the free exchange of experience conducive to the acquisition of new learning.

In like manner, the nurse in her clinic, home and school visits, the sanitarian in his meetings with food handlers or distributors, the social worker meeting with the family in time of crisis, the health educator working with members of a community group, all have a responsibility to help free those they work with from self-imposed barriers to new learning. The experience of each professional in public health has armed him with a wealth of knowledge of crucial value to others. In particular, this special training and experience has provided him with information others do not have regarding new crisis situations that may arise—knowledge of great value in providing anticipatory guidance. A necessary condition to the maximum use of this knowledge by those who most need it is providing an atmosphere receptive to critical inquiry and conducive to learning.

Personal Concerns May Block Discussions

A striking finding by Blackwell in a study of the way people expect to act, should they personally have symptoms of chronic illness, draws particular attention to the importance of public expectations to the control of chronic conditions. Blackwell interviewed matched groups of upper middle-class urban adults to obtain their interpretations of three symptoms of illness, and their judgments as to how they would probably behave, should they personally have these symptoms. With one group, no label was given to the symptom described; with the matched group the symptom was explicitly identified as being suggestive of illness. The symptoms presented to the sample were as follows:

Physical health condition or symptom

As presented without label: ". . . noticing blood in the stool: not a great deal and with no pain connected with it, but noticing it over a period of two days in a row."

Explicit indication of pathology: ". . . noticing blood in the stool: not a great deal and with no pain connected with it but noticing it over a period of two days in a row *and being aware that abnormal bleeding or any change in normal bowel habits are considered among the danger signals of cancer.*"

Psychophysical health condition or symptom

As presented without label: "This condition is one of rather regularly having a burning sensation in the chest after eating and realizing that this has been going on for one week although there has been nothing new or unusual in your eating habits during this time."

Explicit label as pathological: "This condition is one of having *persistent indigestion* and realizing that since there hasn't been any change in your eating habits or in your general routine of living, something must be going wrong with your body's functioning to cause this discomfort. Then there is the added factor that *persistent indigestion is a pain in the chest region which could indicate that something is wrong with the stomach, heart or lungs.*"

Psychosocial health condition or symptom

As presented without label: "This condition is one of generally being easily embarrassed, concerned about making mistakes in both new and routine situations and apprehensive about the future in spite of relative security. It may have been going on for years, but you have just become aware that you seem to be more this way than people around you are. However, you are functioning the same way you always have."

Explicit label as pathological: "This condition is one of generally being easily embarrassed, concerned about making mistakes regardless of whether a task is a routine one at which you have never made a mistake or a new one and apprehensive about the future in spite of relative security. What I am trying to describe is *an abnormal anxiety in which the individual is aware that he is anxious and aware that there is no real reason for feeling this way, but he is still anxious.* You feel that you experience these feelings more intensely than those around you and that as a result you are less efficient in your functioning than you would like to be. You feel that something must be wrong with your emotional functioning for you to feel uncomfortable in this way."[49]

Blackwell found that members of her upper middle-class group expect to delay longer before seeking professional medical care as the condition described becomes more psychosocial. If we consider modal behaviors alone, 87 per cent of those presented the physical health condition expected to delay less than 7 days; 62 per cent presented the psychophysical condition expected to delay from 8 to 30 days; whereas 73 per cent of those presented the psychosocial condition expected to delay more than 30 days before obtaining professional medical care and 20 per cent said they would never seek such care.[50]

When the symptom was presented in the manner that explicitly labeled it as pathological, the modal expectations changed but slightly toward earlier search for help, except for the psychophysical symptom. Eighty-eight per cent of those presented the physical health condition expected to delay less than 7 days; 34 per cent of those presented the psychophysical symptom expected to delay less than 7 days, 39 per cent, from 8 to 30 days, and 23 per cent over 30 days (a striking increase from 8 per cent when symptoms was not so labeled); 64 per cent of those presented the psychosocial symptom expected to delay over 30 days, and 20 per cent indicated again that they would never seek professional medical help. Thus labeling the symptom as pathological tends to decrease delay expectations for a few persons but actually leads to an increase in expected delay for many others.

As shown in Table 4, expectations regarding delay tended to increase significantly for each symptom when the symptom was given an explicit pathological label. Furthermore, when the symptom was so labeled, fewer persons expected to discuss the condition with either family members or colleagues.[51]

Thus many respondents indicated that the identification of the symptom as pathological would tend to increase the delay in seeking appropriate diagnosis and treatment and also tend to decrease the discussions with others who might help the individual learn about appropriate resources. Knowledge of the diagnosis may at once foster delay and psychologically block the individual from taking advantage of sources of information available to him. Rather, they would expect, by themselves, to try to find the cause of difficulty and a way of dealing with it.

TABLE 4. THE "OTHER" OF THE ANTICIPATED INTERACTION
PRIOR TO SEEKING PROFESSIONAL MEDICAL CARE FOR
SPECIFIC CONDITIONS

Condition	Not Explicit Pathology			Explicit Pathology		
	Physical	Psycho-physical	Psycho-social	Physical	Phycho-physical	Psycho-social
Categories of "Other"	Per cent					
Family member	58	61	43	47	46	43
Close friend	4	12	26	1	10	16
Colleague	1	2	9	0	3	10
"Specialist"[a]	1	2	4	0	2	1
No one	36	23	18	52	39	30
Per cent	100	100	100	100	100	100
Number of respondents	81	88	88	86	87	87

[a] "Specialist" means nonmedical or nonpsychiatric professional or expert in some nonhealth field.

SOURCE: Blackwell, Barbara L., "Expectations of Upper Middle-Class Adults About Their Activities Prior to Seeking Professional Medical Care for Physical and Psychiatric Health Conditions. Unpublished doctoral dissertation, University of California, Berkeley, 1963, Table 12, p. 141. Reproduced with permission of the author.

While Blackwell's finding relates to expected behavior rather than to what an individual would actually do in a state of incipient illness, it poses a serious question concerning the role of information and education in chronic illness case-finding. Controlled study of this issue under true program conditions is needed to gain essential knowledge about the extent of such behavior, and the factors underlying it.

THE TRANSFER OF LEARNING

Perhaps all adult learning involves previous learning. What one has learned in the past may either help or hinder one in new learning situations. The term "transfer of learning" or "transfer of training" is employed to refer to these effects of past learnings on new learnings. When previous learning facilitates the acquisition of new knowledge, we speak of positive transfer; when it impedes learning we speak of negative transfer.

Such positive and negative transfer occurs with respect to the acquisition of new content or information, the learning of new skills, techniques, methods, or roles, and the learning of new principles and concepts. It may take place without the knowledge of either teacher or learner, and in ways that may not be recognized. Positive transfer fosters more rapid learning, with its attendant acceptance and praise on the part of others. Since negative transfer tends to interfere with progress, its presence may result in difficulties, disappointment, and misunderstanding on the part of others as to why progress does not take place more rapidly.

The process of generalization that has been mentioned in connection with conditioning illustrates one simple transfer effect most of us have experienced. The child frightened by one furry animal may transfer his learning to apply to other furry things. A child's first experience with men in white coats may have learning effects that become generalized to his experiences with other white-coated men.

Public Health Examples

Mention has been made of a number of public health situations in which past learnings interfere with the acquisition of new learnings. The sanitarian who holds directive or legal responsibilities, as well as educative and persuasive responsibilities, may experience difficult transfer effects in the learning of approaches and roles suitable to these somewhat conflicting patterns of duty. The publics with which he works may have difficulties in working with him when the way they have learned to respond regarding one role and state of affairs is contrary to the way they are expected to respond under other conditions.

New developments in science and technology demand rapid changes in the behavior of public health professionals. When new processes and conclusions are extensions, by increment, of what is already being applied, few difficulties are likely to occur, for positive transfer facilitates new behavioral acquisitions. When major shifts in processes and conclusions are required, however, serious negative transfers may inhibit new learnings. The development of calculators, card sorters, and computers have required significant changes in the way studies must be planned and data analyzed. Both researchers and assistants, in adapting to new ways, will find themselves making hand tabulations or desk records unnecessarily. They may, in fact, delay the research or program actions because of the difficulties they experience in learning to use machines to perform tedious detailed work.

Professionals who enter the public health field from organizations in which administrative control is centrally directed on a national basis, such as some military and industrial organizations, are almost certain to experience negative transfer effects in learning to function within the "looser" public health structure in this country. Similarly, administrators or researchers may experience negative transfer in learning to function in consultant roles without assuming unwarranted responsibility for decisions and actions.

The member of a tightly structured organization who leaves it to accept a university position with greater freedom from responsibility may find himself experiencing difficulty in learning how to use his newly found independence. He may delay in making decisions for himself, as though expecting someone to tell him what to do, or may actually perceive and seek to follow channels of responsibility and communication that do not, in fact, exist.

Other situations common to public health in which the transfer of learning may contribute significantly to successful or unsuccessful functioning include the experience of a change in health officers or departmental administrators with the possible changes in policies, rules, or principles of work, or in ways of giving instructions; the orientation of a new staff member, either as a replacement or as an additional resource to the health team; the education of a new board member, adviser, or consultant; the initiation of a case-finding or immunization program in a new or different disease area; the development of chronic disease programs in departments that have in the past focused primary attention on control of communicable diseases; developing relations and learning to work with new staff, agency, or community groups. In situations like these one may anticipate the presence of a significant amount of positive and negative transfer of learning. To the extent that these effects of transfer are identified, one may profit by making better use of positive transfer and may be able to minimize negative effects.

Conditions Fostering Transfer

Transfer of learning tends to occur whenever there is some degree of similarity between past learnings and what is to be learned with regard to the content, method, role, or principles. To the degree that similarities are present, one would expect positive transfer: a complete duplication of past conditions, with respect both to instructions and to desired response, should lead to complete positive transfer. One is then merely repeating what has previously been learned. Discrepancies of any kind, however, whether with respect to instructions or the desired response, result in interference or negative transfer.

Mednick notes:

> A respected rule of thumb in psychology is that when you move from one situation to another you will always get negative transfer if you keep stimuli constant but change the responses. A good example of this is a person who has learned to drive a car using a clutch and then switches to the same model car with automatic transmission. The stimuli are not terribly different but the responses have changed radically. This individual will find himself stabbing frantically with his left foot looking for the clutch and fumbling around with his right hand in the place where the gearshift should be.[52]

Another type of transfer of learning occurs when we have completed the learning of one task (A) and then learn or practice some other task (B). The study of B may influence the retention of A. If B is similar to A, positive transfer or facilitation may occur; if B is dissimilar to A, the effect may be negative transfer or inhibition.

For example, a student may study for an examination in epidemiology and, after completing his study, may give his attention to administration or health education before taking the examination, or he may relax with a novel or participate in a bull session. In this instance, one would expect either facilitation or inhibition, depending upon the degree of similarity between epidemiology and what he has learned or practiced in the interim before the examination.

As Krech and Crutchfield observe, for an ideal study of the process of inhibition and facilitation one would need to keep a subject in a state of suspended animation and vary the conditions one at a time.

> The nearest approximation is a study by Minami and Dallenbach (1946), who taught cockroaches to avoid a certain corner of their cage which was wired for electric shock, then immobilized half of the cockroaches by placing them for some time in a dark box in bodily contact with tissue paper which inhibits their movements. The other half were permitted freedom of movement. When the immobilized cockroaches were later released and tested, they showed very little forgetting of which corner was to be avoided, while the other cockroaches showed considerable forgetting.
>
> With human subjects the effects of sleep, rather than immobilization, have been studied. Jenkins and Dallenbach in 1924, and Van Ormer in 1932, compared retention during intervals spent in sleep with retention during intervals of waking activities. Both experiments found that

retention was better during sleep, when the *general* level of activity is presumably lower than during waking.[53]

Conclusions

It is not easy to recognize all the effects of transfer of training when they occur, for they are always occurring in varying degrees as part of all learning processes. To the extent that significant influences can be identified, however, efforts can be made to profit from positive transfer when present. Unnecessary duplication of training can thus be avoided. When blocks in the progress of learning are noticed, one can suspect the presence of inhibiting factors resulting from negative transfer, and take efforts to define such effects and deal directly with them.

Major sources of difficulty result from unverbalized assumptions that no transfer effects are present in various training and program situations, and contrariwise, assuming that the transfer of learning is greater, or of a different form, than actually exists.

THE INTEGRATION OF NEW LEARNINGS

The learning process falls short unless new knowledge and understandings are integrated through interpretation into experience so that they may be applied in resolving future problems. Adequate learning, or meaningful change, is most likely to occur when an individual has opportunities to relate the experience through which he has passed to his own way of life, and to draw from this experience suggestions or guidelines that will help him make decisions in the future.

Facts alone do not make the learned man. The man with a storehouse of facts who has not put them together in some useful framework of theory or principles is very shallow indeed. An interpretive review or evaluation of the experience an individual has been through is a most useful means of developing lasting understandings, of identifying criteria and standards against which to judge future courses of action, and of formulating tentative new goals for which to strive.

The integration of experience into new patterns of thought and behavior thus becomes one of the most important phases of the learning or change process. Since basic values, beliefs, and attitudes may be involved in this process of interpreting experience, an analytic review or evaluation of the experience the individual has passed through in achieving change may require extended discussion. Much time may be involved, for the individual needs to consolidate his gains and to gain security with his newly acquired assumptions and behaviors. New knowledge and understanding needs to be integrated so that additional changes will take place from a firm base that is fully understood and accepted by the individual and his group. Should this phase of evaluation and interpretation be moved over too lightly or too quickly, frustrations evolving from attempts to gain new goals, or to achieve further change, may be so overwhelming as to lead to serious reversals of gains already acquired.

Significant contributions to learning may thus occur during the review and evaluative sessions conducted at the end of workshops, institutes, and demonstrations. The gains in learning are likely to be even greater if the group is drawn together again after a reality testing of the knowledge and practices acquired. Such postevaluations serve to reinforce successful experience, to identify errors in practices or barriers to effective action, to facilitate the sharing of ways of dealing with unexpected events, and to stimulate the reformulation of new goals upon the firm base of experience.

Should such evaluations not take place, some members of the group may remain uncertain or confused about ways of applying new knowledge. The sense of ambiguity resulting from half learnings, or conflicting learnings, may lead one to act prematurely and make unwise decisions. Studies of behavior under conditions of ambiguity suggest that a person who feels uncertain about the course of action to take tends to seek an end to the ambiguity by acting without adequate facts or by deciding not to take any action.[54]

It seems axiomatic that public health campaigns and projects are not successful if they are merely demonstrations. Some translation of the demonstration into a continued program is usually a mark of success. Review and evaluation sessions during the course of a demonstration, reconsidering goals, means of improvement, and long-term outcomes help to reinforce the learnings of the demonstration. The process, from the definition of concern, the formulation of goals, the choice of approaches, and evaluation of outcomes, in learning situations generally as in program development, is a continuous process. When such a process is effective, the definition of new concerns will tend to emerge out of the evaluation of previous outcomes. New potentialities for growth are thus crystallized into actions.

It should be noted that academicians are among the strongest violators of this general principle. By giving tests at the end of a school period, without providing an opportunity for students to review and evaluate their test responses, teachers may, without awareness, foster false learnings. Should the student make several serious errors and yet pass with a commendable grade (from his point of view), he may leave the course believing that his responses to the questions were correct. The positive reinforcement received by the final grade may be seen as a positive reward for answers which were, in fact, erroneous.

THE GROWING EDGE

In learning, as in other human processes, the uniqueness of each individual plays a significant role. Each differs from others in his capacities for learning, in his ability to adapt or to cope with a situation, in his patterns of aspiration, in his potential for critical self-evaluation. Education for him needs to take into account these and other special characteristics, as previously discussed, which make him a particular person.

Allport emphasizes that for any teacher, "The target should always be the growing edge of the student."[55] Too often, he notes, the growing edge of the instructor is the one nourished.

Whether in classroom, public meeting, or staff meeting, members of the group present will vary widely in their levels of concern, interest, or commitment, their previous knowledge and understanding of the issue, their coping potentials and access to resources, their patterns of aspiration and expectation. How, then, can one hope to nurture the growing edge of each member of a diverse group?

Of course, one cannot hope to achieve such perfection. Yet many steps can be taken to maximize the possibilities for individual and group learning. By enlisting their participation in obtaining a problem census, by drawing up questions for discussion, by providing opportunities to examine with their neighbors the significance and implications of points made, the possibilities for individual gains are enhanced. The democratic discussion techniques widely known among community educators offer great hope in dealing with this problem.

The importance of timeliness and appropriateness of content from the standpoint of the learner is beautifully stated in Whitehead's golden rule of education, a rule fully as applicable in public health practice as in the classroom.

"The mind is never passive; it is a perpetual activity, delicate, receptive, responsive to stimulus. You cannot postpone its life until you have sharpened it. Whatever interest attaches to your subject-matter must be evoked here and now; whatever powers you are strengthening in the pupil, must be exercised here and now; whatever possibilities of mental life your teaching should impart, must be exhibited here and now. That is the golden rule of education, and a very difficult rule to follow."[56]

NOTES TO CHAPTER 23

1. Mosel, James N., "The Learning Process," *Journal of Medical Education,* vol. 39, May, 1964, pp. 485–496.

2. Shimberg, Benjamin, and Jane S. Harris, "Evaluating a Nutrition Education Program," *Pretesting and Evaluating Health Education,* Public Health Monograph, no. 8, Public Health Service, Government Printing Office, Washington, 1952.

3. See Goodenough, Ward H., *Cooperation in Change: An Anthropological Approach to Community Development,* Russell Sage Foundation, New York, 1963, for an excellent review of the process and principles of community development. See also Bennis, Warren G., Kenneth D. Benne, and Robert Chin, editors, *The Planning of Change: Readings in Applied Behavioral Sciences,* Holt, Rinehart, and Winston, New York, 1961, and Cartwright, Dorwin, and Alvin Zander, editors, *Group Dynamics: Research and Theory,* 2d. ed., Harper and Row, New York, 1960, which provide many research and theoretical papers in this area. S. T. Kimball and Marion Pearsall, in *The Talladega Story: A Study in Community Process,* University of Alabama Press, University, 1954, describe a specific self-survey as viewed by sociologists. The community self-survey projects of the National Health Council follow the general pattern described above.

4. Festinger, Leon, *A Theory of Cognitive Dissonance.* Stanford University Press, Stanford, Calif., 1957, p. 260.

5. Spicer, Edward H., editor, *Human Problems in Technological Change: A Casebook.* Russell Sage Foundation, New York, 1952, p. 292.

6. Berlyne, Daniel E., *Conflict, Arousal, and Curiosity,* McGraw-Hill Series in Psychology, McGraw-Hill Book Co., New York, 1960; *Idem,* "Motivational Problems Raised by Exploratory and Epistemic Behavior, in Koch, Sigmund, editor, *Psychology: A Study of a Science,* Study 2, vol. 5, McGraw-Hill Book Co., New York, 1963, pp. 284–364.

7. *Idem,* "Motivational Problems Raised by Exploratory and Epistemic Behavior," in Koch, Sigmund, editor, *op. cit.,* pp. 303–304. References in the body of the quotation are: (a) Kish, G. B., and Antonitis, J. J., "Unconditioned Operant Behavior in Two Homozygous Strains of Mice," *Journal of Genetic Psychology,* vol. 88, 1956, pp. 121–124; (b) Girdner, J. B., "An Experiment Analysis of the Behavioral Effects of a Perceptual Consequence Unrelated to Organic Drive States," *American Psychologist,* vol. 8, 1953, pp. 354–355; Henderson, R. L., "Stimulus Intensity Dynamism and Secondary Reinforcement," unpublished doctoral dissertation, University of Missouri, 1953; Hurwitz, H. M. B., "Conditioned Responses in Rats Reinforced by Light," *British Journal of Animal Behavior,* vol. 4, 1956, pp. 31–33; (c) Butler, R. A., "Discrimination Learning by Rhesus Monkeys to Visual-Exploration Motivation," *Journal of*

Comparative and Physiological Psychology, vol. 46, 1953, pp. 95–98; (d) Jones, A., H. J. Wilkinson, and I. Braden, "Information Deprivation as a Motivational Variable," *Journal of Experimental Psychology,* vol. 62, 1961, pp. 126–137.

8. Heron, Woodburn, "The Pathology of Boredom," *Scientific American,* vol. 196, January, 1957, p. 52. Other studies in this same area of investigation may be found in Solomon, Philip, and associates, editors, *Sensory Deprivation,* A Symposium held at Harvard Medical School, Harvard University Press, Cambridge, Mass., 1961. For an evaluative review of these and other studies of "brain washing," see Kubzansky, Philip E., "The Effects of Reduced Environmental Stimulation on Human Behavior: A Review" in Biderman, Albert D., and Herbert Zimmer, editors, *The Manipulation of Human Behavior,* John Wiley and Sons, New York, 1961, pp. 51–95.

9. Heron, Woodburn, *op. cit.,* p. 54.

10. *Ibid.,* p. 56.

11. Hochbaum, Godfrey M., *Public Participation in Medical Screening Programs: A Socio-Psychological Study.* Public Health Service, U.S. Dept. of Health, Education, and Welfare, Publication 572, Government Printing Office, Washington, 1958, p. 11.

12. Janis, Irving L., and Seymour Feshback, "Effects of Fear-Arousing Communications," *Journal of Abnormal and Social Psychology,* vol. 48, 1953, pp. 78–92. For some explorations into the nature of anxieties relating to illness, see also Robbins, Paul R., "Level of Anxiety, Interference Proneness, and Defensive Reactions to Fear-Arousing," *Journal of Personality,* vol. 31, June, 1963, pp. 163–178; and *Idem,* "Some Explorations into the Nature of Anxieties Relating to Illness," *Genetic Psychology Monographs,* vol. 66, 1962, pp. 91–141.

13. Hovland, Carl I., Irving L. Janis, and Harold H. Kelley, *Communication and Persuasion.* Yale University Press, New Haven, 1953.

14. Whitehead, Alfred North, *The Aims of Education.* A Mentor Book, New American Library, New York, 1952, p. 30. Originally published by Macmillan Co., New York, 1929.

15. Berlyne, Daniel E., *Conflict, Arousal, and Curiosity,* pp. 296–297. (See Note 6.)

16. *Ibid.,* pp. 289–290.

17. Cantril, Hadley, *The "Why" of Man's Experience.* Macmillan Co., New York, 1950.

18. Berlyne, Daniel E., "Motivational Problems Raised by Exploratory and Epistemic Behavior," in Koch, Sigmund, editor, *op. cit.,* p. 328.

19. Derryberry, Mayhew, "How May the Nurse Become a Better Teacher?," *The Health Officer,* vol. 3, January, 1939, pp. 253–268. Reprinted by Office of Public Health Education, U.S. Public Health Service, Washington, n.d.

20. Hochbaum, Godfrey M., *op. cit.;* Rosenstock, Irwin M., Godfrey M. Hochbaum, Howard Leventhal, and associates, *The Impact of Asian Influenza on Community Life: A Study in Five Cities,* Public Health Service, U.S. Dept. of Health, Education, and Welfare, Publication 766, Government Printing Office, Washington, 1960; Heinzelmann, Fred, "Determinants of Prophylaxis Behavior with Respect to Rheumatic Fever," *Journal of Health and Human Behavior,* Summer, 1962, pp. 73–81; Kegeles, S. Stephen, "Why People Seek Dental Care: A Test of a Conceptual Formulation," *Journal of Health and Human Behavior,* vol. 4, Fall, 1963, pp. 166–173.

21. Hochbaum, Godfrey M., *op. cit.*, pp. 4–5.

22. Gadalla, Fawzy R. A., "A Study of Motivational Factors and Barriers Related to the Utilization of Prenatal Care by Mothers Delivered at Alameda County Hospital." Unpublished doctoral dissertation, University of California, Berkeley, 1962.

23. Gustafson, Harold C., "A Study of Private Physicians' and Public Health Physicians' Perceptions of Community Health Problems, Agency Structure, and Function." Unpublished doctoral dissertation, University of California, Berkeley, 1963.

24. Berlyne, Daniel E., *Conflict, Arousal, and Curiosity*, pp. 195 ff.

25. *Ibid.*, pp. 45–77.

26. Krech, David, and Richard S. Crutchfield, *Elements of Psychology*. Alfred A. Knopf, Inc., New York, 1961, p. 106.

27. Berlyne, Daniel E., *op. cit.*

28. Roshal, Sol M., "Effects of Learner Representation in Film-mediated Perceptual Motor Learning." Unpublished doctoral dissertation, Pennsylvania State College, 1949.

29. Thorndike, Edward L., *Animal Intelligence: Experimental Studies*. Macmillan Co., New York, 1911; Idem, *Human Learning*, Century Co., New York, 1931.

30. Tolman, Edward C., *Purposive Behavior in Animals and Men*, Century Co., New York, 1932; *Idem*, "Principles of Purposive Behavior," in Koch, Sigmund, editor, *Psychology: A Study of a Science*, pp. 92–157, Study 1, vol. 2.

31. For a classical study of latent learning, see Blodgett, H. C., "The Effect of the Introduction of Reward Upon the Maze Performance of Rats," University of California Publications in Psychology, vol. 4, 1924, pp. 113–134.

32. See Tolman, Edward C., *Purposive Behavior in Animals and Men*, Century Co., New York, 1932; Idem, *Behavior and Psychological Man: Essays in Motivation and Learning*, University of California Press, Berkeley, 1958. For his latest views on this topic, see *Idem*, "Principles of Purposive Behavior," in Koch, Sigmund, editor, *Psychology: A Study of a Science*, Study 1, vol. 2, pp. 124ff.; Daniel E. Berlyne, in his *Conflict, Arousal, and Curiosity*, takes a similar position.

33. Kirscht, John P., and Andie L. Knutson, "Science and Fluoridation: An Attitude Study," *Journal of Social Issues*, vol. 17, no. 4, 1961, pp. 37–44; Kirscht, John P., and Andie L. Knutson, "Fluoridation and the 'Threat' of Science," *Journal of Health and Human Behavior*, vol. 4, Summer, 1963.

34. Taylor, William, Accident Prevention Program, U.S. Public Health Service. Personal communication, October, 1962.

35. Hilgard, Ernest R., and Donald G. Marquis, *Conditioning and Learning*. D. Appleton Co., New York, 1940, p. 87.

36. Tolman, Edward C., "Principles of Purposive Behavior," in Koch, Sigmund, editor, *Psychology: A Study of a Science*, Study 1, vol. 2, pp. 92–157.

37. Koos, Earl L., *The Health of Regionville*. Columbia University Press. New York, 1954.

38. Roberts, Beryl J., "A Study of Selected Factors and Their Association with Action for Medical Care." Unpublished doctoral dissertation, Harvard University, 1956.

39. Kelman, Herbert C., "Processes of Opinion Change" in Bennis, Warren G., Kenneth D. Benne, and Robert Chin, editors, *The Planning of Change: Readings in the Applied Behavioral Sciences.* Holt, Rinehart, and Winston, New York, 1961, pp. 509–516.

40. Dewey, John, *The School and Society.* University of Chicago Press, Chicago, 1900.

41. Allport, Gordon W., *Personality and Social Encounter: Selected Essays.* Beacon Press, Boston, 1960, p. 181.

42. Guetzkow, Harold, *Simulation in Social Science.* Prentice-Hall, Inc., Englewood Cliffs, N.J., 1962.

43. Allport, Gordon W., *op. cit.,* chap. 12.

44. Hoff, Wilbur I., "The Prediction of Patients for Rehabilitation." Unpublished doctoral dissertation, University of California, Berkeley, 1963. Attention is also invited to Lofquist, Lloyd H., editor, *Psychological Research and Rehabilitation,* American Psychological Association, Washington, 1960, and Wright, Beatrice A., editor, *Psychology and Rehabilitation,* American Psychological Association, Washington, 1959.

45. Griffiths, William, "The Learning Process," *Bulletin* of the National Tuberculosis Association, vol. 41, May, 1955, pp. 69–70.

46. Spicer, Edward H., editor, *Human Problems in Technological Change: A Casebook,* Russell Sage Foundation, New York, 1952, p. 292; Lionberger, Herbert F., *Adoption of New Ideas and Practices,* Iowa State University Press, Ames, 1960.

47. Cantril, Hadley, *op. cit.*

48. Nyswander, Dorothy B., "Group Dynamics," *Health Education Monograph,* no. 10, 1961, pp. 3–15; Hare, A. Paul, Edgar F. Borgatta, and Robert F. Bales, *Small Groups: Studies in Social Interaction,* Alfred A. Knopf, Inc., New York, 1955; Cartwright, Dorwin, and Alvin Zander, editors, *Group Dynamics: Research and Theory,* 2d ed., Harper and Row, New York, 1960; Lewin, Kurt, *Resolving Social Conflicts,* edited by Gertrud W. Lewin, Harper and Bros., New York, 1948.

49. Blackwell, Barbara, "Expectations of Upper Middle Class Adults About Their Activities Prior to Seeking Professional Medical Care for Physical and Psychiatric Health Conditions." Unpublished doctoral dissertation, University of California, Berkeley, 1963, pp. 65–67.

50. *Ibid.,* p. 88.

51. *Ibid.,* p. 141.

52. Mednick, Sarnoff A., with the collaboration of Howard R. Pollio, *Learning.* Foundations of Modern Psychology Series, edited by Richard Lazarus. Prentice-Hall, Inc., Englewood Cliffs, N.J., 1964, p. 95.

53. Krech, David, and Richard S. Crutchfield, *op. cit.,* pp. 429–430.

54. Frenkel-Brunswick, Else, "Intolerance of Ambiguity as an Emotional and Perceptual Personality Variable," *Journal of Personality,* vol. 18, 1947, pp. 108–143; Smock, Charles D., "The Influence of Psychological Stress on the Intolerance of Ambiguity," *Journal of Abnormal and Social Psychology,* vol. 50, 1955, pp. 177–182.

55. Allport, Gordon W., "The Teaching-Learning Situation," *Public Health Reports,* vol. 68, September, 1953, p. 875.

56. Whitehead, Alfred North, *op. cit.,* p. 18.

Chapter 24

Verbal Conditioning

IN RECENT YEARS psychologists have given increasing attention to the phenomenon known as verbal conditioning, described briefly in the discussion of Greenspoon's pioneer study.[1] It will be recalled that he was able to condition subjects to respond with particular classes of pronouns by employing the verbal reinforcer "mm hmm" when subjects mentioned these pronouns in an operant conditioning experiment.

The use of praise and reproof in operant conditioning is not new to psychology. Thorndike reported many studies in which he employed the terms "right" and "wrong" in guiding conditioning in trial and error learning.[2] However, as Salzinger points out, verbal responses have more often been employed as indices of other behaviors than as behaviors in their own right.[3] Investigators have tended to be more concerned about influencing attitudes, emotions, and other behaviors than in influencing verbal responses, and have looked toward the verbal data as verbal reports.

In an interesting behavioristic description of verbal behavior Skinner has given emphasis to operant conditioning as the primary manner in which we learn to communicate with one another, and with ourselves. He uses the term "verbal behavior" in this situation to apply to all behavior that is reinforced by the mediation of another person, and defines as "verbal" in this sense "any movement capable of affecting another organism."[4] Other theorists would question so broad an interpretation.

Skinner's position as the primary exponent of operant conditioning is stated forthrightly in his text:

> The basic processes and relations which give verbal behavior its special characteristics are now fairly well understood. Much of the experimental work responsible for this advance has been carried out on other species, but the results have proved to be surprisingly free of species restrictions. Recent work has shown that the methods can be extended

428

to human behavior without serious modification. Quite apart from the possibility of extrapolating specific experimental findings, the formulation provides a fruitful new approach to human behavior in general, and enables us to deal more effectively with that subdivision called verbal.[5]

He argues that there is no need to posit such constructs as "motivation" and "meaning" in order to describe, predict, and understand man's communications with man. Reinforcement from the verbal environment is considered to be all that is necessary. More recently he has restated this position somewhat. "An adequate analysis must also reach into the traditional fields of motivation and emotion to determine what is reinforcing and under what conditions."[6]

In his book Skinner draws upon a wealth of fascinating personal observation and literary illustration, but includes no experimental support for his position. His book has, however, led other researchers to seek the experimental evidence his presentation lacks.

Most behavioral scientists do not agree with Skinner's extreme position that the findings from studies on verbal conditioning can be reasonably interpreted without resort to motivation and meaning. Osgood, Suci, and Tannenbaum, for example, have provided ample experimental support for the significance of meaning in verbal responses.[7] A healthy controversy in these areas of research is stimulating much creative effort.[8]

AWARENESS IN VERBAL CONDITIONING

Questions have also been raised concerning the issue of awareness in verbal conditioning. To what extent are subjects undergoing verbal conditioning aware of the nature of the experiment, the kind of reinforcement they are receiving, and the response they are expected to make? Does learning occur without the subject becoming aware at all? Is awareness an important or a necessary condition to better verbal conditioning (and thus to learning under this procedure)?

Awareness and Learning

The role of awareness in learning has long been one of interest. Thorndike offered evidence that learning does occur without subjects apparently being aware although such "unconscious learning is relatively undependable and slow."[9] Thorndike argued for awareness and understanding as being of great significance to learning, contributing to effectiveness through operation of the laws of effect and its corollaries:

> It is natural to assume that the idea of an act plus the ability to perform it plus the will or desire to perform it will produce it. Psychologists, like ordinary folk, have usually accepted this apparent induction from the observation of human behavior. Their modifications of it have been chiefly to note that the will or desire to perform it may be absent, the mere idea of an act that is within a person's repertory being often adequate to produce it. It is also natural to assume that the idea of an act plus the idea of desirable consequences attached to it will be potent to produce it, if it is within one's repertory. The idea of desirable consequences attached to it will, it is assumed, arouse desire to perform it or incline the person toward it in other ways.
>
> So long as we are sufficiently liberal in our definition of "idea of an act" and "idea of desirable consequences," and so long as we restrict our field of observation to the sophisticated behavior of man, these assumptions work fairly well.[10]

Investigators have since provided much evidence that when subjects are aware, learning occurs more quickly, and that this principle holds for verbal conditioning as well as for other learning.[11] Awareness, as Salzinger has pointed out, may take many forms. "A subject can be aware of what constitutes the reinforcement without knowing what the response is that is being conditioned; he may be aware of both the reinforcement and the response; and finally he may be aware of neither the response nor the reinforcement; he may not even know that he is in an experimental situation as in Verplanck's experiment."[12]

Greenspoon, in his study of verbal conditioning, reported that his subjects tended to be unaware of the "mm hmm" reinforcement technique he was using.[13] Since such a finding has important implications for therapy, it stimulated considerable research to learn under what conditions verbal conditioning takes place without awareness.

However, findings in this area of research have been conflicting. Krasner, in his review of 24 studies of verbal conditioning, noted that only about 5 per cent of the subjects were reported to be "aware," and that the learning of this group was not better than the learning of naive subjects.[14] Other researchers have tended to support Thorndike's position that awareness, when it occurs, contributes to learning.

Experimental Study of Awareness

In reviewing some of the conflicting evidence, and in particular a number of studies designed to understand the effects of awareness-unawareness in verbal conditioning, Farber noted that while unaware subjects tended to be "slow and undependable," as described by Thorndike, all aware subjects did not improve.[15]

Farber and his associates designed a novel experiment to gain a greater understanding of the significance of awareness-unawareness. They were interested in knowing the effects of reinforcing verbal responses of different kinds and the effect of giving one experimental group instructions that suggested failure. By employing questions at the end of the interview, they were able to study the extent of awareness and its varying effects. Their experimental approach was described as follows:

Following Taffel's general procedure, each of 120 subjects was shown 80 cards, on each of which were typed four pronouns, "I," "You," "He," "They," in a vertical line, followed by a verb. For one-third of the subjects, the 80 verbs were hostile, ranging from "slew" and "hated" at one end of a good-bad scale to "rebuked" and "pestered." One-third were given neutral verbs, such as "touched" and "observed." And one-third were given nurturant verbs, ranging in good-bad evaluation from "accorded" and "fondled" to "encouraged" and "cherished." Subjects were instructed to make up a sentence for each card, including the verb and beginning with one of the four pronouns. After 20 cards had been presented, there was a brief pause. The experimenter repeated the original instructions for half the subjects. These were called the "neutral" instructions. He scolded the other half for lack of effort, inattention, mumbling, and general ineptitude. Graduate student observers who heard him agreed that he sounded nasty. These were called the "failure" instructions. After this interlude, subjects constructed 60 more sentences, with brief pauses after each block of 20 trials. But now the experimenter said "good" each time a sentence was begun with the pronoun "You."

So, our basic question was very simple. We wanted to know the effect of saying "good" if and when subjects, after being bawled out, say, "You tormented your cat" or "You ought to be lynched," as opposed to "You befriended the needy" or "You will be rewarded."[16]

Following the completion of the 80 cards, subjects were asked to reply in writing to the following questions:

1. Did you notice anything in particular that the experimenter did when you were making up sentences? Circle Yes or No.

2. If "yes," what did you notice, and when?
3. How did you react to this? What did you do?[17]

The design of the experiment thus permitted comparison between those receiving "failure" instructions and those receiving neutral instructions. On the basis of replies to the first two questions, subjects could also be classed in terms of their reported awareness-unawareness.

Twenty-six of the 60 subjects receiving neutral instructions indicated awareness that "good" was being used as a reinforcer as compared with only 17 of the 60 subjects who received "failure" instructions. Thus the report of failing tended to decrease awareness of some subjects. However, subjects in both groups who reported being aware made good progress in learning whereas, as a group, those who were unaware of the use of "good" as a conditioner made no progress. In fact, they regressed during the last trials. Awareness thus seemed closely tied to progress in learning.

The Meaning of Awareness

The responses to the third question, "How did you react to this? What did you do?" yielded interesting new insights regarding the influence of awareness. His findings suggest some of the reasons awareness is not directly reflected in improvement in studies of this nature.

One group of subjects who said that when they became aware they used "you" more often were identified as conformers. About 70 per cent of the responses of this group to the last 20 cards were "you" responses. Subjects who said being aware did not influence their responses were identified as nonconformers. About 35 per cent of their responses to the last 20 questions were "you" responses, whereas less than 20 per cent of the responses of unaware subjects were "you" responses to these questions. Being aware of the reinforcement and conforming—adhering to the demands of the experimental situation thus led to high learning scores.

The verbal reports indicate that the aware, but nonconforming, subjects also learned, even though their responses do not so indicate. Their rejection of experimental demands and their interest in not complying is revealed by some of their comments. One said, "I said 'you' a few more times to prove I was right, then attempted to continue as before and give all pronouns equal utterance." Another aware subject observed, "I felt funny when I said 'you.' "

In general, Farber's studies identify awareness as an important factor in reinforcement of verbal conditioning, but awareness does not necessarily lead to learning as measured by response. "It appears, as Dulaney has nicely put it, 'that a human subject does what he thinks he is supposed to do if he wants to . . .!' "[18]

PUBLIC HEALTH IMPLICATIONS OF VERBAL CONDITIONING

In his text on verbal behavior, Skinner emphasized the importance of research in this area from the standpoint of practical problems of society. His statement reflects his own commitment to behaviorism as the primary explanatory principle of human response.

> The "understanding" of verbal behavior is something more than the use of a consistent vocabulary with which specific instances may be described. It is not to be confused with the confirmation of any set of theoretical principles. The criteria are more demanding than that. The extent to which we understand verbal behavior in a "causal" analysis is to be assessed from the extent to which we can predict the occurrence of specific instances and, eventually, from the extent to which we can produce or control such behavior by altering the conditions under which it occurs. In representing such a goal it is helpful to keep certain specific engineering tasks in mind. How can the teacher establish the specific verbal repertoires which are the principal end-products of education? How can the therapist uncover latent verbal behavior in a therapeutic interview? How can the writer evoke his own verbal behavior in the act of composition? How can the scientist, mathematician, or logician manipulate his verbal behavior in productive thinking? Practical problems of this sort are, of course, endless. To solve them is not the immediate goal of a scientific analysis, but they underline the kinds of processes and relationships which such an analysis must consider.[19]

Research studies are just beginning in the areas Skinner mentioned, and some of these studies are of much interest to public health.

Verbal Conditioning in Therapy

Clinical psychologists were among the first to react to Greenspoon's studies since therapy leans heavily upon verbal response. The verbal exchange of therapist and patient tends to be one in which patients are encouraged to be frank in expressing concerns, conflicts, and emotions as part of the process of seeking personal insights. To the extent that verbal conditioning takes place in this setting it could be a significant factor in either facilitating or retarding therapeutic progress. Krasner, in reviewing research in this area, regarded the verbal conditioning experimental approach as one that might offer a means of systematically isolating and examining significant factors in the therapist-client relationship.[20]

A number of investigators have examined the influence of the prestige of the experimenter in achieving effects. While their findings do not agree, some studies do indicate this factor to be important.[21] One would expect such a relationship on the basis of parallel research on factors influencing communications.[22] An issue in studies of this type, which are most difficult to control because of individual variation, is determining who holds prestige, from the subject's point of view, for a particular purpose and setting. The investigator's estimates as to which therapist has most prestige and acceptability to the patient may be in error.

The influence of verbal conditioning on the content of the therapeutic session has been investigated by Murray, who found that therapists do tend to guide the therapeutic interview by this means. He found that those areas of content of which the therapist approved tended to show an increase in frequency of discussion, whereas those areas which the therapist disapproved of showed a decrease during the course of therapy.[23]

Investigators are only beginning to examine the relative effectiveness of verbal conditioning as a therapeutic approach as used with different kinds of patients and under varying conditions of deprivation, anxiety, or drug therapy. There is some evidence that schizophrenics will be more difficult to condition in this way than manic depressive patients, for example.[24] One would expect finding common grounds for communicating with schizophrenics to be particularly difficult.

Opinion Surveys

The implications of verbal conditioning to surveys of information, attitude, and opinion are highlighted in recent studies. The interest in verbal learning effects has also reawakened interest in much previous research on interviewer rapport and procedure, question wording and manner of vocalizing, question order, the characteristics of the interview, and like matters which Cantril,[25] Payne,[26] and others have examined at length.

In recent studies Hildum and Brown have demonstrated that it is possible through verbal reinforcement to increase statements of opinion in an interview situation, and also to shape these opinions.[27] Another investigator has found that even shaking one's head served as an effective negative reinforcer, leading to a decrease in verbal comments of the type preceding the head shake.[28]

Field, in a public opinion study, found that through the use of praise it was possible to induce respondents to answer with fewer "don't know's." The statements "That's fine," "That's a good answer," and "Lots of people agree with you on that" were used in systematic manner. After the subject's first "don't know" response, the interviewer said, "That's perfectly all right. We're glad to have you say that rather than to give an opinion you don't really have." With a control group the remarks of the interviewer were limited to "all right" or "okay."[29]

A check question about the functions of an imaginary coordinating committee was used to see whether such techniques would influence the quality of response, and another analysis was also carried out as a check on honesty of response. On the check question, significantly fewer of the respondents in the experimental group, as compared with controls receiving no praise, indicated that they had never heard of this committee.

Field concluded, "Here we have seen that praise tended to reduce the number of 'don't know' responses, to increase the originality and number of answers, and that it did not have the negative effects of making the respondents insincere or dishonest in their responses. It would appear, then, that systematized praise might be a valuable tool in obtaining more valid results in public opinion polling."[30]

Diagnostic Interview

To the extent that verbal conditioning guides or shapes responses in the diagnostic interview, which has as its primary purpose obtaining valid and reliable personal information, one might expect it to have a similar influence on other areas of information or data collection. Findings in this area are thus of particular interest to public health research and programs.

Salzinger reports studies in which investigators have been able, through verbal conditioning, to obtain significant differences in the patterns of response to projective tests such as ink blot tests.[31] This is particularly significant since the intention of the projective approach is to promote maximum freedom on the part of the subject in expressing himself. Even a minimum of influence in this area could give a different direction to the diagnosis from that desired.

Salzinger, and Salzinger and Pisoni employed verbal conditioning in the diagnostic interview to increase the number of statements of affect made by patients in which personal pronouns were used.[32] Another investigator showed that one could condition responses to statements which indicated acceptance or rejection of oneself.[33] This issue is of considerable interest to those who use interviews or questionnaires to obtain personal data such as are obtained in health surveys.

Staats followed up Nuthmann's research with studies to learn to what extent verbal conditioning could shape diagnosis in personality. He used for his research items from the Guilford-Zimmerman personality test, supplementing the items in the areas of sociability and activity by similar items to extend them so that each of the two tests would have 100 items. Nuthmann's research had shown that responses to specific items could be conditioned by reinforcement. He wished to learn if verbal conditioning could influence responses to similar, but not identical items. Thus additional personality items were written with both similar and opposite meanings to those used in the original test.[34]

> For example, "You find it easy to start conversation with a stranger," is an original G-Z item. Matching items used were, "It is difficult for you to begin talking to a stranger," and "You enjoy making friends with strangers." Seventy of these items were selected to add to the 30 original items.[35]

Forty "filler items" were then added to the test and the original 100 items were randomly assigned to five blocks of 20 items each so that the type of item would not be a factor in responses.

In his research Staats found that responses to items relating to the two characteristics studied—sociability and activity—were influenced in a striking manner by verbal reinforcement. In both studies the final blocks of items were responded to in a significantly different manner, as predicted. Subjects were thus conditioned to respond to the general class of item, as well as to the specific item. Reinforcing some sociability items led respondents to reply in a consistent manner regarding other items, even though they were worded very differently.

A significant question which Staats raises, but does not answer, concerns the extent to which such verbal conditioning may influence actual behavior in the social setting. He asks whether one can, through such verbal conditioning, actually influence the pattern of personality as Skinner has proposed.

Awareness in Experimental Research

Orne has drawn attention to the importance of this variable of awareness to all experimental situations. He notes that subjects tend to estimate the purpose of experimental procedures and respond to cues they receive while participating in the experiment.[36]

> The subject's performance in an experiment might almost be conceptualized as problem-solving behavior; that is, at some level he sees it as his task to ascertain the true purpose of the experiment and respond in a manner which will support the hypotheses being tested. Viewed in this light, the totality of cues which convey an experimental hypothesis to the subject become significant determinants of subjects' behavior. We have labeled the sum total of such cues as the *"demand characteristics of the experimental situation."* These cues include the rumors or campus scuttlebutt about the research, the information conveyed during the original solicitation, the person of the experimenter, and the setting of the laboratory, as well as all explicit and implicit communications during the experiment proper. A frequently overlooked, but nonetheless very significant, source of cues for the subject lies in the experimental procedure itself, viewed in the light of the subjects' previous knowledge and experience.[37]

Sherman and others have provided experimental evidence that the subjects' expectations regarding hypotheses can have significant influence on findings.[38]

It should be recognized that verbal conditionings, unintentional in these instances, are among the significant cues employed in identifying the experimenter's intentions. Awareness may thus foster learning and response in unintended and undesired ways. As Hall has shown, the kind of instructions given subjects, whether these instructions are task-oriented or ego-oriented, influence the effectiveness of verbal reinforcements employed.[39]

One could scarcely hazard a guess regarding the potential significance of verbal conditioning in experimental research in public health and medicine. Orne, whose association with the Harvard Medical School has drawn him into the heart of this issue in medical research, notes that using placebos in research is not always an adequate solution to the difficult problem of maintaining controls without "contamination."

> The use of placebo experimental conditions is a way in which this problem can be dealt with in a more classic fashion. Psychopharma-

cology has used such techniques extensively, but here too they present problems. In the case of placebos and drugs, it is often the case that the physician is "blind" as to whether a drug is placebo or active, but the patient is not, despite precautions to the contrary; i.e., the patient is cognizant that he does not have the side effects which some of his fellow patients on the ward experience. By the same token, in psychological placebo treatments, it is equally important to ascertain whether the subject actually perceived the treatment to be experimental or control. Certainly the subject's perception of himself as a control subject may materially alter the situation.[40]

UNSETTLED ISSUES

Many issues remain unsettled regarding the nature of verbal conditioning, the necessary conditions for its occurrence, factors influencing its effect, and the extent of its significance in human transactions. Of particular interest are awareness and meaning. How much verbal conditioning takes place in the absence of awareness? Does generalization to broad areas of meaning occur without the subject's being aware that he is influenced? Can verbal conditioning be employed to influence people against their will and regarding issues they consciously oppose?

Farber's evidence[41] raises doubts about the lack of awareness that other researchers report, and suggests that subjects may be responding to the demands of the experimental situation reported by Orne and others.[42] Sarbin[43] and Andersen[44] have provided evidence that subjects in hypnosis experiments tend to be far more alert to what is happening than has previously been assumed. The gap between suggestion and hypnosis is thus very narrow. Is this true also for the gap between verbal conditioning and persuasion?

CONCLUSIONS

These uncertainties regarding the process of verbal conditioning and the underlying dynamics of its occurrence ought not distract us from being aware of its significance in therapeutic, diagnostic, data gathering, and experimental situations, and of its possible significance in all areas involving interpersonal transactions. There is solid evidence that verbal conditioning does shape responses under varying conditions and in unexpected ways.

Whether or not subjects are aware that they are being conditioned to respond in particular ways through reinforcement may be less important in some ways than whether the person or persons providing the reinforcement are aware of the manner and extent of their influence in shaping behaviors. It is most disturbing to think that public health workers of all disciplines may, at times, be unintentionally shaping their data by this means. The evidence reported highlights the importance of employing double blind studies in experimental research.

Verbal conditioning may be in part responsible for the effects of the administrative climate of hospitals on nurses' orientations toward the hospital patient, as reported by Mathews. She found that staff nurses' person-centeredness toward patients was significantly related to the administrative staff's emphasis on social processes. Nurses supervised by a head nurse who perceived this administrative climate as social process-oriented tended to be more person-centered in their activities than staff nurses supervised by nurses who perceived the hospital administrative climate as being more technologically focused.[45]

It is disturbing also to think that the health officer, program director, or supervisor wishing to support creativity, independence, and initiative may unwittingly influence his staff to respond and to act in less flexible manner; or that health workers providing services in homes, clinics, hospitals, and other community settings may unknowingly shape the responses of their clients in unintended ways. The issue deserves far greater attention from researchers than it has been given.

NOTES TO CHAPTER 24

1. Greenspoon, Joel, "The Reinforcing Frequency of Two Spoken Sounds on the Frequency of Two Responses," *American Journal of Psychiatry,* vol. 68, September, 1955, pp. 409–416.

2. Thorndike, Edward L., *The Psychology of Wants, Interests and Attitudes.* The Century Psychology Series. D. Appleton-Century Co., New York, 1935.

3. Salzinger, Kurt, "Experimental Manipulation of Verbal Behavior: A Review," *Journal of General Psychology,* vol. 61, First Half, July, 1959, pp. 65–94.

4. Skinner, B. F., *Verbal Behavior.* The Century Psychology Series. Appleton-Century-Crofts, Inc., New York, 1957, pp. 2, 14.

5. *Ibid.,* p. 3.

6. Skinner, B. F., "Operant Behavior," *American Psychologist,* vol. 18, August, 1963, p. 514.

7. Osgood, Charles E., George J. Suci, and Percy H. Tannenbaum, *The Measurement of Meaning.* University of Illinois Press, Urbana, 1957.

8. See the following for a discussion of the various positions regarding the evidence of mediation in verbal learning: Cofer, Charles N., editor, *Verbal Learning and Verbal Behavior: Proceedings* of a Conference sponsored by the Office of Naval Research and New York University, 1959, McGraw-Hill Book Co., New York, 1961; Cofer, Charles N., and Barbara S. Musgrave, editors, *Verbal Behavior and Learning: Problems and Processes: Proceedings* of the Sec-

ond Conference sponsored by the Office of Naval Research and New York University, McGraw-Hill Book Co., New York, 1963.

9. Thorndike, Edward L., *op. cit.;* see especially chap. 5, pp. 62–70.

10. *Ibid.,* p. 81.

11. For an evaluation of these findings as they apply to verbal conditioning, see Salzinger, Kurt, *op. cit.,* and Farber, I. E., "The Things People Say to Themselves," *American Psychologist,* vol. 18, April, 1963, pp. 185–197.

12. Salzinger, Kurt, *op. cit.,* p. 84.

13. Greenspoon, Joel, *op. cit.*

14. Krasner, Leonard, "Studies of the Conditioning of Verbal Behavior," *Psychological Bulletin,* vol. 55, 1958, pp. 148–171.

15. Farber, I. E., *op. cit.*

16. *Ibid.,* pp. 188–189.

17. *Ibid.,* p. 189.

18. Dulaney, Don E., "The Place of Hypotheses and Intentions: An Analysis of Verbal Control in Verbal Conditioning" in Eriksen, Charles W., editor, *Behavior and Awareness—A Symposium of Research and Interpretation.* Duke University Press, Durham, N.C., 1962, pp. 102–129. Quoted in Farber, I. E., *op. cit.,* p. 192.

19. Skinner, B. F., *op. cit.,* p. 3.

20. Krasner, Leonard, *op. cit.*

21. Salzinger, Kurt, *op. cit.,* p. 80. The reader is also referred to Cohen, B. D., and associates, "Experimental Manipulation of Verbal Behavior," *Journal of Experimental Psychology,* vol. 47, 1954, pp. 106–110; Mahrer, A. R., "The Role of Expectancy in Delayed Reinforcement," *Journal of Experimental Psychology,* vol. 52, 1956, pp. 101–106; Mausner, B., "Studies in Social Interaction: I. A Conceptual Scheme," *Journal of Social Psychology,* vol. 41, 1955, pp. 259–270; Salzinger, Kurt, and Stephanie Pisoni, "Reinforcement of Affect Responses of Schizophrenics During the Clinical Interview," *Journal of Abnormal and Social Psychology,* vol. 57, 1958, pp. 84–90; Salzinger, Kurt, and Stephanie Pisoni, "Reinforcement of Verbal Affect Responses of Schizophrenics During the Clinical Interview: The Effect on Conditioning of Placement of the Period of Reinforcement," Paper presented at the American Psychological Association, New York City, 1957; Verplanck, W. S., "The Operant, from Rat to Man: An Introduction to Some Recent Experiments on Human Behavior," *Transactions,* New York Academy of Science, vol. 17, 1955, pp. 594–601; Wickes, T. A., Jr., "Examiner Influence in a Testing Situation," *Journal of Consulting Psychology,* vol. 20, 1956, pp. 23–25.

22. See Chapter 27 of this volume.

23. Murray, Edward J., "A Content-analysis Method for Studying Psychotherapy," *Psychological Monographs,* vol. 70, No. 420, 1956. Referred to by Salzinger, Kurt, *op. cit.,* p. 74.

24. Salzinger, Kurt, *op. cit.,* p. 88.

25. Cantril, Hadley, *Gauging Public Opinion.* Princeton University Press, Princeton, N.J., 1944.

26. Payne, Stanley Le Baron, *The Art of Asking Questions.* Princeton University Press, Princeton, N.J., 1951.

27. Hildum, D. C., and R. W. Brown, "Verbal Reinforcement and Inter-

viewer Bias," *Journal of Abnormal and Social Psychology,* vol. 53, 1956, pp. 108–111. Referred to by Salzinger, Kurt, *op. cit.,* p. 74.

28. Hartman, C. H., "Verbal Behavior of Schizophrenic and Normal Subjects as a Function of Types of Social Reinforcement." Unpublished doctoral dissertation, State University of Iowa, 1955. Referred to by Salzinger, Kurt, *op. cit.,* p. 77.

29. Field, Joan B., "The Effects of Praise in a Public Opinion Poll," *Public Opinion Quarterly,* vol. 19, Spring, 1955, pp. 85–91.

30. *Ibid.,* p. 91.

31. Salzinger, Kurt, *op. cit.,* p. 73.

32. Salzinger, Suzanne, "Rate of Affect Response in Schizophrenics as a Function of Three Types of Interviewer Verbal Behavior," Paper presented at the Eastern Psychological Association, Atlantic City, 1956; Salzinger, Kurt, and Stephanie Pisoni, *opera cit.* See references to these studies in Salzinger, Kurt, *op. cit.,* p. 74.

33. Nuthmann, A. M., "Conditioning of a Response Class on a Personality Test," *Journal of Abnormal and Social Psychology,* vol. 54, 1957, pp. 19–23. See reference to this in Staats, Arthur W., and associates, "Operant Conditioning of Factor Analytic Personality Traits," *Journal of General Psychology,* vol. 66, First Half, January, 1962, p. 101.

34. Staats, Arthur W., *op. cit.,* pp. 101–114.

35. *Ibid.,* p. 103.

36. Orne, Martin T., "On the Social Psychology of the Psychological Experiment: With Particular Reference to Demand Characteristics and Their Implications," *American Psychologist,* vol. 17, November, 1962, p. 776. See also Orne, Martin T., "The Demand Characteristics of an Experimental Design and Their Implications," Paper read at American Psychological Association, Cincinnati, 1959.

37. Orne, Martin T., "On the Social Psychology of the Psychological Experiment: With Particular Reference to Demand Characteristics and Their Implications," p. 779.

38. Sherman, Susan Roth, "Demand Characteristics of the Experimental Situation as a Factor Influencing the Outcome in Studies of Attitude Change." Unpublished doctoral dissertation, University of California, Berkeley, 1964.

39. Hall, William E., "The Effects of Set and Reinforcement in Verbal Conditioning," *Journal of General Psychology,* vol. 63, Second Half, October, 1960, pp. 239–248.

40. Orne, Martin T., *op. cit.,* p. 782.

41. Farber, I. E., *op. cit.*

42. Orne, Martin T., *op. cit.*

43. Sarbin, Theodore R., "Contributions to Role-taking History: I. Hypnotic Behavior," *Psychological Review,* vol. 57, 1950, pp. 255–270.

44. Andersen, Milton L., "Correlates of Hypnotic Performance: A Historical and Role-Theoretical Analysis." Unpublished doctoral dissertation, University of California, Berkeley, 1963.

45. Mathews, Betty P., "A Study of the Effect of Administrative Climate on the Nurse's Psychological Orientation Toward the Hospital Patient." Unpublished doctoral dissertation, University of California, Berkeley, 1960.

Part Eight

The Communication Process

Part Eight

The Communication Process

COMMUNICATION is the means we have of sharing our experiences with one another. The word "communication" is derived from the Latin *communis*. As Schramm notes, "When we communicate we are trying to establish a 'commonness' with someone. That is, we are trying to share information, an idea, or an attitude. . . . The essence of communication is getting the receiver and the sender 'tuned' together for a particular message."[1]

There is a tendency at times to think of communication as a process whereby one person, the communicator, consciously selects the ideas to communicate, organizes them into meaningful form and presents them in a systematic fashion. The other person may be seen as a sort of open bottle into which this communication flows. Presumably he receives the facts completely accurately and unaltered, sorts them out, evaluates them, integrates them with other facts available to him, all in a conscious, systematic manner. Then he is supposed to act. Of course, if he does not act we may say he is stubborn, or indifferent, or stupid.

Alan Gregg observed that this approach to communication ignores the fact that there must be some suction in the bottle—that there always is suction in the bottle. Not only is there suction, but the suction is selective: many facts do not get in; others are transformed in the process of getting in. Their significance for the individual may also undergo change from that intended by the communicator.[2]

As Gregg's observation implies, the individual on the receiving end of the communication, the communicant, has a most significant influence on the communication process. In spite of the best attempts of our modern advertising agents, the communicant still retains control over the suction of the bottle and consciously or subconsciously selects and organizes the symbols that come into awareness. A growing body of evidence supports the view that the whole communication process from beginning to end is a dynamic process, with undercurrents of need and purpose constantly present, shaping the behavior of both the communicator and the person with whom he is trying to communicate.

There is special merit, therefore, in Cooley's definition of the process of communication as "the mechanism through which human relations exist and develop—all the symbols of the mind, together with the means of conveying them through space and preserving them in time."[3] Gestures, sounds, pictures, words, signs, and actions, too, are the basic means we have for passing along our ideas, feelings, images, and intentions from one person to another and from one generation to another.

Accuracy of communication involves far more than the way we put words together in our attempts to convey meanings. Communication, as a process of transferring meanings, involves the transmission of unique personal significances that we give to the words or other symbols used. The intonations, the pauses, the gestures, the nature of the setting in which the communication takes place, the expectations and anticipations of the other person regarding our expressions, and a host of other factors contribute to the meaning transmitted. A spanking and a love tap may differ only in the intention conveyed.

Cantril, in *The Politics of Despair,* warns that "we must constantly remind ourselves that what exists outside of us has no consistent meaning or relevance to our behavior until we learn its significance *to us.* This significance depends on what we *bring to* a situation, what we *make of it.*"[4]

Man is constantly seeking to reshape his world better to serve his personal and group needs, and employs all the signs, symbols, and other means of influence at his disposal. Even while doing this, however, he is at the same time seeking meaning from the world about him so that he can cope with it more effectively. Nor is man alone in this effort to understand environment. The lowliest of living creatures show signs of irritability that suggest awareness, some crude perceptiveness that enables them to take adaptive actions.

Yet man has a greater capacity than any other animal for using symbols in his communications. By using symbols to represent things, and relations between things, he is able to transmit ideas to other persons whether they are present or not, and about things that may not even exist.

Perhaps his greatest quality is this capacity for creating and giving symbolic labels and values to intangible or abstract things. By making use of this capacity, he is able to extend himself so that he can participate in groups far removed in space and time, and share with others his thoughts, his beliefs, his hopes, his fears, his concerns, his expectations, and intentions. At the same time, by making use of the recorded communications of others far removed, he may draw upon them for guidance, identification, and support in facing situations they could never have directly experienced or specifically anticipated.

Such communication makes possible man's social life, for man as a social being could not exist without this rare human capacity. In communicating with others we draw upon all the capacities we have, both native and acquired, for sensing and perceiving, interpreting and understanding, emoting and expressing. Our efforts throughout are influenced by all the factors previously noted as contributing to the effectiveness of cognitive and emotional functioning. One might, indeed, view communication as a dynamic process into which all of man's capacities, abilities, motives, and expectations become synthesized in action.

Full treatment of the subject of communication at this time would, therefore, involve a focused interpretation of all previous chapters. Those interested in such an approach are referred to more adequate sources. Rather, it seems appropriate at this point to discuss the communication process in terms of some of the special situations of public health. This may at once illustrate the manner in which various physical, social, and personal forces enter into the process and suggest a point of view that may help the reader have a clearer understanding of a unique situation.

NOTES TO INTRODUCTION TO PART EIGHT

1. Schramm, Wilbur, editor, *The Process and Effects of Mass Communication.* University of Illinois Press, Urbana, 1955, p. 3.

2. Gregg, Alan, in Galdston, Iago, editor, and Hans Zetterberg, research associate, *Panic and Morale: Conference Transactions.* New York Academy of Medicine and the Josiah Macy Jr. Foundation, International Universities Press, New York, 1958, p. 32.

3. Cooley, Charles H., "The Significance of Communication," *Social Organization,* 1909, pp. 61–65; 80–103. Reprinted in Berelson, Bernard, and Morris Janowitz, editors, *Reader in Public Opinion and Communication,* enl. ed., The Free Press, Glencoe, Ill., 1953, p. 145.

4. Cantril, Hadley, *The Politics of Despair.* Basic Books, New York, 1958, p. 17.

Chapter 25

The Crisis in Medical Communication

IT WOULD BE DIFFICULT today to magnify the significance of our current problem of communicating scientific health knowledge from scientist to scientific colleague, to practitioner, and to the public to assure its rapid application in the improvement of the public's health. Today great masses of valuable medical research experience and discovery rest unevaluated and unused in scientific publications and reports. One of our greatest communication needs is for the creative development of methods of classifying, collecting, interpreting, evaluating, and distributing these undiscovered discoveries.

Many factors lie behind the research-communication dilemma we now face. Mention of but a few of these will bring many others to mind:

The geometric rate of growth of support for health research during the past two decades.

The availability of a growing number of foreign language sources.

The heavy demand upon teacher and researcher for published writings which build a mass of reports of unequal worth, varying in validity and reliability.

A shift from individual researchers working alone to groups of researchers producing findings in industrial fashion.

The rapid movement of research teams into new areas of theory and yielding reports that are often beyond the grasp of other members of the same discipline who have not acquired the new jargon.

The extension of health research and development across disciplinary lines, with an awareness that many of the most significant problems can only be solved by interdisciplinary approaches.

The lack of agreement, even among related disciplines, on meanings of scientific terminology and their relationships.

The lack of common frameworks of theory in the behavioral sciences to serve as a unifying scheme for coordinating and interpreting discoveries.

The shortage of trained scientific reviewers and abstracters competent to give this mass of publications the critical evaluation required.

The low status given to abstracters and reviewers in our scientific culture, which results in this critical work being carried out by inadequately trained reviewers.

The inaccessibility of libraries, abstracting services, bibliographic references, and review facilities to many researchers who might profit by knowing what others have done.

An increase in the educational level of the public, accompanied by a greater social awareness and concern about scientific developments and the practices of scientists.

Growth in the variety and number of mass media of communication, together with a vast corps of communication "gatekeepers" whose livelihood depends upon new knowledge to transmit.[1]

THE PUBLIC HEALTH COMMUNICATION CHAIN

Any attempt to consider the dynamics of public health communication must take into account what was called this "crisis in medical communication" by Vice President Hubert H. Humphrey[2] when as senator he was chairman of the Subcommittee on Reorganization in International Organizations. The communication problem of the public health leader rests not alone with his relationships to his publics, but also concerns the communication problems of the research scientist, his professional scientific colleague, and the professional practitioner, who together form a chain of new discovery to the public health practitioner and lay leaders. Weakness in communication at any point in this chain will lead to inadequate health communication. In looking at this chain of communications, one must also recognize that the communication is not only from scientist to layman, but also from layman to scientist, and must be so if the research scientist is to explore research areas of crucial significance to the practitioner and the publics he serves.

The Research Scientist

From the standpoint of the research scientist in health, rapid and efficient communication facilitates the discovery of knowledge and greater understanding of its meanings. Research effort may be wasted if the research scientist does not have readily at his command knowledge of the findings of other researchers, the techniques and methods they use, and the theories they have developed. Awareness of both past successes and failures contributes to improvement in methods, approaches, and the organization of ideas, and minimizes the necessity of worthless rediscovery.

As Grey has pointed out, information is an essential raw material for every researcher; as research generates knowledge, so knowledge generates research. The processing and dissemination of research findings and method are an integral part of the total research sequence. When the processes of synthesizing, classifying, and distributing information are inadequate, research efforts may be futile or sterile.[3]

The Public Health Practitioner

Professional health practitioners lean upon the research scientists and their colleagues in attempting to apply new knowledge rapidly and soundly. This applies both in facilitating efficient and effective administration, and in developing plans for sound decision-making. The validity of public health objectives, and the validity and reliability of public health standards, procedures, and organization efforts rest upon the adequacy and validity of the findings upon which they are based. While a question may be raised as to whether public health administration is itself a science, there is no question that its effective application rests upon the quality of findings available to the administrator. Public health objectives, standards, methods, and procedures need constantly to be revised in tune with new knowledge regarding public needs, facilities, and organization, and with new evidence regarding the validity of specific practices, approaches, and techniques for meeting objectives.

The public health practitioner is in a most difficult position in the communication channel, between research scientist and layman. As Christensen has pointed out, scientists communicating with scientists can often proceed on the assumption that their colleagues have a certain background of scientific knowledge against which to evaluate and interpret new facts or ideas; further, they have a strong motivation to learn, for new facts or ideas may contribute to the effectiveness of their research efforts.

But when we move into the world of application, all these assumptions totter. When we are transmitting to professional groups—physicians, dentists, and their many allies—we must be conscious of a wide diversity of preparation and degree of interest. Further, we must recognize that our messages compete for their attention with many others and may even conflict with other pressures and goals.

And the problem becomes still more complex when we include official and private organizations, voluntary associations, teaching and service institutions, community leaders, and the general public without whose support and participation programs have no purpose.[4]

The public health practitioner, even more than other members of this communication chain, is faced with problems involving the accuracy of communication, for on his shoulders rests the major responsibility for translating scientific concepts and jargon into lay language and meaning. Often this involves integrating new findings into old information which may be known to some, but not to other members of the lay populace. The problems of integrating such findings into existing patterns of concern and practice may involve considerations of major public health significance.

Expert Communication "Gatekeepers"

The public health practitioner, in his attempts to reach the public with new or significant health information and recommendations for action, must lean heavily for guidance upon many expert communication gatekeepers. Included among these are the public relations and information personnel, the health educator, the news editor and science writer, television and radio commentators. These experts serve in a variety of roles concerned with estimating public interests, needs, and wants, and means of reaching the public, and they make many decisions of significance regarding content to present and methods of presentation.

In a challenging review of a number of studies of these gatekeepers in the flow of scientific information, Tannenbaum reports evidence that some of the expert communicators who are most eager to help may muddy the waters for lack of valid conceptions regarding the public's interest and views. Investigations carried out under his direction at the Mass Communications Research Center of the University of Wisconsin, together with the research of other investigators, suggest a need for great caution in accepting the estimates made by communication experts regarding the knowledge, attitudes, interests, or wants of the lay public concerning science information unless these estimates are based on valid research findings.[5]

One such series of studies was related to the conceptions of mental illness held by experts, by the public, and by scientific communicators as related to presentations in television programs on this topic. The scientists, television commentators, and a sampling of the public were found to be in high agreement in their conceptions of mental illness. All three groups, however, were far removed in their judgments from the image of mental illness presented by the mass media. The study revealed that the mass media presentations were in agreement with what the television commentators erroneously judged public beliefs and conceptions to be, rather than in terms of what the public's conceptions and beliefs actually were.

In discussing the implications of these findings, Tannenbaum concludes:

> Spokesmen for the mass media have long justified their selection and presentation of subject matter by saying that they are "giving the public what it wants." Giving the public what it wants may or may not constitute a legitimate and equitable basis for regulating our cultural industries, but the fact remains that if you are to operate by such a principle you should at least know what the public *does* want. In the mental health area, at least, the mass media gate-keeper may be badly mistaken: The public does not believe what the media people think it believes, and it may not want what the media people think it wants.[6]

Studies of the use of scientific terms and phrases in the mass media suggest that regular readers of scientific information find the original scientific terms meaningful. Their judgments regarding the use of these scientific terms were more like the judgments of the scientists and science writer, whereas nonreaders of science tended to find lay terms more meaningful. Science writers may be writing more for people who are not regular readers than for their regular readers who are scientifically oriented. One public health implication may be the importance of looking closely at ways in which the regular science readers in health may serve as a link in communications to the broader lay public.

CONCLUSIONS

Studies such as those reported by Tannenbaum suggest that while there is an urgent need to identify, evaluate, and interpret research findings currently available for immediate use in public health practice, there is an equal need to determine how to communicate such knowledge effectively in order to elicit improvement in public health behaviors. Research on the utilization of research findings deserves high priority, for the gap between scientific knowledge and its utilization grows wider each year. Scientific research on the communication process itself has not as yet yielded the valid and reliable evidence necessary to plan and develop communication programs with assurance of their success.

NOTES TO CHAPTER 25

1. *Surgeon General's Conference on Health Communications,* November 5–8, 1962, Public Health Service, U.S. Dept. of Health, Education, and Welfare, Publication 998, Government Printing Office, Washington, 1963; Neal, Helen, editor, *Better Communication for Better Health,* National Health Council, New York, 1962.

2. Humphrey, Hubert, Memorandum from Senator Hubert Humphrey, Chairman, Subcommittee on Reorganization in International Organizations, re: An Action Program for Strengthening Medical Information and Communication, 1962.

3. Grey, Blake E., "Information and Research—Blood Relatives or In-laws? Dissemination of the Results of Experimentation Is an Integral Part of the Total Research Process," *Science,* vol. 137, July, 1962, pp. 263–266.

4. Christensen, Aaron W., Address in *Surgeon General's Conference on Health Communications,* November 5–8, 1962, p. 83. (See Note 1.)

5. Tannenbaum, Percy H., "Communication of Science Information," *Science,* vol. 140, May 10, 1963, p. 580.

6. *Ibid.*

Chapter 26

The Communicator for Public Health Agencies

THE OFFICIAL REPRESENTATIVE of an organization who attempts to communicate its values, policies, and aims to a particular audience or the public is guided in his efforts by the way he perceives the world of which he is a part. His judgments are limited by the boundaries of his private reality world. His predictions as to what means of communication will be effective are governed by the quality and accuracy of his perceptions or awarenesses concerning the audience with whom he is attempting to communicate. He cannot anticipate what he is unaware of, nor can he know what he has not personally experienced.

The role of the communicator is not a distinct one. To be effective he must constantly employ all the sensory mechanisms at his disposal so as to sharpen his understanding of the interests and reactions of the individuals with whom he is attempting to communicate, and take advantage of any changes in their behavior or reactions which have predictive value in his efforts to influence them. Unless he maintains this constant awareness of change, he may employ channels no longer in use, appeal to needs long since satisfied, or instill fear or insecurity in those he seeks to influence.

The communicator is only one of the many sources of stimulation competing for the attention of his audience. His success in the race for attention depends on his ability to adapt his message so that it has immediate meaning within the reality world of his audience. He is limited in his efforts, since what he perceives in this situation also is influenced by his own pattern of personal and group motives. His wants and hopes may not be in accord with the desires and expectations of his audience.

The tasks of the communicator are many and challenging. In the following discussion brief attention will be given to some of these

455

tasks that have particular relevance for the public health communicator.

REPRESENTING AGENCY POLICIES

The role of communicator for a health organization, such as a health department or voluntary agency, is complicated by the fact that it carries with it the responsibility of presenting values, policies, or aims that may be other than the communicator's own. First there is the problem of determining what to communicate and then the task of presenting values and content with a minimum of personal bias.

In discussing mass communication, Wiebe warns us that we cannot afford to preserve the illusion that any communication is, or can be, unbiased. The crucial question is not whether or not the communication is biased, but rather *"toward what value system is the communication biased."*[1] This is a question that concerns both the representative of an organization and the group to whom he presents his message. The health representative usually is obliged to present his information or message in a manner consistent with the value orientation and policies of the agency even while seeking to be objective in his approach. The message itself is likely to be his interpretation of that value system and current policies although he personally may attempt to be unbiased in his presentation.

The task of an organization's representative is also complicated by the fact that other persons within the organization, and also past members of the group, compete for the attention of the audience. Their ideas may not agree with his; actually they may express values or policies that are contradictory to those he seeks to communicate. Such persons may even be unaware of changes in policies or principles, and of the implications of such changes for health practices.

The image of the organization, including its value orientations, its policies and practices, is slowly developed in the minds of leadership, staff and public, and is not easily changed. This image may have been developed in past years when policies or goals were different. Yet this image, acquired through years of experience, may still govern expectations in the current situation. An agency that has once applied the means test in accepting clients may some time later be identified as being primarily concerned with the care of the destitute, even though the current program emphasis is much changed. The early association of a local health department with sanitation and contagious diseases may be retained long after a significant part of the budget is expended on problems of chronic illness.

Determining the value orientation and policies of an organization with respect to any particular area of communication is fraught with difficulty. One might expect to be able to obtain them quickly from the governing board or from the administrator chosen by this board to represent the organization. But values and policies become crystallized in subtle ways at the action levels far removed from the direct influence of the administrator. National foreign policy, for example, may be established in many subtle ways by persons acting on specific issues in overseas posts. The pediatrician in the well-baby clinic, the nurse visiting a new mother in her home, and the telephone operator trying to help a distraught mother find appropriate help, all interpret policies, and in attempting to interpret may establish policies and strengthen the value orientation of the health department.

The "top level bias" that Kornhauser described as tending to develop in organizations increases the problems of the public health communicator who is seeking to present his agency's program policies as faithfully as possible.[2] There is always a danger that the communicator, who represents an organization at some particular point in this hierarchy, will overemphasize certain value orientations he believes to be of prime significance to those above him, or he may translate them in ways that are not intended by the leadership group.

CLARIFYING INTENTIONS

Few tasks of the public health communicator are as difficult to perform as that of obtaining a clear and specific statement of the purpose of his efforts. In some way he must answer the question: "What should the communication accomplish?"

One who seeks to represent the values and intentions of many others must select from a wide range of expressions of interest and purpose, those that are consistent with one another and have general acceptance. He must identify and obtain decisions regarding those conflicts that are certain to emerge. Unless his goal is to show disagreement, he needs to make sure that the common statement of intentions, filtered out of many statements, has general acceptance or, at any rate, is not in serious disagreement with the intentions of persons involved. Yet the product of this search for agreement needs to be specific enough to have special meaning for the person who is to receive the message. If the final product is to gain acceptance and support within the agency, and the backing of staff members, it must represent the desires of many; yet to be effective, it must be specific in orientation, it must have singleness of purpose.

Anyone who has participated in preparing an exhibit for an agency will appreciate the observation that "a camel is a horse built by committee." One intensive study of 50 scientific exhibits of public health agencies revealed that some of them had as many as a dozen specific purposes, often of equal or nearly equal significance. The analysis suggested that exhibitors were attempting to satisfy the ideas of members of their organizations who were not in agreement with one another and, at the same time, to reach various specific audiences with equal effect.

A serious difficulty in making sure of intent lies in the problem of distinguishing content and intent, the form of a communication as distinct from its purpose. Preoccupation with the manner of telling, showing, or illustrating may divert attention from the primary goal of influencing behavior.

Exhibitors at the annual meetings of the American Public Health Association are requested by the Exhibit Committee to complete the statement for their exhibit, "The main purpose of this exhibit is . . ." in 25 words. As one way of evaluating the effectiveness of these exhibits, a representative sample of members of the association is asked to complete the same statement while viewing the exhibits. Experience using this approach has revealed innumerable instances where exhibits have completely failed to achieve their objectives for lack of primary focus on those objectives. To illustrate, in one instance several evaluators independently stood in front of an exhibit and completed the sentence in this way, "The main purpose of this exhibit is to demonstrate the various uses of isotopes." The exhibitor, in completing the same sentence, had stated, "The main purpose of this exhibit is to demonstrate new techniques for testing laundry equipment." The uniqueness of his approach attracted attention to the exhibit but diverted attention from its purpose.[3]

Such simple pretests or evaluations of attempts to communicate through exhibits, pamphlets, films, or speeches draw attention to the extent of uncertainty that exists in regard to agency philosophy, objectives, and policies. Steps can then be taken by the group to deal directly with uncertainties regarding intent.

Lack of agreement regarding purpose often passes unnoticed, however, when present in the less formal means of communication, such as discussions, talks, responses to inquiries, and the like. Uncertainty, confusion, misunderstandings, or even conflict reflected in the informal communications of different staff members may prove to be serious barriers to program achievement.

Unrecognized disagreement or misunderstanding may first emerge into staff awareness when serious efforts are made to formulate in writing an agency's philosophy, objectives, or policies. The very difficulty that staff groups have in formulating simple statements of policy and intention is evidence of the significance of disagreement on the issues involved. Staff members may work at cross purposes for years without becoming aware of their differences regarding purpose until written statements of agreement are attempted. Yet unless members of the agency are in close agreement regarding the intentions of communication, the image of the organization as presented in their various communications is likely to be perceived by the outsider in varying, possibly conflicting, ways.

In the area of communications, as in other areas of program development, intentions often become clarified when they can be stated in terms of specific health actions desired of specific individuals: *What* is *who* expected to do and in *what way* as the result of our communication effort? When such a question is clearly answered, both the content and the methods of communication can be more purposefully selected. The likelihood of effectiveness will be thereby increased.

DEFINING THE IMAGE OF THE AUDIENCE

Another major responsibility of the public health communicator is to acquire a clear and valid image of his audience.[4] He has the responsibility also of keeping alert to changes in that audience so that appropriate adjustments in communication can be made as the orientation of his audience changes. Communication, of whatever kind, is going to fail in its purpose unless it effectively reaches its target group.

An adequate description of the audience for planning communications includes many factors, information regarding some of which may not even be at hand or attainable, and can only be estimated. Yet even an awareness that these factors may be important will sharpen sensitivity in planning. Significant data may at times be available, but overlooked for lack of awareness of its pertinence to the task.

Many studies have called attention to the importance of being alert to the interests, wants, and concerns of the audience, their opinions, attitudes and beliefs, the values they hold, their psychological sets or readiness to accept or reject information, and the assumptions that govern their health behaviors. Such information regarding the audience is of crucial significance to one who would practice the art of persuasion. Of equal importance is the knowledge they have regarding the possibilities for action in relation to the health problem under consideration, and the possibilities for action they perceive as feasible and appropriate for themselves. Attention needs also to be given to the types of relationships they prefer to have with the communicator, their independent or dependent patterns of behavior, and their preference regarding the manner of communication from the expert.

When adequate information regarding such factors is not available to the communicator, a serious danger exists in the tendency he has, as do we all, to draw upon existing stereotypes for descriptions. Thus the communicator may assume, on the basis of stereotypes, that the poor are lazy, the uneducated are unintelligent, the businessman is indifferent to problems of social welfare, and so on. Such invalid stereotypes may guide communication efforts in hidden unverbalized ways. Studies have shown that the stereotypes we hold of different minority and national groups often lack a valid basis in experience, yet play an important role in governing our approaches to them. Even though one sees his own group as including members widely differing in their patterns of interest and behavior, one tends to assume that other groups, with some common identifying characteristic such as color, religion, nationality, or occupation, are all alike. The tendency to assume this similarity in the behavior of other groups ignores evidence that each individual is unique and possesses his own communication system.

When data are not available for describing the audience, the communicator needs to be alert also to another tendency toward invalid judgment. This is a tendency to assume that one's own values are represented in others, that one's own preferences are the preferences of others, and that others want and seek the same things. While the gap between the educated layman and the professional is narrowing rapidly in areas of general information, the gap between professional and the uneducated layman grows broader. As studies previously cited have suggested, these differences may involve not only patterns of want, concern, and interest but also basic value orientations toward life and illness, and the limits placed upon man in dealing with the problems of God and nature on matters concerning his health.

Obtaining a valid image of the audience means, therefore, obtaining as full and accurate an understanding as possible of the private world of the communicant and the setting in which his behavior occurs. To the extent that one has a clear picture of the private world of the communicant, it is possible through the overlap of experience to adapt ideas to his patterns of thought and action in ways that make them more acceptable within his own way of life. Since a full and valid picture of his private world is never available, adaptation on the basis of best judgment is always necessary. In applying this principle of best judgment, however, one needs to make certain that one's own biases, prejudices, and values are not significantly distorting his judgments.

Consideration of Special Factors and Conditions

Many health communications never reach their intended audience because special physical, physiological, or situational factors germane to that audience have not been considered. The health communicator should be aware that all individuals do not have equal opportunities to be exposed to the medium or content of the health program being promulgated. It is his task to know whether the communication technique or approach he is using is the one best attuned to the special situation of the audience with which he is primarily concerned.

In one instance, for example, an experimental program was developed to communicate new information to diabetics on ways of dealing with their special problems. Included in the program was a series of 12 slide films which was presented in successive sessions, together with adequate time for discussion by the audience, thus providing them with an opportunity to translate the new information into their own ways of life. The setting planned for the series of meetings, however, was on the second floor of a walkup public building. Many older persons with diabetes who might have profited greatly from the experience were unable to attend the meetings because they were unable to climb the stairs. A new setting had to be chosen. Changes also had to be made in the size of type in some of the printed materials used, for in preparing them adequate attention had not been given to the fact that many diabetics have poor eyesight and need large type in any printed materials they will use.

Audience Understanding of Health Jargon

Health educators, and others who pretest their materials, have become sensitive to widely varying meanings that lay groups give to what may appear to be simple public health terminology. Their explorations have amply demonstrated that public health communicators have a serious responsibility to know what special meanings words and concepts in common usage in public health programs have for their audiences.

What seems simple to the professional is often confusing to persons with other patterns of experience, even for the well educated. Charts, diagrams, graphs, pictures, figures, objects, photographs, and words which seem self-explanatory to the health communicator may be unfamiliar to others. This may lead to serious error in interpretation, to creating anxieties, to the rejection of recommendations, or to the spread of misinformation, rumor, or superstition.

At times, for example, the application of a simple health recommendation may require judgment in using some system of classification. If the classification used is in any way inconsistent with common usage of words, confusion arises. In the health professions, for example, burns are often classified as first, second, and third degree burns, according to severity of tissue damage, and different action recommendations are associated with each type of burn. An exploratory study involving this classification revealed much public confusion. Many persons identified the first degree burn as most severe—it ranked first in significance. The findings suggested that the message regarding the treatment of burns might be more effectively imparted to the layman, for whom it was intended, if some classification more in accord with common usage had been employed. Possibly the terms "slight," "medium," or "bad" burns would better serve the purpose in communicating intent.

The public health communicator, whose message is intended to influence behavior, should make certain that the practice he recommends is meaningful from the point of view of the other person's habit patterns. Adapting recommendations to habit patterns facilitates acceptance of the recommended action with a minimum of disruption of one's present way of life. It is unreasonable to expect ready acceptance of new practices that conflict with deep-seated habit patterns, and it is wasteful to attempt to reeducate people to a greater degree than necessary to achieve adequate improvement in their health practices. If communications can be patterned in tune with current patterns of behaviors, the likelihood of recommendations being accepted is greatly enhanced. Recommendations, and even laws, as our prohibition era demonstrated, will be ignored if they are in conflict with widely held practices. Few in our society would, if they could, brush their teeth within twenty minutes after eating. Yet more than now do, might acquire the practice of rinsing their mouths thoroughly after eating. It is meaningless to suggest to laboring people who cannot control their working hours to "take a rest in the afternoon," or to urge annual physical examinations for those who see the cost in money and loss of time from work as prohibitive. "Avoid heavy work" is a meaningless recommendation if given without full understanding of the type of work done, the time and manner of performance, the tools or aids available, the urgency of completion, the rest opportunities, and the like.

Many of Brown's insightful observations regarding patient care in hospitals are fully applicable to public health waiting rooms and clinics.[5] Familiar practices such as the opportunity for social coffee while waiting might foster more effective interpersonal communications. Early morning clinic hours or evening clinics when possible might facilitate the participation of those who want checkups but feel they cannot remain away from their jobs.

Pretests of nutrition educational materials reveal that poorly educated laymen are confused about the concepts of proteins, carbohydrates, minerals, vitamins, and fats; that these terms convey various meanings. This raises the question as to whether such concepts are necessary for imparting the important nutrition information. Do people shop for proteins, carbohydrates, and fats, for well-balanced diets, or do they buy meat, vegetables, and bakery goods for breakfast, lunch, or dinner? Can the communication be patterned to improve their food habits with a minimum of change in the way they look at foods in the market and their current patterns of buying and preparing meals?

Studies of semantics have drawn attention to many of the ways in which word choices, the structure of language, and the assumptions we make regarding the use of language influence communication. These studies are at once interesting and profitable reading for those who seek to improve their approach. In *The Process of Persuasion,*

Miller has reviewed some of the techniques employed by the former Institute for Propaganda Analysis, and has illustrated in many ways the use of these techniques in interpersonal and mass communications.[6]

Social scientists, educators, and marketing research specialists have developed many techniques for testing communications prior to wide usage to assure adequate understanding. Some of these methods have already received good public health acceptance, and readers are referred elsewhere for a more adequate discussion of their applications in health communications.[7]

Basic Orientation to Authority

A personal and group characteristic to which little attention has been given in public health, and yet which is of considerable significance to the professional trying to communicate with laymen, concerns what Sanford has called "the recipient's *basic orientation to authority*."[8] Individuals differ in their accustomed way of responding to authority and to persons in authority. They vary in their orientations along the dimension of dependence and independence. An independently oriented person demands the privilege of thinking critically about his own problem and making his own decision regarding action. The dependently oriented person, on the other hand, tends to look to authority for direct guidance. As Sanford notes,

> The point here is that communicatees vary widely with respect to dependence and independence. The skillful communicator, interested in producing behavioral results, will gauge his communication with respect to the dependence or independence of the system he confronts. To talk directively and to play God in the presence of the independent system is very probably to fail. To be non-directive in the presence of great dependency is to create perhaps more confusion than the dependent system can possibly stand.[9]

The public health representative, whether communicating with individuals or groups, will profit by learning what he can regarding the dependent-independent orientation of his audience. Those who like to run their own lives, make their own decisions, plan their own ways of doing things are likely to seek information of use to them in this process. They will wish to know the sources of the information and make their own evaluations and judgments of its validity and usefulness. They are likely to inquire about meanings and sources and to reject authorities who fail to satisfy their inquiries. Their dependent counterparts, on the other hand, tend to look to authority for guidance, being happier in the presence of a communicator who enjoys a father figure or authoritarian role with them. Thus while one discounts the voice of authority, the other leans heavily upon it and may almost blindly follow directives given by a professional leader in an authoritarian way.

As Sanford notes, while individuals differ along this dependency-independency orientation, each of us varies in his orientation, depending on his current state of need. A desperately ill individual, who might otherwise question authority, may lean heavily upon it. Under conditions of emergency or disaster individuals, and groups also, tend to depend greatly for direction on authoritative appearing sources, as was shown in Cantril's study of the "Invasion from Mars." In the public reaction to Orson Welles' radio broadcast, many individuals responded without question to the radio communiqué. This was particularly true of those least prepared to cope with the emergency situation described.[10]

This tendency to lean on authority in time of crisis may account, in part at least, for the unusual response of the public to emergency situations in public health and their apparent indifference to take steps to prevent such emergencies before they arise. Each health officer will recall experiences of his own in tune with this observation. The mass response to the New York City's smallpox scare some years ago and the mass response to recommendations to obtain immunization during the Connecticut floods illustrate this point.

This greater tendency of individuals and groups, under conditions of disaster or emergency, to follow authority or assumed authority may stem in part from the fact that the emergency creates a common state of expectations or "set" on the part of the audience. As discussed elsewhere, the frame of reference that an individual brings to a communication situation strongly influences his response to it. If we are planning to buy something, we notice advertisements that otherwise we would ignore. If some health symptom is described in terms we have experienced, it has direct meaning for us. These psychological "sets" we bring to a situation serve us in selecting items of importance and may lead us to disregard things we do not perceive to be significant for us. When emergencies arise, these same items of information may suddenly have high personal significance.

MAINTAINING A TRUSTWORTHY IMAGE

Public health leaders have long applied the general principle that *who* communicates an idea has a significant bearing on the acceptance of the communication by an audience. Extensive research supports this principle.[11] As Klapper has pointed out, the significant factor seems not to be the true qualifications of the communicator or source but the "image of the source" held by the audience. The person or source perceived as trustworthy, reliable, and expert tends to be more effective than one not so perceived in influencing attitudes.

It is of interest, however, that while the qualifications attributed to the source of information tend to influence acceptance, they do not seem to affect the amount of information learned,[12] provided, of course, that the audience "attends" the communication given by the communicator of less repute. Except under "captive" conditions, an audience is not likely to remain present and attentive if the source is not respected.

A strange phenomenon known as "the sleeper effect" may be of great importance to the public health communicator who seeks to influence attitudes on controversial issues. Studies of "captive" audiences suggest that people tend to forget the sources of information after a period of time. When this occurs, information associated with some negative or untrustworthy source, and initially rejected, may gradually become accepted. Should the information be again associated with the negative source, it will lose this so-called "sleeper effect."

For example, a food faddist who lacks acceptance as an expert and a nutritionist respected as an authority may compete for the acceptance of their conflicting recommendations regarding food attitudes and practices. Other things being equal, the nutritionist, if perceived as the more respected source, probably would be initially more effective with the audience. After some time, however, neither food faddist nor nutritionist may be remembered as a source for his recommendation, even though this information is retained. Then the "sleeper effect" may result in the food faddist's recommendations gaining favor and the nutritionist's losing favor with the audience. Unless the audience is again reminded of the positive and negative sources associated with the two recommendations, both will end up being about equally acceptable.

Since studies of this "sleeper effect" have thus far been limited generally to student or other captive audiences, their applicability to public health situations must be considered with caution. To the extent that this effect occurs, however, it may contribute over a period of time to the loss of public support in a community on such controversial issues as fluoridation of the community water supply.

THE ORDER AND MANNER OF PRESENTATION OF ISSUES

The public health official is often responsible for presenting controversial issues to the public, to professional groups, to members of his boards or budget committees. Then he is faced with the matter of estimating what order and manner of presentation is likely to be most effective. If he speaks on fluoridation, for example, how can he most effectively present his position? Should he seek to speak first or last in a situation where others opposing his point of view are on the same platform? Should he mention and discuss counter-arguments? Are there any ways of inoculating his audience against the counter-effects presented in the arguments of his opposition?

The Laws of Primacy and Recency

Questions such as those posed above have been subjects of many research studies since Lund formulated the "Law of Primacy and Persuasion" in 1925. When the first of two positions tends to have a major influence upon attitude and recall, the law of primacy is said to be in effect. However, Lund's Law of Primacy has not been a very stable law, for under many circumstances the recency effect seems to be more influential; that is, the last of two arguments is frequently the one remembered better. The relative significance of primacy or recency upon the listening individual will vary according to many factors, some known, and some unknown.[13]

One important effect to consider is the time at which measurements and estimates of effect are made. Since forgetting occurs rapidly following any communication, the time between the presentation of the primary and secondary positions and the taking of measures will influence the outcomes. Here, as in so many other cases, one's method determines the response to his facts.[14] As the time interval between two communications increases, there tends to be an increase in the recency effect on both opinion and recall when these are measured immediately after the second communication. When there is a longer lapse in the time between communication and the measurement, the recency effect is not so great.

Other factors that seem to influence the relative significance of these two "laws" concern the degree of familiarity with the material and the degree of exposure the audience has had to the two positions on the issue. The naive listener is more likely to be influenced by primacy than is one who is familiar with the material and has perhaps already formulated some attitude regarding it. Once he has acquired some information either in advance of the communication or during the primary communication, he may tend to become committed to the position he holds and not permit himself to be fully exposed to the contradictory position.[15]

Commitment

Hovland and his colleagues have critically reviewed the various studies regarding primacy and recency effects, and note that one significant feature to be considered is the matter of commitment on the part of the listener. If the audience listening to the person offering the primary argument accept this argument, if they commit themselves to it by talking with one another, discussing it with others, or voting upon it, this factor may itself lead to the greater significance of primacy under certain conditions. This suggests that the health officer might well take advantage of this tendency on a critical issue to obtain an expression of opinion from the public to which he is speaking. On the other hand, if he wishes his audience to make up their minds in a most critical manner, he may avoid any action that leads to early commitment.

One-Sided versus Two-Sided Presentation

The question as to whether or not to discuss one's opponent's arguments in one's own presentation has also been subjected to experimental research. During the war a series of experiments was carried out on mass communication in the armed forces as part of the "Why We Fight" program. Under these conditions it was possible to match groups and conduct rigorous experimental studies, one of which concerned the matter of discussing counter-arguments.

One group of soldiers was presented a one-sided argument as to how long it would be before Russia would be able to produce atom bombs. The other group received both sides of this argument. The person presenting the issue discussed the counter-arguments as part of his presentation. In the study it was found that, with an educated audience, presenting both sides of the argument was a more effective means of influence than discussing only one side. However, persons of lower education who lack the background to evaluate the issue critically and to recognize inconsistencies and contradictions tended to be confused by the counter-arguments.[16]

Somewhat similar findings were obtained in a study conducted on the "Voice of America" program in postwar Germany. Programs that included admissions of the weaknesses in American living conditions, government, and foreign policies, along with the arguments in favor of the American position, tended to be perceived by the audience as more credible.[17]

Presenting both sides of an argument tends to leave the educated listener with a feeling that one is less biased and more objective. The speaker probably tends to be seen as more honest in his approach, particularly by the better-educated members of the audience and those who already have some exposure to the issue under discussion.[18] When the audience holds a position in opposition to the speaker, his presenting only one side of the issue may lead the listeners to reject the entire argument without even considering it. On the other hand, if they have not been previously exposed to the issue, presenting the counter-arguments, discussing their values and weaknesses, and indicating the basis for the position taken helps the uninformed to think through the total issue and come to a more reasonable conclusion. Later, when the counter-arguments are presented by the opponent group, the members of the audience who have heard the counter-arguments and have given them serious thought will be better prepared to deal with the arguments then raised. They have, in a sense, been "inoculated" against the opposing position.[19]

Research suggests that in presenting counter-arguments to one's own position in such a situation, a serious attempt should be made to include all significant counter-arguments. The omission of some significant fact or point known to some members of the audience tends to detract more from the effectiveness of the presentation than not discussing the other side of the issue at all. Those members of the audience who notice the omission may then believe the speaker to be more biased in his approach than he would be in presenting only a one-sided argument.[20]

While the presentation of counter-arguments tends to contribute to the effectiveness of persuasion with an educated audience, it is not wise to leave the conclusions entirely to the audience; a clear and concise summary of the speaker's position contributes to effectiveness even with well-educated members of the group, and is most essential with those less educated or less informed. While findings on this matter are not unequivocal for all situations, the odds favor the speaker who concludes with a clear summary of his position and the grounds on which it is based.[21]

Implications for Action

Under most circumstances, of course, the public health worker will not present his position in open debate from a platform. Rather, he is likely to discuss the issue in open meeting with an audience, some of whom are supportive, some in doubt, and others opposed. He may be alone in the speaker's position, accompanied by colleagues, or with a community leadership group. Under these circumstances, of course, it is possible for him to take advantage of both recency and primacy in presenting his position. The odds are in favor of his position being better accepted if he includes, in the middle of his discussion, a reference to, and analysis of, the kind of arguments that may later be raised. To the extent that the data reported here are valid for such a community situation, his most effective presentation would include, first, a clear statement of the issue, relating it to the interests and concerns of the audience; then, an unequivocal discussion of his own position; followed by a discussion of counter-arguments, their implications, and why he feels that his position is better; and, finally, to take advantage of recency, a summary supporting his point of view.

Unfortunately, or perhaps fortunately for the public, conclusions based on studies such as these are always contingent upon "other things being equal." Yet other things are never equal. Psychological "sets" and frames of reference which members of the audience bring to the meeting, their interest and concern with the issue, their motivations to learn or to reject, their acceptance or rejection of the speaker as an individual or as representing an agency they accept or reject, the physical arrangements of the meeting, the degree of tension involved in the subject matter, the evaluations of peers, the ego-involvement of members of the audience in the decisions, and a host of other factors make each public health meeting or discussion unique. Studies of the order of presentation based on experiments with soldiers or students under controlled conditions have some limits in validity when applied to such a public setting. From their conclusions we identify variables that seem to have better than chance significance—hence worthy of application "other things being equal."

THE USE OF FEEDBACK

The effective communicator is at the same time both a provider and receiver of information and ideas. The way he selects and organizes his facts, and the way he expresses the ideas are influenced by his patterns of personal motivation. His motives are expressed in devious ways he may not be fully aware of. His actions, both as a receiver and giver of information and ideas, are guided by his perceptions of the world in which he lives. His communications are patterned to the requirements of his private world, a world of assumptions built out of the successful and unsuccessful "efforts after meaning."

Man's search for meaning in the communications of others is matched by his constant search for feedback from others regarding his own communications. As Lewin and his associates have demonstrated, discussions with others provide him with an opportunity to test out his own ideas verbally and obtain feedback from his peers before using them in other life situations.[22]

Potential Barriers in Communication

Barriers or potential barriers to effective communication are always present for at least some members of the intended audience. Success in communication depends upon the ability of the communicator to discover these barriers early in order that remedial actions may be taken. Early actions taken to correct weaknesses may contribute significantly to success.

The potential barriers to communication are many and varied. They relate to any step or transaction in the entire communication process. The nature of these possible barriers and the way they may influence effectiveness may be suggested by noting some of the critical aspects of this dynamic human transaction.

Some potential barriers may reside in the communicator himself: his possible lack of direction; his unawareness of the influence of personal values, assumptions, and prejudices; the limits he has, as we all have, in personal capacities and abilities.

Others reside in the communicant: his personal values, motives, and psychological orientations; his limits in capacity to receive input at variance with his way of life; his tendency to modify input and to give it unique, personal meaning, which may at times actually be different from that intended by the communicator.

A third set of potential barriers relates to the order and manner of presentation: the possible effects of primacy or recency factors; the strength, nature, and manner of the discussion of counter-arguments; the potential impact of early or tardy commitment to action by members of the audience.

A fourth set of potential communication barriers relates to the media used and the channels through which the message must pass in order to reach the intended audience: the accessibility of the medium to the audience; the adequacy, clarity, and completeness of the transmission; factors present within the channel itself that might obstruct or distort the message; the availability of intermediate opinion leaders to help interpret the message in terms of its specific personal relevance for others; the effects of competing messages which also seek to attract the attention of the audience; the influence of peer and reference groups upon acceptance of the message, upon the commitments to action.

No communicator could hope to maintain constant awareness of this host of factors that might influence the effectiveness of his attempts. One of the best means of dealing with such factors is for him to develop an effective feedback mechanism for determining whether and in what form the message reaches the potential audience. Where errors of omission or distortion occur, such a feedback mechanism will help to identify the barriers responsible and to suggest means of improvement. When unusual success in communication occurs and is identified through the feedback, significant vectors may be identified so that advantage may be taken of them in developing more effective communication with other groups.

Types of Feedback

Many methods of feedback are available to the alert communicator. They range from the casual observations of a colleague to the rigorously controlled research or evaluation of an independent, outside group. Simple methods, such as pretests, and progress evaluations, serve as positive means of evaluation. Applied systematically, they provide excellent means for guiding communication efforts, thus making them more effective.[23]

The use of feedback is a part of all communication processes, whether of a personal, group, or large-scale type. It is constantly employed by the communicator, often without conscious awareness on his part. It is systematically employed in interpersonal settings by the interviewer, diagnostician, therapist, administrator, or salesman who will need feedback in order to achieve specific professional purposes. It may also be systematically used by one who works with groups to determine the group climate, the direction of movement, and the sources of tension or conflict. And, of course, it is widely used in advertising, marketing, or program development by organizations whose success often rests upon the effectiveness of pretests, pilot studies, and action research used in developing approaches.

In the give and take of interpersonal communication we employ feedback methods so constantly to guide conversation that we may be unaware of its significance. The gestures, expressions, or other responses of the person with whom we converse tell us whether he is concerned or indifferent, eager or uncertain; whether he thinks he understands or is doubtful. Most of us cannot converse long with an expressionless, cold, or unresponsive person who does not provide feedback. We desperately need response to our output on issues of significance in order better to gain an overlapping of our private worlds and gain fuller agreements on the meaning and significance of things about us.

Within staff or other group settings, the use of discussion, committee reports, or the various techniques developed by the group process specialist may be used to facilitate feedback. "Buzz sessions" have been developed as an effective way of obtaining the reactions of members of larger groups when feedback is desired from all members and there is a likelihood of a few dominating the general discussion. In the smaller group or "buzz session" an individual may test out his idea without embarrassment and gain the confidence necessary to express it publicly. This means that the ideas developed are more likely to be formulated with a consideration of the framework of the private world of less vocal members.

Self-surveys and other types of action research that have gained favor in public health are often unusually valuable to the program director for their feedback qualities. Members of a self-survey or action research group may identify problems within settings unfamiliar to the program director. They may then be able to recommend approaches for solving these problems in ways consistent with the private worlds of the public involved.

Pretesting and progress evaluations as means of improving public health communications offer people an opportunity to provide significant feedback in terms of the way they perceive specific aspects of the program. Their systematic use facilitates feedback on aspects of program communications and lessens the chance factors involved in obtaining responses from larger groups. They offer, for large groups, some of the opportunities for response that we constantly employ to give assurance that our interpersonal communications are on the mark.

CONCLUSIONS

Research in public health communications has increased in both number and quality of studies in recent years. Findings from studies completed are beginning to provide us with guidelines for increasing our effectiveness as communicators.

Public health leaders tend to look toward the research conducted in their own special areas as having greater validity than findings drawn from other fields of study. One should recognize, however, that general principles of communication cut across disciplinary and professional areas so that research in one area of communication can have direct meaning for another. It would be most difficult to summarize the primary principles of mass influence of significance to public health more brilliantly than has Cartwright, whose study of factors influencing the sale of war bonds is considered a classic in communications research:

> What happens psychologically when someone attempts to influence the behavior of another person? The answer, in broad outline, may be described as follows: To influence behavior, a chain of processes must be initiated within the person. These processes are complex and interrelated, but in broad terms they may be characterized as (i) creating a particular cognitive structure, (ii) creating a particular motivational structure, and (iii) creating a particular behavioral (action) structure. In other words, behavior is determined by the beliefs, opinions, and "facts" a person possesses; by the needs, goals and values he has; and by the momentary control held over his behavior by given features of his cognitive and motivational structure. To influence behavior "from the outside" requires the ability to influence these determinants in a particular way.
>
> It seems to be a characteristic of most campaigns that they start strongly with the first process, do considerably less with the second, and only lightly touch upon the third. To the extent that the campaign is intended to influence behavior and not simply to "educate," the third process is essential.[24]

NOTES TO CHAPTER 26

1. Wiebe, Gerhart D., "Mass Communications" in Hartley, Eugene L., and Ruth E. Hartley, *Fundamentals of Social Psychology.* Alfred A. Knopf, Inc., New York, 1952, p. 179.

2. Kornhauser, Arthur, "The Problem of Bias in Opinion Research," *International Journal of Opinion and Attitude Research,* vol. 1, December, 1947, pp. 1–16.

3. Knutson, Andie L., "Progress in Evaluating APHA Exhibits," *American Journal of Public Health Yearbook,* vol. 43, no. 5, 1953, pp. 83–93.

4. Hartley, Eugene L., and Ruth E. Hartley, *op. cit.*, pp. 39 ff.

5. Brown, Esther Lucile, *Newer Dimensions of Patient Care.* Part 1, The Use of the Physical and Social Environment of the General Hospital for Therapeutic Purposes. Russell Sage Foundation, New York, 1961.

6. Miller, Clyde R., *The Process of Persuasion*, Crown Publishers, New York, 1946; Chase, Stuart, *The Tyranny of Words*, Harcourt, Brace and Co., New York, 1938; Hayakawa, S. I., *Language in Action*, Harcourt, Brace and Co., New York, 1941; Hayakawa, S. I., editor, *Language, Meaning, and Maturity, Selections from Etc.: A Review of General Semantics, 1943–1953*, Harper and Bros., New York, 1954; Korzybski, Alfred, *Science and Sanity: An Introduction to Non-Aristotelian Systems and General Semantics*, Science Press Printing Co., Lancaster, Pa., 1933.

7. Knutson, Andie L., Benjamin Shimberg, Jane S. Harris, and Mayhew Derryberry, "Pretesting and Evaluating Health Education," *Public Health Monograph*, no. 8. Public Health Service, Government Printing Office, Washington, 1952.

8. Sanford, Fillmore H., "Inter-Personal Communication," *Industrial Medicine and Surgery*, vol. 25, June, 1956, p. 262.

9. *Ibid.*, p. 263.

10. Cantril, Hadley, Hazel Gaudet, and Herta Herzog, *The Invasion from Mars.* Princeton University Press, Princeton, N.J., 1940.

11. Hovland, Carl I., and Walter Weiss, "The Influence of Source Credibility on Communication Effectiveness" in Schramm, Wilbur, editor, *The Process and Effects of Mass Communication*, University of Illinois Press, Urbana, 1955, pp. 275–288; Klapper, Joseph T., *The Effects of Mass Communication*, The Free Press, Glencoe, Ill., 1960, pp. 99 ff.

12. *Ibid.*

13. Lund, F. H., "The Psychology of Belief: Part 4. The Law of Primacy and Persuasion," *Journal of Abnormal and Social Psychology*, vol. 20, 1925, pp. 183–191.

14. Insko, Chester A., Jr., "The Order of Communication," unpublished doctoral dissertation, University of California, Berkeley, 1963; Miller, Norman, and Donald T. Campbell, "Recency and Primacy in Persuasion as a Function of Timing of Speeches and Measurements," *Journal of Abnormal and Social Psychology*, vol. 59, July, 1959, pp. 1–9.

15. Hovland, Carl I., "The Role of Primacy and Recency in Persuasive Communication" in Maccoby, Eleanor E., Theodore M. Newcomb, and Eugene L. Hartley, editors, *Readings in Social Psychology*, 3d ed., Henry Holt and Co., New York, 1958, pp. 137–149; Hovland, Carl I., Irving L. Janis, and Harold H. Kelley, *Communication and Persuasion*, Yale University Press, New Haven, 1953; Hovland, Carl I., editor, *The Order of Presentation in Persuasibility*, Yale University Press, New Haven, 1957.

16. Hovland, Carl I., Arthur A. Lumsdaine, and Fred S. Sheffield, *Experiments on Mass Communication*, Studies in Social Psychology in World War II, vol. 3, Princeton University Press, Princeton, N.J., 1949, pp. 201–227; Lumsdaine, Arthur A., and Irving L. Janis, "Resistance to 'Counterpropaganda' Produced by One-sided and Two-sided 'Propaganda' Presentations" in Maccoby, Eleanor E., Theodore M. Newcomb, and Eugene L. Hartley, editors, *op. cit.*, pp. 131–137.

17. Carlson, Earl R., and Herbert I. Abelson, *Factors Affecting Credibility in Psychological Warfare Communications.* Human Resources Research Office, George Washington University, Washington, D.C., 1956.

18. Hovland, Carl I., Arthur A. Lumsdaine, and Fred D. Sheffield, *op. cit.*

19. Lumsdaine, Arthur A., and Irving L. Janis, *op. cit.*

20. Hovland, Carl I., Irving L. Janis, and Harold H. Kelley, *op. cit.;* Hovland, Carl I., editor, *The Order of Presentation in Persuasibility.* (See Note 15.)

21. Hovland, Carl I., Irving L. Janis, and Harold H. Kelley, *op. cit.*

22. Lewin, Kurt, *Resolving Social Conflicts.* Edited by Gertrud W. Lewin. Harper and Bros., New York, 1948.

23. Knutson, Andie L., "Pretesting: A Positive Approach to Evaluation," *Public Health Reports,* vol. 67, January, 1952, pp. 73–77. Knutson, Andie L., "Evaluating Program Progress," *Public Health Reports,* vol. 70, March, 1955, pp. 305–310.

24. Cartwright, Dorwin, "Some Principles of Mass Persuasion: Selected Findings of Research on the Sale of United States War Bonds," *Human Relations,* vol. 2, 1949, pp. 253–267. Also in Katz, Daniel, and associates, editors, *Public Opinion and Propaganda,* Henry Holt and Co., New York, 1960, pp. 382–393.

Chapter 27

Frames of Reference in
Public Health Communications

WHAT WE PERCEIVE, how we interpret what we perceive, and the attitudes we hold toward what we perceive tend to be influenced by what we have previously seen or learned as well as by what is "out there." We learn through experience to expect certain things and our cognitive life is largely influenced by our expectations.

A century of experimental research has been focused on gaining a better understanding of the nature and function of the psychological "sets" we bring to any situation we observe. One conclusion supported by this research is that cognitive activities such as perceiving, remembering, judging, and recalling are selective in nature and tend to be influenced by the individual's initial orientation to the situation in which he finds himself.

The findings of this research further suggest that the structure of the situation being perceived, the organization of the setting or "field" perceived must also be considered. External as well as internal factors influence behavior, even though what is perceived as "figure" and what is perceived as "background" in any situation is influenced by a host of value and motivational factors.

The term "frame of reference" has been used to refer to these internal and external factors, past or present, which together tend to influence the way a situation is perceived or judged. It refers both to those factors within the individual himself that tend to influence his expectations and to those factors within the environment or field that tend to influence the direction of his initial response.[1]

In perceiving, remembering, recalling, and judging, all of us tend to be influenced by such frames of reference. When they are internally structured or are "psychological sets" they are subject to influence by personal motives, concerns, desires, or expectations. When they are externally structured they tend to be influenced by the order or pattern of the "field" situation presented to the observer. More often, however, the frames of reference of any individual tend to be the product of a subtle combination of internal and external influences.

It is not difficult to think of many illustrations in daily life in which the "frame of reference" we bring with us to a situation tends to influence our reactions. A person who moves from a home with a five-step entrance to one with a six-step entrance will tend to stumble for a while until he becomes adjusted to the new situation. He will continue to "expect" only five steps. A person who comes to a committee meeting expecting conflict may perceive conflict in minor disagreements. If accustomed to perceiving minority members in subservient roles, he will so identify minority group members present no matter what quality of abilities, training, or experience they possess.

One can likewise think of many instances when the way a situation is presented can influence the way the stimulus is perceived. A pleasant smile orients the receiver toward a favorable response. A cluttered desk may suggest untidiness; neat clothes and grooming may suggest order and efficiency. An exhibit theme set in large type and highlighted is more likely to serve as an organizing guide to the observer. Some party games take advantage of our tendency to be influenced by order or the way information is presented. Ask anyone to pronounce the following words as you spell them in this sequence without the person's seeing the words: MacIntyre, MacIntosh, MacHenry, Machinery.

However, a frame of reference is not always so easily established. Persons who approach a situation with strong convictions or deeply held beliefs are not easily swayed by the order in which information is offered. When one meaning or significance of the situation is clear in terms of personal purpose, the individual is not easily reoriented to other meanings.

THE INFLUENCE OF PREPAREDNESS-UNPREPAREDNESS

Sherif and Cantril suggest as a working hypothesis that *"All other things being equal, the rôle played by internal and social factors decreases with the stability, clarity or structuredness of the stimulus situation and with the strength of frames or points of reference already established."*[2]

Persons who have witnessed a panic, a lynching, a mob in action, a revival, or some other emotionally charged social experience, such as those described by Cantril in his *Psychology of Social Movements,* will note that while some individuals are readily drawn by social pressures, others are less easily moved.[3] Those who approach the situation with strongly established frames of reference are not likely to shift quickly from their initial points of view. More easily influenced are those who lack a firm frame of reference to serve as an anchor in judging the experience, or those who may be guided by several alternative points of view from among which they have difficulty in choosing. If such an individual has a great need for an interpretation of the ambiguous situation, he may grasp the first plausible explanation offered.

For example, an individual may believe he is experiencing the vague and ambiguous symptoms of a chronic illness. The recurring symptoms have led to a heightening of his sense of threat and concern. He needs some frame of reference to help him interpret the situation so that appropriate action can be taken. If such a person holds a firm positive orientation toward modern medical diagnosis, he is likely to seek such a diagnosis. If he lacks a positive orientation, however, and holds instead a favorable orientation toward faith healing, this frame of reference may govern his behavior. On the other hand, he may feel much concerned and in need of assistance but lack a positive frame of reference toward any particular channel of action. Then he may be more easily attracted by the appeals and promises of pseudomedical advertising.

Studies of the responses of individuals to nondirective or projective tests or questions, such as the Rorschach or ink blot test, the thematic apperception or tell-a-story type of test, sentence-completion tests, and the like, yield convincing evidence that people tend to respond to questions about ambiguous pictures or situations in terms of personal needs, concerns, hopes, or fears. The frame of reference they employ in responding to ambiguous situations tends to be influenced by personal motivations.

Persons who have had no previous experience with such test situations have not, as yet, developed standardized ways of responding. Their response patterns are less influenced in such situations by the individual's ideas about how he "ought" to respond, by what he thinks a "good response" ought to be.

Many tests used for the diagnosis of mental illness have been developed on the principle that when people are offered an ambiguous situation in which to respond, they can better express their personal needs, concerns, fears, and expectations than when the situation is more formal. Not only do they find the ambiguous situation an easier one to talk about, they are more likely in such a situation to escape from culturally derived patterns of response that block free expression. There is little question that under such ambiguous conditions personal or internal motivating factors do influence the type of frame of reference in which individuals respond.

THE SEARCH FOR COGNITIVE CLARITY

Schachter proposes that individuals require affiliation with their fellow men for two general purposes. First, others help them achieve goals they cannot achieve alone. Secondly, individuals seek approval, friendship, support, prestige, status, and the like that can be satisfied only through interpersonal transactions.[4] In the first instance, the social group serves as an aid in goal attainment; in the second, the interpersonal transactions or affiliations themselves may represent goals. This second function, served by others, includes help as a sort of "sounding board" in interpreting and understanding events, and thus also appears to be of much importance to communications.

Theory of Social Comparison

According to Festinger's theory of social comparison, people draw upon one another for evaluations of their own judgments, opinions, and attitudes, and for assistance in defining their personal feelings, emotions, and experiences.

> The drive for self-evaluation concerning one's opinions and abilities has implications not only for the behavior of persons in groups but also for the processes of formation of groups and changing membership of groups. To the extent that self-evaluation can only be accomplished by means of comparison with other persons, the drive for self-evaluation is a force acting on persons to belong to groups, to associate with others. And the subjective feelings of correctness in one's opinions and the subjective evaluation of adequacy of one's performance on important abilities are some of the satisfactions that persons attain in the course of these associations with other people. How strong the drives and satisfactions stemming from these sources are compared to the other needs which people satisfy in groups is impossible to say, but it seems clear that the drive for self-evaluation is an important factor contributing to making the human being "gregarious."[5]

Schachter extends Festinger's theory to suggest that a "drive for cognitive clarity" may lead people to make efforts to reduce ambiguities that they encounter. For this purpose they seek intensive social contact, and discussion when possible, to interpret events and reduce uncertainties they experience.

In one experiment Schachter and Burdick created for study an unusual state of uncertainty in a girls' school by having the principal call out of class in the morning one girl from each classroom "to be gone for the rest of the day." The remaining girls were given no explanation for this unusual action. The girls remaining in class engaged in intensive transaction and communication throughout the day in their attempt to resolve their uncertainties regarding the event and to understand what had happened.[6]

It should be recognized that such a tendency to seek cognitive clarity when faced with ambiguous events is consistent with evidence cited in Chapter 23 regarding exploratory tendencies, perceptual curiosity, and the disturbing effects experienced by individuals under conditions of boredom or isolation.[7]

The Influence of Anxiety

How anxiety influences this tendency of man to seek cognitive clarity through interpersonal transactions when ambiguity exists is a matter of much significance for those who serve the public on matters relating to health. People who believe they have symptoms of some dangerous physical condition are likely to be in a high state of anxiety. This is perhaps also true when they fear that the public health or welfare is threatened. Such anxiety is likely to be greatest when the definition of the condition or the expected outcomes seem ambiguous. It has been noted by Frenkel-Brunswick that under such conditions people may seek an end to their intolerable feelings of uncertainty by acting prematurely without adequate evidence regarding the most appropriate course of action to take.[8]

In her study of what adults said they would expect to do if they were experiencing an ambiguous symptom suggestive of illness, Blackwell found that people expected first to make efforts to achieve an adequate definition of the condition. They expected to seek clarification through self-study, discussion with friends or members of the family, or consultation with specialists. However, when the symptom described was explicitly labeled as pathological and, in Schachter's terms, a state of cognitive clarity was achieved, their behavior changed. They then expected to decrease the transactions with friends, family members, colleagues, and specialists and to try to work out solutions by themselves. This tendency was particularly evident for psychosocial symptoms. In this instance they expected to try to identify the personal or social conditions responsible and to try to deal with them personally before seeking help.[9]

The role of other persons in helping one to achieve cognitive clarity thus seems to be quite different from the role of others in providing emotional or social support.

Experimental Studies of Anxiety and Affiliation

Schachter employed a novel experimental approach in a series of studies to learn more about the relationship between anxiety and this tendency to seek affiliation with others. His samples for these studies were girls, strangers to one another, most of whom were students in psychology at the University of Minnesota. Those enrolled in psychology received a unit of credit for participating in the experiment if they remained until the experiment was completed.

The purpose of these studies was to learn whether subjects preferred being alone, with other members of the same group, or with other students not in the group during a period of waiting before participating in an experiment that presented different conditions of ambiguity and threat. In these studies two types of experimental conditions were employed. One setting was designed to induce a high state of ambiguity and anxiety; the other was designed to produce a low state of ambiguity and anxiety.

In the high anxiety situation the girls were brought together in a room where they found themselves facing "a gentleman of serious mien, horn-rimmed glasses, dressed in a white laboratory coat, stethoscope dribbling out of his pocket, [and] behind him an array of formidable electrical junk." He introduced himself as "Dr. Gregor Zilstein of the Medical School's Departments of Neurology and Psychiatry" and explained that the girls would participate in an experiment concerned with "the effects of electrical shock."

Dr. Zilstein presented a seven or eight-minute discussion of research in this area, the nature of electroshock therapy, the danger of accidents when employing electricity, and the like. He advised the students that each would receive a series of shocks as part of an experiment. "Now, I feel I must be completely honest with you and tell you exactly what you are in for. These shocks will hurt; they will be painful. As you can guess, if, in research of this sort, we're to learn anything at all that will really help humanity, it is necessary that our shocks be intense." He called attention to the electrical "junk" behind him that would be used in the experiment and then again emphasized that the experience would be a painful one that would result in no permanent damage.

In the low anxiety situation the electrical gadgetry was not present, but the setting of the room was in other ways similar. Dr. Zilstein introduced himself to the group as before and advised that the students would participate in an experiment involving electrical shock. "I hasten to add, do not let the word 'shock' trouble you; I am sure that you will enjoy the experiment." He described with care the procedures to be used and then reemphasized that the experiment would only involve mild shocks. "It will resemble more a tickle or a tingle than anything unpleasant."

From this point on the two experimental approaches were identical. The experimenter, following his introduction, first obtained from members of the group their reactions in response to the question, "How do you feel about being shocked?" This question was employed to provide a measure of the effectiveness of the anxiety manipulation. Students responded to the question by indicating their feelings on a 5-point scale with alternatives ranging from "I dislike the idea very much" to "I enjoy the idea very much." Needless to say, striking differences in response were found between the two groups.

Subjects were then advised that about a ten-minute delay would occur while the room was being prepared for the experiment and they were asked to leave the room and wait elsewhere. It was recognized that some would prefer waiting alone, whereas some would rather wait in the company of other girls. Comfortable rooms were available for them either to wait alone or with other girls, and each girl was asked to express her preference on this matter. To get a measure of intensity of feeling on this preference to be alone or with others, subjects were asked to complete another 5-point scale with alternatives ranging from "I very much prefer being alone" to "I very much prefer being with others." Those who wished to do so were then permitted to indicate that they would like to drop out of the experiment. This provided a final measure of anxiety.

With this final recording of responses completed, the experiment was over, and subjects were so advised. They were told the purpose of the experiment and the reasons for deception, and were requested not to discuss the experiment with other students. From the questionnaires they had completed it was possible to determine their personal judgments regarding the anxiety they experienced as related to their preferences for waiting alone or with others.[10]

Many variations of this general experimental design permitted Schachter to study the influence of self-estimates of anxiety and of hunger on affiliation preferences. By continuing the experiment through the ten-minute waiting period for some groups, under varying conditions, additional measures could be obtained. The research focused on the effects of waiting alone, waiting with others who were strangers but participating in the same experience, and with persons not participating in the study on feelings of anxiety. It was possible to gain some insights into what people sought in choosing to spend time with others under such experimental conditions.

In general, the states of anxiety and of hunger, produced by approximately twenty hours of food deprivation, tended to increase preference for affiliation with others, and preferably others involved in the same experience, even though strangers. Some groups, while waiting in the presence of their colleagues, were permitted to talk about anything they wished, including the experiment; others were permitted to discuss other things, but not the experiment; still others were asked not to talk while waiting. Regardless of which of these alternative choices was presented, as opposed to waiting alone, subjects who were highly anxious tended to prefer waiting with others, and in all three settings this affiliation helped to lower their feelings of anxiety during the waiting period.

Data obtained in postexperimental questionnaires revealed that in addition to lowering anxiety, the experience of being with others helped subjects evaluate their own feelings and experience. They wanted to see how others acted under these conditions. As one stated, "By seeing that they weren't worried then I wouldn't be."[11] Nonverbal means of communication, as well as verbal means, were employed in obtaining this confirmation regarding the way others felt. It would appear that "ambiguous situations or feelings lead to a desire to be with others as a means of socially evaluating and determining the 'appropriate' and proper reaction."[12]

It should be noted that the experiments described were concerned with average differences in response under varying conditions. Some important individual differences were also determined. Most interesting is the finding that original position of birth in the family, regardless of family size (in this study most of the families represented had two to four children), proved to be directly and strikingly related to the preference to wait with others under conditions of anxiety. This finding was consistent with other evidence cited that first-born children tend to be more anxious and are more likely to seek social assistance in dealing with problems.

THE "AUTOKINETIC PHENOMENON"

Ingenious methods have also been developed for studying the influence of field or environmental factors, especially social pressures, on the development of frames of reference in ambiguous situations. Among the most interesting studies in this area are some that have been conducted in studying responses to what is known as the autokinetic phenomenon—the apparent movement of a small stationary spot of light when seen in darkness.[13]

It has long been known that in a pitch-dark room a single point of light, when observed for a short period of time, seems to move in one or more directions. When the observer continues to look at this light for a period of time a certain pattern of movement will become stabilized, provided nothing else influences the person's judgment. When other points of light are introduced into the situation, or when sounds are included in the area, these seem to have some effect on the type of stabilization that develops; that is, they seem to influence the development of a frame of reference.

Sherif and other psychologists have conducted many experiments to learn how an individual develops a frame of reference in an ambiguous situation and how to identify factors which influence this development.

In one such study, individuals were placed alone in a position to observe such a spot of light, and were asked to describe what they saw. It was found that each individual can and does tend to establish for himself a certain pattern of movement which he ascribes to the light. Once such a pattern of movement was established, it tended to be maintained in subsequent experiments. This pattern became his frame of reference in viewing the point of light. Yet the person was usually unaware that he had acquired a way of looking at the spot of light, and that this acquired manner of approaching the experience was influencing his judgments.

In subsequent experiments the subject was accompanied by a colleague who viewed the autokinetic phenomenon at the same time as the subject. Both viewers were asked to state in what direction, and how far, the light was moving. Under these conditions it was learned that the frame of reference of the subject could be influenced by the judgments of his colleagues. The subject tended to adapt his perception of the situation to the judgments of the colleague who was responding to the same situation. In some way he was influenced by the social pressure of the other member without being aware that his perceptions were being influenced.[14]

Many subsequent studies of this pattern have been carried out under varying conditions and they support the conclusion that social factors such as social pressures, the judgments of others, or suggestions from others do tend to influence the nature of the frame of reference developed or held in an ambiguous situation. This occurs even with highly intelligent individuals and with professional persons trained to be cautious observers. It occurs under experimental conditions with respect to a wide range of situations.

IMPRESSIONS OF OTHER PEOPLE

Asch, a social psychologist interested in learning more about how we gain our impressions of people, carried out a series of small studies that have broad potential significance for public health practice.[15] Much of our knowledge about the people we work with is obtained from the impressions we receive from others. How are their impressions acquired? What internal and situational factors govern our judgments of colleagues, associates, and clients?

Asch noted that certain personal qualities tend to serve as "key" factors in organizing our impressions of others. In testing his hypothesis, he read identical lists of terms descriptive of a person to two groups, except that one group heard the individual described as "warm" and the other group heard him described as "cold." Group A: "Intelligent, skillful, industrious, *warm,* determined, practical, cautious"; Group B: "Intelligent, skillful, industrious, *cold,* determined, practical, cautious."[16]

Members of the two groups were then asked to write sketches of the person, and then indicate on a list of pairs of adjectives those that were the most descriptive. Striking differences were found between the two groups in their adjective choices, with far more of those who heard the person described as "warm" classifying him as "generous," "wise," "happy," "good-natured," "imaginative," and so on. Thus their generalizations about the person were clearly influenced by hearing the person described as "warm" or "cold." Other terms used, such as "polite" and "blunt," failed to yield such differences.

In another classical experiment, Asch read the following list of terms descriptive of a person to two different groups. Note that in this study the identical terms were used with the two groups except that their order was reversed: Group A: "Intelligent, industrious, impulsive, critical, stubborn, envious"; Group B: "Envious, stubborn, critical, impulsive, industrious, intelligent." Again considerable differences in the descriptions by the two groups resulted. The order of presentation established a frame of reference which tended to influence judgment, even though there was no difference in the content presented to the two groups.[17]

VALUE AND ATTITUDE CLIMATES

Newcomb has documented, in an interesting comparative study, the extent to which individual and group attitudes and value orientations influence the patterns of new knowledge acquired. He chose for study three student communities that differed significantly in their orientations toward the Spanish Civil War which was then in progress. His purpose was to test the hypothesis that the differing orientations of the student bodies toward the Spanish Civil War would influence the kind of facts they held regarding it.[18]

The student body at Bennington College, where Newcomb was engaged in a long-term study of student orientations, was chosen to represent a liberal student group. The Bennington students at that time tended as a group to be strongly pro-Loyalist and frequently participated in activities in support of the Loyalist cause. An unnamed Roman Catholic university student body was selected to represent an anti-Loyalist position, and the Williams College students were selected to represent a somewhat more neutral position.[19]

The extent to which different orientations regarding the Spanish Civil War were held by the three groups chosen for study is illustrated by the responses of a sample of students from each school to the statement, "I hope the Loyalists win the war." Eighty-two per cent of the Bennington sample either "strongly agreed" or "agreed" with this statement; 64 per cent of the Williams sample "strongly agreed" or "agreed," whereas only 11 per cent of the unnamed Roman Catholic university students "strongly agreed" or "agreed," and 76 per cent of the Roman Catholic students either "strongly disagreed" or "disagreed."[20]

Student responses were obtained to tests of three different types of information:

> A test of neutral information regarding the War. "Care was taken to include information items of strictly neutral content, that is, such that knowledge of the correct answer would not dispose the individual toward either a favorable or unfavorable attitude."
>
> A test of pro-Loyalist information. It "consisted of true-or-false items, the true answers to which were presumably disposing toward pro-Loyalist attitude (e.g., the statement, true at the time, that 'General Franco's government has been recognized as the legitimate power in Spain only by governments which are overtly fascist, or near-fascist.')."
>
> A test of information of a type presumed disposing to anti-Loyalist attitudes "(e.g., the true statement that 'Indisputable evidence has been adduced showing that some clergy have been executed and many persecuted by Loyalist sympathizers.')"[21]

Bennington students were found to hold a pattern of facts decidedly different from those held by the Roman Catholic student group, and Williams students tended to be similar to Bennington students. The mean information scores for the three groups regarding these three different tests of information concerning the Spanish Civil War were as follows:

MEAN INFORMATION SCORES OF:

Type of Information[a]	Bennington	Williams	Unnamed Catholic student group
Neutral	7.4	7.0	4.1
Pro-Loyalist	9.8	10.1	1.7
Anti-Loyalist	2.7	1.2	7.2

[a]An adaptation from Table 10 in "Some Patterned Consequences of Membership in a College Community" by Theodore M. Newcomb. (See Note 18, p. 497.)

Newcomb interprets these striking differences as reflecting the influence of different attitude climates in the three schools:

> As a result of these attitude climates, students in either community found it easier to get one sort of information than the other; they were more likely to acquire and to retain that kind of information which supported their attitudes than the kind which undermined them; and both information and attitudes were simultaneously influenced by degree of concern over the issue. At Bennington those most concerned over the

issue became most pro-Loyalist in attitude; they acquired and retained most information supporting the attitude; and they were least able to accept as "fact" such information as tended to undermine their attitudes. Those most concerned over the issue at the Catholic university became most anti-Loyalist in attitude, and were most likely to retain and to reject, respectively, those kinds of information which supported or undermined their attitudes.[22]

Personal and family values probably have a guiding influence over an individual's choice of a college to attend, provided adequate economic means are available and entrance requirements are satisfied. Thus students with similar values probably tend to choose similar schools. Once enrolled, however, the individual tends to adapt to the prevailing norms with respect to issues of public interest, as Newcomb's studies have shown. One might thus view the findings reported here as reflecting the combined effects of individual and group values and attitudes on information acquired and accepted.

THE PERSISTENCE OF FRAMES OF REFERENCE

The frames of reference people acquire help them attain and maintain a sense of security and stability, and a sense of purposive continuity in an ever-changing social and physical world. All perceptual and judgmental behavior takes place within such frames of reference. One's values and standards, the behavior of one's reference groups, and the expectations one holds for oneself serve as anchorages in the development of such frames of reference. Without frames of reference based on such anchorages one would be at a loss in making even simple decisions, for one would have no means of judging alternatives.[23]

Frames of reference are developed out of the evaluations of previous experience. They serve the purpose of linking past behavior to future behavior in terms of meaning and purpose. By helping the individual in his efforts to organize and to give meaning to the wide range of physical and social stimuli which compete for attention, they help to prepare him for action in new situations. An established frame of reference is in this sense a psychological readiness to behave in a particular way.

It is not surprising, then, that a frame of reference once firmly established has a high persistence quality. It tends to remain stable even in the face of strong contrary evidence, and may thus govern behavior in situations far removed in time and type from those in which it was initially acquired. Since frames of reference may function without personal awareness, they may lead even unwilling persons to behave in ways that mock both logic and intent.

Public Health Illustrations

This persistent quality of frames of reference, therefore, has high public health significance. Understanding the illogical manner of their functioning may help the administrator identify behaviors so influenced, whether these behaviors are those of members of the public, employees, staff members and professional colleagues; or whether his own behavior is involved.

One observes the persistent functioning of conflicting frames of reference in the stubborn conflicts of the conference table, in the stereotyped reactions of one profession to another, in standardized patterns of response to authority, and in reactions of those with power and responsibility to the demands of those whom they control. A century of experience working together has led physicians to see nurses, and nurses to see physicians, with particular patterns of role, responsibility, and behavior. Even though major changes in training and function of both physicians and nurses have occurred over the century, the standardized frame of reference within which the physician and nurse view each other, and respond to each other, persists.

Persistence of the frame of reference is also discernible in the responses of patients to physicians and nurses, in the reactions of waitresses and dishwashers to physical checkups, in the responses of restaurant owners to the arguments of the sanitarian, and, of course, in the counter-reactions of the professional health worker in each of these instances. The mother of a low-income family who has learned of the means test through an ego-crushing experience in the health clinic will not quickly discard the negative orientation acquired. Rather, this negative frame of reference is likely to be generalized by the mother to the clinic in general and to health workers as a group. A negative orientation toward the idea of accepting charity will not be wiped out by statements that "the clinic is designed to serve you" or "everyone is welcome." The costs of a means test program may thus be reflected, in untreated illness, the spread of contagion, and in manners not directly revealed.

This persistent quality of frames of reference deserves the serious consideration of health change agents—whether physicians, nurses, sanitarians, or health educators. It is frequently much more difficult to change a frame of reference already firmly established than it is to establish a new frame of reference. As Dr. Applewhite so aptly observed, "Nothing is so hard to light as a burned-over stump."

Our national civil defense educational program has floundered, in part, from efforts to establish civilian orientations prematurely, with officials urging conflicting actions from "Hide!" to "Flee!" before there was valid evidence available to support either action. In succession, the public has been advised to seek cover in the basement; to build a cement shelter and store necessary rations; to keep extra gasoline in the car in order to flee from the cities by the quickest escape route; to store food in some shelter outside the city; and finally, again, to seek shelter in the basement, and build a cement shelter there, or nearby. Either all of these actions are appropriate, or the public has been trained to take many false steps. Thus many conflicting frames of reference to guide action in disaster have been established, and are likely to persist as barriers to the development of new frames of reference. They may contribute to bewilderment should a disaster occur.[24]

Experimental Findings

One of the most interesting, and disturbing, studies of the persistence of established frames of reference was conducted by Leeper a quarter-century ago. For his experiment he prepared three pictures: a picture of a young woman, one of an old woman, and one in which the two other pictures were fused to make a composite picture.

A person who is first shown the figure of the young woman, and then shown the composite picture, will see the young woman but not the old woman in the composite picture. Conversely, a person who is first shown the figure of the old woman and then the composite figure will see the old woman, but not the young woman in the composite figure. The frame of reference established by the first picture viewed persists. A considerable lapse of time occurs before anyone shown either single figure first will see both young and old women in the composite picture.

When Leeper's young woman and old woman were shown to separate groups of public health students, the responses obtained were fully consistent with Leeper's findings. Representatives of the two groups were then asked to draw crude outlines of the faces of the person they saw in the composite figure. These outlines were put on the

FIGURE 14

FIGURE 15

FIGURE 16

Figure 14 represents a Young Lady, Figure 15 represents an Old Lady, and Figure 16 represents the composite. Only one figure should be viewed at a time, with the others blocked out, the order of presentation being from Figures 14 to 16 or from 15 to 16.

SOURCE: Leeper, Robert W., "A Study of a Neglected Portion of the Field of Learning—the Development of Sensory Organization," *Journal of Genetic Psychology,* vol. 46, 1935. Reproduced with permission of the author.

blackboard. Members of the class tended to identify strongly with the person who drew the figure they had first seen. Some students could not see the opposite figure until it was traced out with a finger on the composite picture. Even the brief exposure was sufficient to establish a surprising degree of persistence in the frame of reference established.[25]

Influence on Council Activities

Members of the American Public Health Association who attended the first meeting of the Governing Council at the annual meeting in 1959 observed an example of the extent to which an established frame of reference influenced the decision-making process of a governing body. The issue was a statement in the report from the chairman of the Executive Board to the Governing Council. Involved were a change in practice with respect to the ways of dealing with proposed resolutions and the manner in which this change was presented to the members.

It has been the practice of the Governing Council to consider resolutions brought to it by a Committee on Resolutions. These resolutions and recommendations were solicited from the members, usually through the action of the Section Councils. Following a review by the Resolutions Committee to eliminate duplication and to establish common patterns of wording, and so forth, the resolutions were usually published and made available for review of the Council as a whole.

Previous to 1959 the Executive Board had not been seen as a source of new resolutions or recommendations to the Governing Council, nor had it been the practice of the Board previously to call attention to specific recommendations or resolutions brought to the Association Council. Accordingly, members of the Council were faced with a new pattern of procedure when presented the following statement at the end of a report of the chairman of the Executive Board to the Governing Council:

"A number of policy matters will come to the Council's attention by way of resolutions at the second session. Several other matters of moment to the Association will be brought to the Council's attention by Committee reports. The Board calls your attention to the following recommendations. . . ." A list of recommendations was then offered for the Council to consider at its next meeting, together with other resolutions that had been brought to its attention in the customary way.

The new practice of the Executive Board, in calling attention to resolutions for the Council to consider, caused a flurry of action on the floor. It was apparent from the discussion that the Council did not object to the idea of resolutions being transmitted by the Board for Council consideration. Rather, there was concern that in accepting the Board's report the Council might imply support for the resolutions. Someone might interpret the resolutions as having the approval of the Council. Several members of the Council indicated, in the discussion and in response to questions following the discussion, that in accepting the Board's report they were, in effect, supporting the resolutions presented by the Board just as they were approving other Board actions.

One member of the Council, interviewed later, expressed the opinion that approval of the Board's report with the recommended resolutions in it might be erroneously interpreted by outsiders. The resolutions might be seen as having been passed by the APHA. This might lead to serious public misinterpretation.

The discussion resulting from this recommendation to the Council lasted an hour. No progress was made in spite of repeated statements by the chairman of the Board and the parliamentarian that in accepting the report the Council was neither accepting nor approving the recommendations, but merely agreeing to consider them. The Council would not accept the report of the Board as presented. It was necessary to carry the issue over as unfinished business until the report was revised so that it would be more clearly in tune with the expectations of the Council members.

This incident illustrates the difficulties involved in obtaining or bringing about changes even in the order of the activity of formal groups. Patterns of norms, once established, carry great weight in the minds of those concerned. The implications of even minor changes may be interpreted quite differently from the way in which the person initiating the change intended.

Of considerable interest here, also, is the degree or extent to which the frame of reference, once established by the report, persisted in the minds of the Council members even though serious attempts were made to clarify the meaning of the report. In this instance, a highly educated leadership group found themselves held up for hours because of the difficulties involved in instituting a minor change in the way of doing business. This occurred even though there was no apparent disagreement regarding the intent of the change.

IMPLICATIONS FOR PUBLIC HEALTH

The implications of studies of the frame of reference for public health practice are many and varied. Perhaps most significant of all is the evidence that professional people, such as public health leaders themselves, have, or acquire, frames of reference with respect to all situations they perceive, judge, and evaluate. The frame of reference they may take toward any situation may seriously influence their behavior in that situation without their being aware that it is occurring. Only by maintaining a highly critical attitude in ambiguous situations, by seeking outside sources of evidence, and by seeking to validate judgment against rigorous criteria can the leader protect himself from such insidious influences.

Many different frames of reference are likely to be present in any group brought together to work on a problem, to plan a program, or to evaluate progress. Different members, exposed to the same experience and to the same data, will react in contrary ways. Much give and take in the manner of discussion may be necessary before the reasons underlying the varying conclusions can be identified. In the differing points of view lies the potential for high creativity if full consideration is given to alternatives so that richer group decisions emerge. But if the varying viewpoints cannot be brought into the discussion and objectively evaluated, the same situation holds the potential for lasting misunderstanding and frustration. The individual members of the group may then never learn in what ways they agree or disagree with their colleagues, or what factors underly these disagreements.

Attempting to prepare materials, posters, exhibits, or movies for a given audience involves predicting to some degree the frame of reference that the group will take for the material presented. When the educator and the audience come from the same socioeconomic and cultural background, the chances of error are considerably less than when they come from different backgrounds or when there is wide variation within the group as to the social or cultural experience. Under such circumstances, particularly, some method of feedback from the individuals in the group, through asking questions or through getting reactions, is imperative if the educator is to know the frame of reference the individuals bring to the experience and whether or not the materials or approaches selected are being properly understood.

When people do not come to a situation with strongly established frames of reference, then the order and manner of the educator's presentation of material and his manner of defining the situation or setting up the conditions for learning are of great importance. Members of the group may be influenced to a considerable degree by the pattern of structure the situation offers them. If no structure is consciously offered, then the clutter of the situation will result in some structure being developed in the mind of the individual concerned, which may be quite contrary to that intended.

When similarly trained professional leaders approach new situations they, too, are likely, because of training, to view them in similar ways and to be influenced in like manner by the structure of the organization they observe. Even though they may approach the situation independently, their judgments may confirm one another and yet tend to be invalid when compared with that of another judge who considers the situation from another point of view. Error may thus be confirmed, rather than identified, by two judges viewing the same situation from the same background of value and experience. This may be a matter of serious concern with regard to advisory, review, or evaluative committees. High agreements, influenced by common experience and values, may at once conceal error, foster complacency, and stifle creativity.

Even in our approaches to one another in an interview situation, such as applying for a job or meeting with an executive board, the manner of our approach may influence the type of frame of reference within which we are perceived. Such quickly established orientations may have serious long-term effects in interpersonal relations. In such instances, also, a frame of reference, once established, is most difficult to change.

NOTES TO CHAPTER 27

1. Sherif, Muzafer, and Hadley Cantril, *The Psychology of Ego-Involvements, Social Attitudes, and Identifications*. John Wiley and Sons, New York, 1947, p. 34.

2. Sherif, Muzafer, and Hadley Cantril, "The Psychology of Attitudes," Part I, *Psychological Review*, vol. 52, no. 6, 1945, p. 317.

3. Cantril, Hadley, *The Psychology of Social Movements*. John Wiley and Sons, New York, 1941.

4. Schachter, Stanley, *The Psychology of Affiliation: Experimental Studies of the Sources of Gregariousness*. Stanford Studies in Psychology, I. Stanford University Press, Stanford, 1959.

5. Festinger, Leon, "A Theory of Social Comparison Processes," *Human Relations*, vol. 7, 1954, pp. 135–136.

6. Schachter, Stanley, and Harvey Burdick, "A Field Experiment on Rumor Transmission and Distortion," *Journal of Abnormal and Social Psychology,* vol. 50, 1955, pp. 363–371.

7. See discussion and references in Chapter 23 of this volume.

8. Frenkel-Brunswick, Else, "Intolerance of Ambiguity as an Emotional and Perceptual Personality Variable," *Journal of Personality,* vol. 18, 1947, pp. 108–143.

9. Blackwell, Barbara, "Expectations of Upper Middle Class Adults About Their Activities Prior to Seeking Professional Medical Care for Physical and Psychiatric Health Conditions." Unpublished doctoral dissertation, University of California, Berkeley, 1963.

10. Schachter, Stanley, *op. cit.,* pp. 12–14.

11. *Ibid.,* p. 41.

12. *Ibid.,* p. 132.

13. Sherif, Muzafer, *The Psychology of Social Norms.* Harper and Bros., New York, 1936.

14. *Ibid.;* Sherif, Muzafer, and Carolyn W. Sherif, *Groups in Harmony and Tension: An Integration of Studies on Intergroup Relations,* Harper and Row, New York, 1953; Idem, *An Outline of Social Psychology,* rev. ed., Harper and Row, New York, 1956; Idem, *Reference Groups: Exploration into Conformity and Deviation of Adolescents,* Harper and Row, New York, 1964.

15. Asch, Solomon E., *Social Psychology.* Prentice-Hall, Inc., Englewood Cliffs, N.J., 1952, pp. 205–229.

16. *Ibid.,* p. 209.

17. *Ibid.,* p. 212.

18. Newcomb, Theodore M., "Some Patterned Consequences of Membership in a College Community" in Katz, Daniel, and associates, editors, *Public Opinion and Propaganda.* The Dryden Press, New York, 1954, pp. 435–446.

19. Newcomb, Theodore M., *Personality and Social Change: Attitude Formation in a Student Community.* The Dryden Press, New York, 1943. Reprinted, 1957.

20. *Idem,* "Some Patterned Consequences of Membership in a College Community," *op. cit.,* p. 439.

21. *Ibid.*

22. *Ibid.,* pp. 439–440.

23. Sherif, Muzafer, and Hadley Cantril, "The Psychology of Attitudes," *op. cit.;* Part II. *Psychological Review,* vol. 53, no. 1, 1946, pp. 1–24.

24. Cantril, Hadley, *op. cit.;* Cantril, Hadley, Hazel Gaudet, and Herta Herzog, *The Invasion from Mars,* Princeton University Press, Princeton, 1940.

25. Leeper, Robert W., "A Study of a Neglected Portion of the Field of Learning—the Development of Sensory Organization," *Journal of Genetic Psychology,* vol. 46, 1935, pp. 41–75.

Chapter 28

The Role of Mass Media
in Public Health*

By William Griffiths and Andie L. Knutson

Mass media are intensively employed in public health. Vast sums are spent annually for materials and salaries that have gone into the production and distribution of booklets, pamphlets, exhibits, newspaper articles, and radio and television programs. These media are employed at all levels of public health in the hope that three effects might occur: the learning of correct health information, the changing of health attitudes and values, and the establishment of new health behavior.

During the past decade there have been strong disagreements among public health leaders regarding the effectiveness of mass media in achieving these ends. In one camp are those who believe that mass media are highly effective and deserve recognition as the primary means of public health education. Opposed are those who strongly question such a point of view, and argue that health education must use more dynamic methods. Some educators go so far as to assign mass media a relatively limited role.

Those who support the wide use of mass media maintain that mass media provide the best means of imparting the latest scientific information to large groups of people. It has been the experience of health workers that the general public possesses a great deal of incorrect information about traditional health problems and at the same time lacks an understanding of the advances in numerous public health fields. The mass media are assumed to be the means whereby changes in knowledge can be achieved. The correct information is supposed to produce

* This chapter was previously published as a paper in the *American Journal of Public Health,* vol. 50, April, 1960. Reprinted with the permission of the publisher.

a trigger-like reaction whereby new health facts lead to a change in health attitudes and values, which in turn bring about changes in health practices. This assumption is based partly on the observation that industry spends considerable sums of money for advertising through mass media, and would not do so unless results were achieved.

Others feel that even the best of mass media will not reach members of those groups which most need the services public health has to offer. Some more personalized approach would seem necessary both to reach such groups and to influence the values, beliefs, and attitudes which bind them to outmoded health behaviors. Furthermore, selling health is different from selling cigarettes or soaps. A business may be successful if only a small percentage of the public is influenced to become customers, and for many firms this means making only a single purchase. What a far cry this is from influencing the vast majority of our population to follow a particular health practice day after day for the rest of their lives.

The two sets of arguments seem poles apart, yet each has a ring of truth. They pose for us a most serious question to consider: What is the role of mass media in public health programs?

In approaching this question we are fortunate that a wealth of excellent research evidence is available. Since the beginning of World War II mass communications have been the subject of intensive research, and many excellent studies have been reported. It is the purpose of this paper to review some of the most significant of these studies insofar as they have a bearing on our question.

Mass Media Tend to Reach Select Audiences

There is ample evidence, and certainly no reason for presenting details, to show that the mass media in this country reach millions of people, yet they are more likely to reach persons of somewhat better socioeconomic status, educational status, and those more active in the community activities than those of lowest socioeconomic status, education, and participation in community affairs. They are somewhat more likely to reach the persons in leadership positions than those in followership positions, those who have prestige and status in their intimate groups rather than those who lack these characteristics.

This conclusion is supported by a wealth of interesting data pertaining to the number of people reached by the various media.[1] It even applies with respect to the use of the public library.[2]

The major concern, of course, is not one of reaching people but rather of reaching the desired audience. A pamphlet intended to recruit young girls into the nursing profession has no chance of achieving its purpose unless the pamphlet is read either by those individuals eligible to enter the nursing profession or by others who will communicate the contents to the eligible group. In many cases, when we can define precisely the desired audience, it is possible to devise ways of reaching the group through mass media. On the other hand, certain desired audiences, such as men between the ages of 50 and 60 with cardiac disorders, or the 15 per cent of the population which was not reached in the county x-ray survey, are sometimes nearly impossible to reach by means of mass media alone.

At times it is necessary to reach every citizen in the community. It may be important for everyone to take action regarding an impending epidemic, or to take essential health precautions during a period of crisis or disaster. The success of some major health effort may depend on the participation of groups that cannot be reached directly through mass media channels.

Most health workers are only too familiar with the fact that such groups as the PTA are attended by the parents who least need to be reached. The parents who would benefit most from the health talk or movie are rarely in attendance. The audience is free to select or reject.

Even when people are exposed to a communication, they may neither read nor listen to what we have to say. During one of the war bond drives in World War II every household in Baltimore, Maryland, received a pamphlet urging the occupants to buy bonds. After a short period of time a large number of people were interviewed, 83 per cent of whom did not recall receiving a pamphlet.[3]

People read, listen to, or see primarily those things with which they agree. During World War II, every possible communication channel was used to persuade people in a certain community to see a particular movie, the purpose of which was to heighten citizens' identification with the war effort. Only 5 per cent of the adults in the community attended the movie. When those persons who attended the movie and those who did not attend were interviewed, it was found that the former group had already manifested more behavior encouraged by the movie than the latter group. For example, 40 per cent of those who attended the movie had given blood to the Red Cross prior to attending the movie, compared to 20 per cent of those not attending.[4]

Klapper, in commenting on the large number of researches on this process that he calls "self-selection," writes: "Whether a person voluntarily reads at all, what kind of material he reads, what kind he listens to, and what type of movie he chooses to see are apparently determined by his cultural status. Taste, in the widest sense of the term, seems a product of formal education rather than of attendance on given kinds of mass media material. Tastes, indeed, seem so fixed that mass media have little chance to do anything about them. For it now appears that a given kind of material distributed through the mass media, reaches only those persons who already like such material."[5]

Effects May Be Specific and Limited

If we can reach and hold our desired audience, how effective will mass media be in imparting the intended message? One of the most careful and intensive research investigations in mass communication was conducted in World War II and we believe it is significant enough to report in some detail. Hovland and his associates, working in the War Department's Information and Education Division, investigated the effectiveness of numerous training films, including the "Why We Fight" series. This series consisted of seven 50-minute films, used especially in orienting new recruits during basic training. The films outlined the history of World War II from the rise of Fascism in Italy and Germany through America's entrance into the war. As the general purpose of the films, Hovland states: ". . . their purpose was not purely instructional in the manner of a training film, but was rather to get across particular interpretations of facts, overcome prejudices, arouse motivations, and in general to modify attitudes rather than merely to convey factual information."[6]

Two basic assumptions were made in preparing the "Why We Fight" series: first, that a large group of men entering the Army lacked knowledge of the world events leading to America's entrance into the war; second, that if the men understood the facts of the situation they would accept their role in the Army more readily.

Without describing in detail the experimental design and procedure of the research, it will be of value to know that for a number of the films experimental and control groups were devised; in the former were men who had seen the films, while the control group consisted of men who had not seen the films. The films were pretested through interviews and questionnaires and the same methods were used in securing information after the films had been seen. The major findings of this research make a real contribution to understanding the effects of mass media.

First, the films were found in general to be quite effective in imparting factual information. Men who had seen the films increased considerably their knowledge about the war and knew much more about various national and international events than the men who had not seen the films.

Second, the films were effective in changing opinions when the opinions dealt with specific facts covered in the films. For example, a greater number of men who had seen the film "Prelude to War," as compared to those who had not seen it, agreed with the statement that the German Army had about the best trained officers in the world. Although the films were effective in changing opinions, changes in opinions were not as great as changes in information.

Third, in analyzing the films in relation to motivation, Hovland writes: "The films had no effects on the items prepared for the purpose of measuring effects on the men's motivation to serve as soldiers, which was considered the ultimate objective of the orientation program."[7]

A similar method of analysis was used in the study of the reaction to a mass x-ray survey conducted with strong mass media support in Mishawaka, Indiana, in 1947 and 1948. Random adult samples of approximately 400 were obtained prior to and after the intensive information campaign lasting almost a year.

> In general, the study indicates that the survey was effective in imparting specific information publicized in the survey, and was successful in motivating a little over 60 per cent of the adult population to obtain x-rays during the year. The findings suggest, however, that people were not always left with a thorough understanding of the items of information they had picked up; that the survey failed to increase knowledge or influence attitudes in areas of information and attitude not specifically covered in the survey; and that it was unsuccessful in influencing some of the basic attitudes related to tuberculosis control.[8]

Schramm, in an evaluative review of the effects of mass media, concludes that mass media are valuable in increasing factual information and changing attitudes when the media are highly specific. He believes that ". . . the amount of attitude and opinion change tends to be proportional to the specific quality of the attitude or opinion. If the desired response is specific, it is more likely to be learned than if it is general. . . . It appears that few persons can be counted on to learn the unstated implications of a mass communication."[9]

In the health field, Greenberg and his associates have attempted to determine whether the pamphlets "Pierre the Pelican" met the objectives for which they were written. This series of pamphlets distributed widely by health agencies and intended for parents of first-born children was designed to motivate parents to use certain child-rearing practices. The series consisted of 12 pamphlets, simply and attractively designed, each dealing with various areas of child growth and development. Once a month, for the first year, a pamphlet would be mailed to the parents.[10]

Greenberg set up experimental and control groups of parents of first-born children, based on four strata according to degree of urbanization. The experimental group received the pamphlet series while the control group did not. A questionnaire-interview schedule was developed and tested in pilot studies. Skilled interviewers were selected and underwent a three-day training course. Through the interviews, information was secured in various areas of child care and training: eating, sleeping, and toilet habits; linguistic and motor development; social development; and parents' present attitudes and future plans in relation to the child's growth and development.

Preliminary analysis of the data obtained reveal few differences in parents' feeding practices existing between the group receiving the "Pierre the Pelican" series and those not receiving it. The authors conclude with the statement: "This evaluation shows that in order to affect attitudes and practices, more must be known about how to utilize the complex psychological factors which stimulate persons to action. Also, the alteration of established patterns of behavior may be too much to expect from a single instrument."[11]

We may summarize with reference to the health field. If mass media are skillfully prepared, we may expect health facts to be learned. An attitude toward a health subject may be altered quite easily if the attitude is neutral in character and the subject matter of the mass media relates specifically to the health attitude. It is very difficult, however, for mass media to change attitudes embedded in tradition and strongly held.

Many health workers have been enthusiastic about the importance of using mass media techniques because of the success of mass media in the advertising field. Lazarsfeld and Merton show the fallacy of this deduction. They write: "Prevailing beliefs in the enormous power of mass communications appear to stem from successful cases of monopolistic propaganda or from advertising. But the leap from the efficacy of advertising to the assumed efficacy of propaganda aimed at deep-rooted attitudes and ego-involved behavior is as unwarranted as it is dangerous. Advertising is typically directed toward the canalizing of pre-existing behavior patterns or attitudes. It seldom seeks to instill new attitudes or to create significantly new behavior patterns."[12]

Thus cigarette advertisers do not spend their money on attempting to convince the nonsmoker to smoke, but rather on attempting to persuade the smoker to switch his brand. The behavior change mechanism involved in this is quite different from the behavior change mechanism involved in persuading longshoremen to visit a physician at regular intervals, when longshoremen view doctors as persons you visit only when you are seriously ill.

Wiebe feels that radio and television can sell citizenship objectives as well as soap provided certain specific conditions exist—conditions which have been found essential in the successful merchandising of commodities. These conditions are not easily met.[13] One important condition of selling a commodity is having a retail outlet. Retail sales people play an important facilitating role, for they supply the link between the radio and television advertisement and the completion of the purchasing act. Retail sales clerks, often located in the nearby neighborhood, have the advertised commodity ready and attractively packaged for immediate distribution. In the field of public health, health agencies might be thought of as retail stores and health workers as sales clerks who are enthusiastic about their products and eagerly await the general public. Unfortunately, however, health agencies have very few products in attractive, easy-to-carry packages for quick and immediate delivery. The process of achieving the objective is much slower and more complex.

Personal Appeals May Influence Effects

While mass media cannot, except under most extraordinary conditions, be expected to move people to action if the action is in opposition to strong beliefs and attitudes, they can be effective in moving people to action if the desired course of action is in the direction of basic personal and social motives, and particularly if the action is supported by leaders holding acceptance and prestige in the eyes of the laymen. It is important that these leaders have the capacity to translate the action meaningfully into the behavior patterns of those concerned.

One amazingly successful demonstration of the effectiveness of mass media as a motivating force was that of Kate Smith in one of her war bond appeals. In one day, through the medium of radio, she received pledges amounting to thirty-nine million dollars. Merton, in analyzing this particular radio program, studied the types of motivating themes used by Kate Smith in her appeals. Previous war bond drives had emphasized the themes of sound investment and future security, but these were entirely omitted in the Smith program. Almost one-half of her themes related to sacrifice and another third to participation and competition. These themes are illustrated in the following statements taken from her talks:

"Could you say to Mrs. Viola Buckley . . . Mrs. Viola Buckley whose son Donald was killed in action . . . that you are doing everything you can to shorten the war . . . that you are backing up her son to the limit of your abilities?"[14]

"We can do it together. . . . We can put this greatest of war bond drives across."[15]

"I was a little disappointed to discover that the good old town of New York was behind Los Angeles . . . now we're going to hold the switchboard open to give New Yorkers a chance to catch up to and surpass Los Angeles. Are you with me?"[16]

Although the Kate Smith program is in no way comparable to health programs, it does illustrate the point that health programs attempting to bring about some change in behavior must give attention to the motivational factors employed. Professional health workers might not be very enthusiastic about heavy emphasis upon sentimental themes, but they must realize that formal and scientific presentations will do little toward changing behavior.

It is important to recognize that Kate Smith's success did not stem solely from her ability to communicate effectively with the public and from the fact that she held unusual prestige in the eyes of laymen. The campaign which she touched off was the result of months of planning. Many persons who intended to purchase bonds held up their purchases to take advantage of the publicity in support of the program under way. Weeks of intensive work with leadership groups intermediary between the broadcast station and the lay public were involved in developing this project. Their efforts were timed with great care in order that a bandwagon type of appeal might be developed. Unfortunately, data are not available on the amount of funds spent for war bonds resulting from the preplanning and the amount resulting directly from the appeal of Miss Smith. One must be cautious, therefore, in estimating the effectiveness of her drive even though the evidence suggests that her appeal was most potent.

Psychological Set Influences Interpretation

When unusual conditions of psychological readiness exist, the mass medium may play an exceptional, and in fact frightening, role in influencing public action. This is well illustrated by the panic created by the broadcast of Orson Welles's now famous "Invasion from Mars" play in 1938. Cantril, in his study of the panic, observed that "long before the broadcast had ended, people all over the United States were praying, crying, fleeing frantically to escape death from the Martians. Some ran to rescue loved ones. Others telephoned farewells or warnings, hurried to inform neighbors, sought information from newspapers or radio stations, summoned ambulances and police cars. At least six million people heard the broadcast. At least a million of them were frightened or disturbed."[17]

Cantril's study suggests that while no single personality variable consistently related to the panic reaction, a lack of critical ability seemed most conducive to fear under the stress situation. His study suggests that an insecure and bewildered people under pressure of domestic insecurity and international tension, lacking adequate information or appropriate standards for judging the events, and threatened by a situation in which they stood to lose all their values at once, were triggered into panic.

The credibility of persons interviewed with respect to the experts cited on the program, and the fumbling attempts of many to obtain advice from experts of their own choosing, call attention again to the importance of prestige suggestion in influencing behavior through any means of communication. Hovland and his associates, on the basis of many studies of source credibility, conclude that "the characterization of the communicator as trustworthy or biased has relatively little effect on the learning of factual material but markedly influences the degree to which the communicator's conclusions and recommendations are accepted."[18]

Trusted Informal Leaders Can Serve Key Function

The evidence suggests that achieving long-term attitude and behavior change requires communications of a more personal type to assure full understanding of the meaning of the change and to help in translating the change into the personal behavior of the individual concerned.

Other things being equal, communication is likely to be more effective if the person communicating is perceived as one who can be trusted, who is an expert, or who holds prestige in our eyes. A very popular and trusted health science writer may be more effective in communicating scientific opinions than a great scientist who lacks status in the eyes of the public. Local health leaders may be better able to capture opinion than national leaders of greater stature who lack experience in the local area. The unrecognized leader in the local group may be more effective than either of the former with the group by whom he is trusted.

It is with this informal leader that the group may be able to test out new ideas verbally or in action before trying them out in life. The discussion with him may provide an opportunity to test reality in a non-threatening situation. It may afford also an opportunity to determine the relation of the change to the solution of the problem of concern. When this happens the person who is ego-involved in the problem may be better able to understand how it applies to him, and therefore may be more willing to adopt the new practice.

Many of the group discussion-decision studies point to the importance of this more personal type of education as a means of providing people with a better opportunity to exchange ideas and make decisions for themselves. Workshops, buzz groups, self-surveys are all means of reality testing which help individuals to achieve change with a minimum of personal threat. In these interpersonal situations the communicator can better adapt to the needs and concerns of his audience, and can better adjust to discussion in terms of the expectations or motivations of those he is seeking to influence.

Tinker to Evers to Chance?

In what ways, then, do mass media really influence patterns of personal change? Mass media do serve a significant function in providing information and support to selected groups of the population. Often, however, they do not reach those populations with which public health is primarily concerned. When they do reach those groups, the effects have been less satisfactory than might be desired.

Research suggests that mass media have varying and often limited effects, both by failing to reach all members of the population, and because the selective nature of communication does not assure adequate exposure and reinforcement. Therefore, significant behavioral changes may not result. Among those most frequently reached, however, are persons of somewhat greater than average education and of somewhat better than average socioeconomic status. These are people who tend to be active participants in informal social webs of their communities; because of their superior education and better orientation to current affairs they are more likely to understand and accept new scientific information. They are more likely also to recognize their own community's stake in new public health approaches and to see the value of action both for themselves and for those less alert and less informed.

Is it possible that these persons are key communication gatekeepers to the people of their communities? One is reminded of the famous Chicago double play team of Tinker to Evers to Chance. Are these leaders the community "Evers" who receive and evaluate communications from the mass media sources, and are in a position to pass on the communications selectively to persons who look to them for leadership?

Katz and Lazarsfeld have found that such an interrelationship between mass media sources and the interpersonal networks of communication in local areas does actually exist. In their investigations they have identified certain individuals they call "opinion leaders" who are more influential than other members of the population in their local settings. The opinion leaders they have identified are not status people in any formal way, rather they are the everyday type of person found in all socioeconomic groups, to whom people ask questions and to whom people listen. The research suggested that there is, indeed, a "two-step flow of communication" from the sources of mass media to these informal opinion leaders, and from these opinion leaders to persons they meet in everyday social contacts.[19]

The significance of the Katz and Lazarsfeld investigation, as compared with some of the earlier studies in mass communication, is that the audience is perceived not as a mass of disconnected individuals, but rather as individuals who belong to groups and whose beliefs and attitudes are influenced by these groups. These are individuals also who share the values and beliefs of groups to which they belong and are better able than outsiders to communicate effectively with members of these groups.

As Katz and Lazarsfeld suggest, there may be a hidden network of these informal opinion leaders who are themselves affected by communications received through the mass media and who, in turn, influence others about them. To the extent that this is true, the role of mass media in public health education may be quite different from the role we frequently assign to it. It is a potent role, and a most significant one for health educators to consider; one, in fact, that none can afford to ignore.

Research is needed to learn what different types of informal leaders exist in areas of concern to public health. Are there opinion leaders who are key communication gatekeepers—in child health, in chronic diseases, in alcoholism? If so, how can the mass media be employed in such a way that these opinion leaders are more effectively utilized in the communication networks they informally serve? How can we best give "Evers" the backing he deserves?

NOTES TO CHAPTER 28

1. Klapper, Joseph T., *The Effects of Mass Media,* Bureau of Applied Social Research, Columbia University, New York, 1949; Lazarsfeld, Paul F., and Patricia L. Kendall, *Radio Listening in America,* Prentice-Hall, Inc., Englewood Cliffs, N.J., 1948; Schramm, Wilbur, and David M. White, "Age, Education, and Economic Status as Factors in Newspaper Reading: Conclusions," *Journalism Quarterly,* vol. 26, June, 1949, pp. 155–157. Republished in Schramm, Wilbur, editor, *The Process and Effects of Mass Communication,* University of Illinois Press, Urbana, 1954, pp. 71–73.

2. Campbell, Angus, and Charles A. Metzner, *Public Use of the Library and of Other Sources of Information.* Institute for Social Research, University of Michigan, Ann Arbor, Mich., 1950.

3. Cartwright, Dorwin, "Some Principles of Mass Persuasion: Selected Findings of Research on the Sale of United States War Bonds," *Human Relations,* vol. 2, no. 3, 1949, pp. 253–267. Republished in Katz, Daniel, and associates, editors, *Public Opinion and Propaganda,* Henry Holt and Co., New York, 1960, pp. 382–393.

4. *Ibid.*

5. Klapper, Joseph T., *op. cit.,* p. 11.

6. Hovland, Carl I., Arthur A. Lumsdaine, and Fred D. Sheffield, *Experiments on Mass Communication.* Studies in Social Psychology in World War II, vol. 3. Princeton University Press, Princeton, N.J., 1949, p. 21.

7. *Ibid.* pp. 64–65.

8. Hoyt, Cyril J., Andie L. Knutson, and C. Mayhew Derryberry, "What the People Know," *Monthly Bulletin,* Indiana State Board of Health, vol. 53, December, 1950, p. 282.

9. Schramm, Wilbur, "The Effects of Mass Communications: A Review," *Journalism Quarterly,* vol. 26, 1949, p. 405.

10. Greenberg, B. G., Mary Ellen Harris, C. Frances MacKinnon, and Sidney S. Chipman, "A Method for Evaluating the Effectiveness of Health Education Literature," *American Journal of Public Health,* vol. 43, September, 1953, pp. 1147–1155.

11. *Ibid.,* p. 1155.

12. Lazarsfeld, Paul F., and Robert K. Merton, "Mass Communication, Popular Taste and Organized Social Action" in Bryson, Lyman, editor, *The Communication of Ideas.* Harper and Bros., New York, 1948, p. 114.

13. Wiebe, Gerhart D., "Merchandising Commodities and Citizenship on Television," *Public Opinion Quarterly,* vol. 15, Winter, 1952, pp. 679–691.

14. Merton, Robert K., *Mass Persuasion: The Social Psychology of a War Bond Drive.* Harper and Bros., New York, 1946, p. 52.

15. *Ibid.,* p. 55.

16. *Ibid.,* p. 65.

17. Cantril, Hadley, Hazel Gaudet, and Herta Herzog, *The Invasion from Mars.* Princeton University Press, Princeton, N.J., 1940. Summary in Maccoby, Eleanor E., Theodore M. Newcomb, and Eugene L. Hartley, editors, *Readings in Social Psychology,* 3d ed., Henry Holt and Co., New York, 1958, pp. 291–292.

18. Hovland, Carl I., "Effects of the Mass Media of Communication" in Lindzey, Gardner, editor, *Handbook of Social Psychology.* Addison-Wesley Publishing Co., Reading, Mass., vol. 2, 1954, p. 1072.

19. Katz, Elihu, and Paul F. Lazarsfeld, *Personal Influence: The Part Played by People in the Flow of Mass Communications.* Free Press, Glencoe, Ill., 1955.

Chapter 29

Interpersonal Communication
Within Organizations*

IN DISCUSSING some of the research findings concerned with interpersonal communication in organizations, one might be tempted to
focus entire attention on the conscious and unconscious needs and
purposes that influence communications. To do so, however, would
be to ignore a most important fact: the possibility of effective interpersonal communication does not exist equally for all members of an
organization. Certain conditions relating to time, space, and function
need to be satisfied before there is much chance for personal or
group purposes to be expressed, or for needs to be satisfied through
interpersonal communications.

We need to consider:

First: How are communications influenced by when and where people in the organization do their work? How are they influenced by the
way the building is constructed, the way the rooms, halls, and stairways are placed, the way the rooms are organized and the desks are
arranged, the placement of washing and eating rooms, the kinds of en-
trances and exits, and the formal and informal passages through the
building? All of these things may be of importance in determining
what possibilities exist for interpersonal communications.

Next: How are communications influenced by the formal and informal arrangements developed to carry on the business—by the
philosophy of leadership, the pattern of authority and responsibility,
the patterns of prestige and status, and the kinds of roles performed?

Finally: How are communications influenced by the need and response patterns of the individuals concerned—their unique patterns
of motivation and perception, and their unique patterns of reaction.

* Previously published as a paper by the author in *California's Health,* vol. 15,
May, 1958. Reprinted with the permission of the publisher.

In brief, we need to consider first the physical situation, second the web of relationships within which individuals function, and finally the unique qualities of the communicating individuals.

Physical Situation

There is a wealth of evidence that the way a building is constructed tends to influence the patterns of communication within it. We recognize and speak to people we meet frequently in the halls; we tend to stop for a chat with the person who has a desk nearby. But the person who can come and go through a side entrance may have to go out of his way to learn the latest gossip.

It seems reasonable that the same kinds of counting and observational techniques used by businessmen in testing out a new location should be useful in studying the pattern of traffic through a health department. Studies of museums and exhibits do, in fact, indicate that people tend to follow particular pathways. This may result in their missing out on important displays.[1]

Festinger and others, in studying interaction and communication within a housing development, found in a sociometric study that persons living in apartments that opened directly onto the stairways tended to be chosen more often by others. Apparently living close to the flow of traffic helped them become known. Likewise, people living in the center of the court tended to be chosen more often than those at the end of the court.[2] This general principle tends to apply in staff meetings and group discussions, and at parties also. The person who sits in the corner or on the outer fringes of the group tends to be left out of the conversation.

This does not mean, of course, that mere proximity will lead to more effective communications. Rather, nearness permits an increase of interaction to occur, and this in turn may lead to participation and the possibility that an acquaintanceship or friendship will develop.

In brief, the convenient path tends to be the one most frequently used, and when convenient paths cross, communications tend to be facilitated.

One might ask, are the physical arrangements within the health department such that they encourage or discourage communications across professional lines? Do the physical arrangements encourage communications upward, or downward? Is the physical placement of staff people such that it encourages or discourages their interaction and communication with members of groups with whom they are expected to work? Is the health educator, for example, located where interactions frequently occur? This may not necessarily be the place of greatest status.

The Web of Relationships

In thinking about my second question, "How are communications influenced by the formal and informal arrangements developed in carrying on the business of the organization," I was led immediately to consider the tremendous differences in the communication pattern in a dictatorship as compared with that within a democracy. A dictator maintains power in part by limiting the type and amount of information available to those he is attempting to control. He protects members of the group from adverse or unnecessary communications, and by protecting them gains and maintains a monopoly over the information to which they are exposed. In such a situation communication is primarily downward. When upward communications do occur, they are likely to be patterned to satisfy the expectations of the leader or the leadership group.

We tend to forget that this same type of information monopoly sometimes develops, perhaps unintentionally, within our own administrative situations. Passing on information may be a burden, and we may not have time to communicate adequately. We make decisions for others regarding the information they should have. We say, "Let's not bother him with this," or "This won't really concern him," or "He's not going to have time to read this."

Such administrative decisions are often necessary. Yet they are potentially sources of communication difficulty. For when we start to protect others from information, we are, in a way, controlling their possibilities for interaction.

In a democratic organization where distribution of power is desirable, intragroup and intergroup communications and interaction must be encouraged.

The philosophy of leadership may, therefore, greatly influence the kinds of interpersonal communication possible within an organization. Active intragroup and intergroup communication is not likely to occur unless the leader encourages such communication, and unless the members of the group clearly recognize that such communication is being encouraged.

For any organization to function effectively, the members must carry out different roles, each with a different kind of responsibility.

Depending on the importance of these roles, those who perform them acquire different levels of status within the group. This status may be of either a formal or an informal nature. In either case the role and status patterns of the group influence the nature of interpersonal communications.

Wessen, for example, reported that in one large general hospital 75 per cent of the doctors' conversations were with other doctors; 60 per cent of the nurses' conversations were with other nurses; and 60 per cent of the conversations of the workers of other groups tended to be with others in their own group.[3] Other researchers have reached somewhat similar conclusions.

This might reasonably be expected, since there is evidence that people of different occupational groups within a hospital setting tend to differ in their patterns of values and in their areas of striving.[4] A person of a particular status level within an organization is, therefore, likely to have more in common to converse about with persons of similar training, experience, and status.

Since status is an important social goal, it is not surprising that, in their communications outside their own status groups, individuals tend to try to communicate upward. They seek communication with persons who may be able to help them achieve their individual and group goals; likewise, they tend to avoid communication with persons of lower status, or others whom they do not perceive as being potentially helpful. An exception to this is the person with supervisory responsibilities who has much to gain through effective communication with persons of lesser status.[5]

Since health educators have both staff and consultant responsibilities, it may be of interest to mention briefly some of the special problems of role identification and communication that have been identified by Dalton in his studies of the line officer and staff officer relationship.[6]

A person responsible for a line job or a direct program job usually has his responsibilities and role rather clearly delineated. His goals tend to be somewhat more specific than those of the consultant; often they can be measured by tangible evidence. He may have the responsibility for both initiating and controlling the action necessary for achieving these goals.

A staff consultant, on the other hand, has an ambiguous role. He is expected to assist or advise on ways of introducing new ideas or techniques for improving the program, but does not have the authority to put his suggestions or recommendations directly into action. He works with others on their programs and may sometimes be seen by them as a competitor—or even as a threat—because his training, his abilities, and his channels of communication differ from their own. His influence is likely to be ambiguous. Achievements cannot be easily measured; rewards, if any, are likely to be intangible. Frequently he is in such a position that the line officer must communicate downward to him, and the line officer may resent the idea of communicating downward when asking for help.

Staff officers tend to associate and communicate with members of their own groups; program officers tend to associate and communicate with members of their own groups. The problem of developing and defining staff and line roles in such a way that interaction and cross communication will be facilitated is a very real one indeed.

May I ask, with whom did you lunch most frequently last week? With whom did you have coffee most frequently? With which members of your organization do you get together after hours? With whom in your organization do you have the greatest difficulty in communicating —in getting together and exchanging ideas and in reaching satisfactory agreements? What factors might have influenced these interactions?

The physical and social structure of an organization has a great deal to do with the amount and kind of interpersonal communications that are possible. In the end, however, whether or not interpersonal communications actually occur and are effective depends on the unique characteristics of the individuals directly concerned—the communicator and the person with whom he is attempting to communicate. One cannot adequately discuss the role and behavior of either the communicator or the communicant without taking into consideration the role and behavior of the other. I have chosen here to discuss the process first from the standpoint of the communicator and second from the standpoint of the person with whom he is communicating. As we go on I am sure you will agree that this separation is artificial.

The Unique Qualities of the Communicator

The behavior of the communicator in any act of communication is motivated. The needs, values, and purposes that the communicator has acquired through experience influence both what he selects to communicate and how he expresses it. His behavior is ruled by needs and purposes of which he may be unaware, as well as by his conscious decisions and intentions.

Freud led the way in demonstrating to us that all behavior is motivated. In his challenging *Psychopathology of Everyday Life* he called attention to the hidden needs and wishes that govern the remembering and forgetting of things, and to the motives that lie behind our slips of the tongue, slips of the pen, misreadings, faux pas, and other errors of commission and omission.[7] Sometimes we are willing to admit that there may be purpose in error. Often, however, the motives are so intimate or so unflattering that we cannot admit them, even to ourselves. In fact, we may not even notice the slip made in expression or gesture. It is not surprising, therefore, that others can sometimes recognize and interpret these errors more accurately than we can ourselves.

As infants, our first communications with other persons in this world are through nonverbal gestures, soft, warm pressures, touches and pats, caresses, facial expressions, waving, and pointing. We learn to respond to them with appropriate nonverbal symbols of our own. We learn such nonverbal symbols, and we discover them to be reliable for predicting how to act successfully at a time when we know few safe and effective guidelines.

As we grow older and begin to learn to use words, our nonverbal communications are suddenly ignored. We are urged to speak, and to react to spoken words, and to discard the techniques which have proved so valuable during our first years of life.

But we may never completely discard these valuable means we have acquired for interpreting the reactions of others. Long after we have learned to understand spoken symbols, we continue, in varying degrees, to be sensitive to the expressions on people's faces, to the movements of their bodies, to the way they turn their heads or move their eyes as we speak, to the shrugs or nods that may be almost imperceptible, yet tell so much about their reactions.

Is it any wonder that the nonverbal means of expression also remain with us even after we have learned adult ways? Is it any wonder that we use them without even knowing it—sometimes when we do not even mean to do so? And is it any wonder that other persons may find such signs, which may be given without conscious intent, more reliable in judging our true intentions than the words or expressions we consciously employ?

We distrust the man whose actions or expressions belie his words; and on the positive side we may share deep feelings and understandings with one another without even being aware of the symbols we are using or the signs we perceive. The silence of lovers, for example, may impart deep feelings, and not always the same feelings.

When it comes to communicating across the boundaries of social groups, difficulties arise because we tend to perceive others as having the same personal needs, desires, and purposes that we have. The communicator as a unique individual with unique motives, beliefs, and attitudes selects interpretations which have personal meaning for him and which he believes will have meaning for others. When he has a background of experience different from that of his audience, he may be quite unable to communicate because he cannot see things in the same way they do. Yet he may sincerely believe he is being successful because he tries so hard—and his audience try so hard to make him feel comfortable.

In many ways you and I may be better able to communicate effectively over language and cultural barriers with our professional friends in other parts of the world than we are able to communicate effectively with members of our own organizations whose patterns of experience would lead them to differ more sharply with us in some areas of value and belief. One of the greatest challenges we face is that of developing effective communication bridges across the channels that separate professional groups.

The other person and the social and physical situation which helped to shape his behavior must always be uppermost in the mind of an effective communicator. This means that the effective communicator must be a sensitive receiver and evaluator of information even while he is performing his communication role.

The Unique Qualities of the Communicant

As Sanford has so neatly put it, "It is the recipient of communication who determines whether communication has happened at all. He validates communication. Through his behavior and only through his behavior can we tell whether the communication has been more than interpersonal noise. It is perhaps true that much of the intended communication of the world misfires or miscarries or fails entirely because the communicator pays more attention to his bow and arrow than to his target."[8]

My next major point, then, is that the behavior of the communicant in any communication process is motivated. The needs, values, and purposes that he has acquired through experience, his psychological "set," and his expectations with respect to the communicator are of primary significance in influencing the meaning the information will have for him and the way it becomes integrated into his patterns of knowledge, belief, and action.

Some years ago the chief of the Swazi people of Africa visited England with a group of his tribesmen to obtain settlement of a land dispute. After the party returned to their homeland, the British settlers in the area were eager to learn the Swazis' main impressions of England. The one thing that remained most vividly in their minds was the picture of the English "bobbies" directing the traffic with uplifted hands.

Why did this simple action make such an impression? For the Swazis this was a familiar gesture. It was the gesture they used in their homeland for greeting their friends and neighbors. To them it was one of the few things they experienced that fitted in with their own customs. It had an immediate personal significance for each one of them.

This is one of the many incidents reported a quarter of a century ago by the dean of British social psychologists, F. C. Bartlett, in a book which brought together many years of field observation and laboratory research under the title *Remembering*. Here Bartlett called attention to the tendency of the mind to reshape and organize all experience in a way that is meaningful and useful to the individual. His central theme was, "It is fitting to speak of every human cognitive reaction—perceiving, imagining, thinking, and reasoning—*as an effort after meaning*."[9]

Bartlett's phrase, "an effort after meaning," expresses very well the dynamics which underlie the role of the communicant. People seek meaning from experience. The meanings they attach to specific experiences tend to be those which make the best sense to them and have the greatest significance for them in terms of their patterns of value and experience.

Each of us charts his course through the world by means of his perceptions. During any specific moment of life our sense organs are bombarded by a wide array of light and sound waves, which we in psychology call stimuli. It would be physically and mentally impossible for any of us to be consciously aware of every one of these light and sound waves, much less pay attention to them and react accordingly. Fortunately, we learn through experience to organize this mass of stimuli into meaningful wholes that make sense to us and have meaning for us—wholes that help us decide how to act.

But what determines how this mass of light waves, sound waves, heat waves, and other stimuli are organized into meaningful wholes? What is the underlying process which results in some of these groups of stimuli or symbols being given a prominent position in perception while others remain in the background? As we say in psychology, what determines "the figure" as compared with "the ground"?

The best evidence available suggests that perception is an active, motivated process. What we perceive in the world about us is governed by personal interests, wants, concerns, anxieties, fears, hopes, and expectations—a network of motivating forces which grow out of our daily experiences. As Cantril expresses this principle, . . . "What is 'real' is whatever an individual experiences as real, whatever affects his behavior, not something existing with invariable characteristics in its own right outside of man himself. . . ."[10]

Words Are Perceptions

You may be thinking that words are different from perceptions—what has perception to do with verbal communication?

Words *are* perceptions. Spoken words are organized groups of sound waves to which we give meaning; written words are organized groups of light waves to which we give meaning. Early in life we learn to give meaning to these groups of sound and light waves, so that we can act more effectively in adjusting to the world. This is part of the slow process of learning, the process of gradually differentiating specific groups of stimuli out of an unorganized mass. The meanings we associate with words are the meanings that help us most to act successfully in achieving the purposes of daily living.

Each person has his own special pattern of experience, values, concerns, and purposes which serve him in making his "effort after meaning." It helps him shape an unorganized mass of stimuli into a meaningful environment. The world he creates through his perceptions—his psychological world, or his assumptive world—is his own private world, different from anyone else's private world. As Kelley observed, "He can share this universe with others through communication, but only in part; because those with whom he attempts to communicate must interpret what he offers in accordance with the receiver's own unique background."[11] The possibility of the communication being successfully accomplished requires, then, that the assumptive worlds of the two or more individuals concerned *overlap* in the content area covered by the communication.

This concept of an assumptive world is, I firmly believe, a most valuable concept to use in thinking about communication and interpersonal relations. It helps us understand why what we say has so frequently a different meaning for the person with whom we talk. It helps us understand why each has a tendency to see and interpret any situation in the light of his own pattern of experiences and motivations, regardless of the means whereby this information is received. It helps us understand the growing evidence that new knowledge alone is not likely to be effective in changing beliefs and actions, but that after some changes in belief have occurred or new values have been acquired, the individual is likely to seek new information that will be helpful to him in supporting the new beliefs or serving the new values.

Cantril has suggested that our perceptions of other people, that is, our social perceptions, differ from our perceptions of things, in that we are concerned as to what intentions the other individuals have which might be of importance to us.[12] We need to know how their purposes or desires relate to our own personal and group goals. Any gestures, signs, or actions giving us an inkling as to what we can expect other people to do which is significant to our goals is of primary importance to us in determining how to act toward them.

This may help to explain why, other things being equal, communication is likely to be more effective if we perceive the person communicating as one who can be trusted, who is an expert, or who holds prestige in our eyes. A popular and trusted health science writer may have more status in the eyes of the public than an outstanding scientist. Trusted local health leaders may be better able to capture public opinion than national leaders of great stature who have never met the test of years of experience in that local community.

We speak to an individual, watch his expression, notice whether he smiles or frowns, wait for his interpretations, seek guidelines which will tell us whether we are moving in the right direction or not. If he frowns or in some way indicates he has not agreed, we change our tones, use other arguments, give and take with him until we find a point of agreement. If his interpretation suggests that he does not understand, we change our words, try to find out how he interprets the problem, and use his terms as a bridge to better communication. This is the process whereby we gain entrance into his private world, his world of assumption. This is the means whereby he, and we, are able to gain an *overlapping* of our private worlds in the area of mutual significance.

Summary

Communication is a means of sharing our experiences with one another. Communication within an organization may be either limited or facilitated by physical and structural arrangements, and by the unique web of formal and informal relationships developed to carry out the business of the organization. The effective communicator within the organization is at the same time a provider and receiver of information and ideas. Both the way he selects and organizes the facts and the way he expresses the ideas are influenced by personal motives of which he may not be fully aware. His actions, both as a receiver and giver of information, are guided by his perceptions of the world in which he lives. This world he perceives is his private world, a world of assumptions, built out of successful and unsuccessful "efforts after meaning" and the experiences he has had in seeking ways to satisfy his personal and group purposes.

NOTES TO CHAPTER 29

1. Yoshioka, J. G., "Direction-Orientation Study with Visitors at the New York World's Fair," *Journal of General Psychology,* vol. 27, 1942, pp. 3–33.

2. Festinger, Leon, Stanley Schachter, and Kurt Back, *Social Pressures in Informal Groups: A Study of Human Factors in Housing.* Harper and Bros., New York, 1950.

3. Wessen, Albert F., "The Social Structure of a Modern Hospital: An Essay in Institutional Theory," unpublished doctoral dissertation, Yale University, 1951; Mishler, Elliot, and A. Tropp, "Status and Interaction in a Psychiatric Hospital," *Human Relations,* vol. 9, no. 2, 1956, pp. 187–206.

4. Knutson, Andie L., "Personal Security as Related to Station in Life," *Psychological Monographs,* vol. 66, no. 4, 1952, pp. 1–31. Whole number 336.

5. Jackson, J., "Analysis of Interpersonal Relations in a Formal Organization." Unpublished doctoral dissertation, University of Michigan, 1953.

6. Dalton, Melville, "Conflicts Between Staff and Line Managerial Officers," *American Sociological Review,* vol. 15, June, 1950, pp. 342–351.

7. Freud, Sigmund, *Psychopathology of Everyday Life.* Macmillan Co., New York, 1948. This was the authorized English translation from the 4th German edition.

8. Sanford, Fillmore H., "Inter-Personal Communication," *Industrial Medicine and Surgery,* vol. 25, June, 1956, p. 261.

9. Bartlett, Frederic C., *Remembering.* Cambridge University Press, Cambridge, England, 1932, pp. 31 ff.

10. Cantril, Hadley, *The Politics of Despair*. Basic Books, New York, 1958, p. 16.

11. Kelley, Earl C., "Education Is Communication," *Etc.: A Review of General Semantics,* vol. 12, 1955, pp. 248–256.

12. Cantril, Hadley, *The "Why" of Man's Experience*. Macmillan Co., New York, 1950.

Index

Index

ABELSON, Herbert I., 469, 476
Activity value orientation, 283
Adair, John, 188, 193
Adler, Alfred, 200
Affiliation, 480–485
Allee, Warder C., 203, 210
Allport, Floyd H., 159, 178
Allport, Gordon W., 38, 41, 43, 56, 60, 171, 174, 178, 179, 217, 219, 222, 223–224, 262, 274–276, 290, 291, 307, 309, 310, 322, 332, 410, 423, 427
Allport-Vernon "Study of Values" scale, 274
Ambiguity, 479–482
American Public Health Association, 10, 99, 107, 110–115 passim, 116, 301, 458, 493–494
Ames, Adelbert, Jr., 160, 178
Anastasi, Anne, 61, 63, 67, 68, 70
Andersen, Milton L., 438, 441
Antonitis, J. J., 390, 424
Arnold, Mary F., 120, 131
Asch, Solomon E., 182, 192, 486–487, 497
Attitude change, 307–308
Attitude climate, 487–489
Attitudes (and beliefs), 293–310: action and, 305–306; authority and, 300–301, 464–465; commitment, 468; communication and, 303–305; components of, 294–295; definition of, 294–298; formation of, 218, 299–302, 315–332 passim; measurement of, 217–222, 298–299; motivational basis of, 302–303; persuasion and, 307–308, 504–506; role and, 302; socializing agents of, 328–330; values and, 259, 261–292 passim, 299; verbal conditioning and, 433–443
Autokinetic phenomena, 485–486
Awareness in conditioning, 429–433

BACK, Kurt, 512, 521
Bakke, Edward W., 250, 255

Bales, Robert F., 413, 427
Ballachey, Egerton L., 98, 100, 115, 248, 255, 298, 308, 309, 310
Barker, Roger G., 42, 43
Bartlett, Frederic C., 518, 522
Becker, Howard S., 300, 309
Behavioral cycle, 72–83: of adults, 75; in childbirth, 79–82; of children, 73–74; and food, 134–135; in program planning, 75–82; and research, 75–82 passim; in tuberculosis, 76–79. See also Life cycle
Beliefs. See Attitudes
Benedict, Ruth, 48, 51
Benne, Kenneth D., 289, 292, 387, 424
Bennis, Warren G., 387, 424
Bentley, Arthur F., 29–30, 36, 37
Berelson, Bernard, 303, 310
Berlyne, Daniel E., 389–390, 393–394, 399–400, 406, 424, 425, 426
Bernard, Luther L., 200, 210
Bertalanffy, Ludwig von, 39, 43
Biderman, Albert D., 390, 425
Bierman, Jessie, 10, 275, 291
Bills, Robert, 276, 291
Binet, Alfred, 66
Bird, Charles, 184, 192, 216, 223
Birren, James E., 61, 70
Blackwell, Barbara L., 414–417, 427, 481–482, 497
Blake, Robert R., 159, 178
Blandford, Donald H., 293
Blodgett, H. C., 406, 426
Bloom, Samuel W., 48, 51
Blumer, Herbert, 319, 332
Bond, Betty, 161, 178
Borgatta, Edgar F., 413, 427
Boring, Edwin G., 150, 158, 159, 178
Bowlby, John, 324, 333
Braden, I., 390, 425
Brehm, Jack W., 294, 309
Brim, Orville G., Jr., 10, 266, 290, 331–332, 333
Brodbeck, Arthur J., 341–342, 350, 352

Brown, Esther Lucile, 10, 463, 475
Brown, R. W., 434, 440
Brozek, Josef, 251–253, 255
Bruner, Jerome S., 175–177 *passim,*
179, 295–298 *passim,* 302, 309
Bruvold, William H., 65, 70
Buell, Bradley, and associates, 40, 43
Bumstead, Charles H., 336, 351
Burdick, Harvey, 481, 497
Burton, John, 267, 290
Butler, R. A., 390, 424

CALIFORNIA Research Corporation, 173
Cameron, Dale, 57
Campbell, Angus, 308, 310, 499, 509
Campbell, Donald T., 467, 475
Cannon, Walter B., 40, 43, 201, 210
Cantril, Hadley, 10, 47, 51, 54, 60,
157, 158, 159, 160, 161, 166, 178,
180–181, 192, 213, 216, 223, 228–
230, 233, 241, 242, 271–273, 275,
291, 292, 294, 309, 336, 351, 393,
412, 425, 427, 434, 440, 446, 447,
465, 475, 477–478, 479, 489, 491,
496, 497, 506, 510, 519, 520, 522
Caplan, Gerald, 75, 83
Carlson, Earl R., 469, 476
Caron, Herbert S., 189, 190, 193
Cartwright, Dorwin, 387, 413, 424,
427, 474, 476, 500, 509
Cassel, John, 142, 143
Caste, 105–106
Caudill, William, 39–40, 43, 95, 97
Centers, Richard, 102, 107, 115
Chase, Stuart, 464, 475
Chein, Isidor, 238, 242
Cherkasy, Martin, 48, 51
Child, Irwin L., 315, 332
Chin, Robert, 387, 424
Chipman, Sidney S., 503, 509
Chisholm, Brock, 373–374, 379
Christensen, Aaron W., 357, 358, 451–
452, 454
Clark, Margaret, 280, 282, 292
Classical conditioning, 359–361
Clausen, John A., 104, 105, 115
Cofer, Charles N., 429, 439
Cognitive clarity, 480–485
Cognitive-dissonance: and attitude
change, 306; and learning, 388
Cognitive strain, 175–179
Cohen, Arthur R., 294, 309
Cohen, B. D., 434, 440
Cohen, Morris R., 184, 192
Combs, Arthur W., 181, 192, 230,
242
Communicant, 517–519
Communication: and anxiety, 481–
484; attitudes and, 302–304; audience image in, 465–466; authority
and, 300–301, 464–465; barriers to,
471–472; cognitive-dissonance and
attitude change, 306; commitment
in, 468, 470; counter-arguments,
468–469; definitions of, 445–447;
feedback in, 470–473; frames of reference in, 475–487; in infancy,
316–319; nonverbal, 428–441 *passim,* 486–487, 516–517; opinion
leaders and, 449–455 *passim,* 506–
509; order of presentation and,
467–470; personal appeals in, 504–
506; physical arrangements and,
512–513; private world and, 518–
521; psychological set and, 506;
reference groups in, 106–116 *passim,* 487–489; research on values
and, 267–268; sleeper effects of,
466; social class and, 99–103 *passim;* social structure and, 513–515;
source credibility and, 464–465,
506–509; status and, 513–515; stereotypes in, 108, 452–453, 460. *See
also* Learning
Communication accuracy, 58–59
Communicators in public health, 449–
454, 455–476, 515–517
Conger, John J., 350, 353
Consistency-inconsistency, 238–239
Constancy, perception of, 162–165
Constitutional types, 68–70
Converse, Philip, 308, 310
Cook, Stuart W., 218, 223, 298, 306,
309, 310
Cooley, Charles H., 446, 447
Cottrell, Leonard S., Jr., 10, 61, 70
Crutchfield, Richard S., 98, 100, 115,
244–248 *passim,* 255, 296, 298, 308,
309, 310, 359, 361, 378, 399–400,
420–421, 426, 427
Culture: distinguished from society,
91–92; functions of, 94–95; influ-
ences of, 95–96; internalization of,
96

DALTON, Melville, 121–122, 131, 514,
521
Davis, Allison, 103, 115, 282, 292
Davis, Robert C., 280, 292
Day, Ella J., 343
Death, meaning of, 288
DeCecco, John P., 366, 378
Defense mechanisms and perception,
172–174
Deficiency motives, 243–246
DeFleur, Melvin L., 306, 310
DeMartino, Manfred F., 224
Dennis, Wayne, 338, 352

Deprivation, 334–353 *passim*
Derryberry, C. Mayhew, 10, 76, 83, 214, 223, 394–395, 425, 464, 475, 502, 509
Deuschle, Kurt, 188, 193
Deutsch, Morton, 43, 218, 223, 238, 242, 298, 309
Dewey, John, 29, 30, 36, 37, 149, 410, 427
Dillehay, Ronald C., 11, 18, 293–310; cited 304, 310
Dobzhansky, Theodosius, 53, 60, 61–62, 70
Dukes, William F., 269, 276, 290, 315, 332
Dulaney, Don E., 433, 440
Dunham, Barrows, 279, 291
Dunlap, Knight, 200, 210
Dunn, Leslie C., 53, 60
Dunne, Margaret R., 11
Dye, Harold B., 344–345, 353

Eaton, Joseph W., 48, 51
Ebbinghaus, Hermann, 361–362, 378
Eberhart, John C., 10
Edwards, Allen E., 298, 309
Edwards, Ward, 156, 158
Effect, law of, 363, 405–409
Ego, 230–242 *passim:* changes in, 232–238; development of, 230 ff.; and identity, 318–319; meaning of, 230 ff. *See also* Self
Ego insults and threats, 230–241 *passim,* 245–246
Ego-involvements and identifications, 231–232; as anchorages, 237–238; and health definitions, 231–232, 233–237; and learning, 410 ff.
Ego-satisfactions, 230–241 *passim,* 245–246
English, Ava C., 213, 223, 262, 290, 315, 332, 369, 379
English, Horace B., 213, 223, 262, 290, 315, 332, 369–371, 379
Environmental change, 34–36
Erikson, Erik H., 73–75, 82, 83
Estes, William K., 359, 378
Ethnic groups, 107–108
Exploratory behavior, 399–405

Family planning, as value, 286
Farbarow, Norman L., 288, 292
Farber, I. E., 430–433, 438, 440, 441
Feifel, Herman, 288, 292
Feshback, Seymour, 391, 425
Festinger, Leon, 294, 306, 309, 310, 388, 424, 480, 496, 512, 521
Field, Joan B., 435, 441

Field theory, 181–192 *passim:* applications of, 184–192; approach of, 181–182; and perception, 181–184
Fiske, D. W., 276, 291
Flavell, John H., 339, 352
Food: changing practices, 138–140; definitions of, 132–134; as dependent variable, 142; emotional meanings of, 142–143; as incentives for change, 140–141; influence of starvation on motives, 251–253; and life cycle, 134–135; meaning of, 132–144, 204–205; as motives, 204–205; and personality, 138; and religion, 135–136; and social organization, 136–138; and social status, 140–141; symbolic uses of, 140–141; and work, 136–138
Foote, Nelson N., 61, 70
Forgetting: of controversial material, 305; curve of, 361–363
Foster, George M., 91, 95, 97, 280, 292
Fowler, William, 336, 341, 351, 353
Fox, Renée, 130, 131
Frames of reference, 477–497: definition of, 477–478; impression of persons and, 486–487; persistence of, 489–494; value and attitude climates as, 487–489
Frank, Lawrence K., 31, 37, 96, 97, 181, 192, 202–203, 210, 337, 352
Franklin, Joseph C., 251–253, 255
Franzen, Raymond H., 76, 83
Free, Lloyd A., 263, 291
Fremont-Smith, Frank, 412
Frenkel-Brunswick, Else, 422, 427, 481, 497
Freud, Sigmund, 172, 179, 200, 201, 516, 521
Fromm, Erich, 200
Fry, Edward B., 366, 379
Fuller, John L., 54, 60

Gadalla, Fawzy R. A., 285–286, 292, 397–398, 426
Gaffey, William R., 70
Galiher, Claudia B., 110, 115, 187, 193
Gardner, B. B., 282, 292
Gardner, Mary R., 282, 292
Gatekeepers in communications, 450–454
Gaudet, Hazel, 465, 475, 491, 506, 510
Geertz, Clifford, 91, 97
Geography: and behavior, 32–33; and language, 34; and symbolic life, 33–34
Gesell, Arnold L., 73

Gewirtz, Jacob L., 208–209, 211
Gibson, James J., 165, 178
Girdner, J. B., 390, 424
Glacken, Mildred, 11
Glaser, Robert, 366, 379
Glass, David C., 11
Goffman, Erving, 122, 131, 230, 242, 319, 332
Goldenson, Robert M., 328, 333
Goodenough, Ward H., 387, 424
Graham, Stanley R., 108, 115
Granger, G. W., 172, 178
Greenberg, B. G., 503, 509
Greenspoon, Joel, 365, 378, 428, 430, 433, 439, 440
Gregg, Alan, 445, 447
Grey, Blake E., 451, 454
Griffiths, William, 10, 11, 22, 411, 427, 498–507
Group influences on health, 36, 39–40, 44–51 passim, 87–88
Groups: differences in intelligence in, 66–68; ethnic, 107–108; individuality in, 53–54; man's development in, 44–45, 53–54; membership, 106–115; placement in, 98–115; professional, as reference, 109–115; psychological, 98–99; reference, definition of, 106, 98–115 passim; religious, 107–108; types of, 98–99, 106
Grout, Ruth, 110, 115
Growth motives, 243–246
Guetzkow, Harold, 410, 427
Gustafson, Harold C., 398, 426
Guttman, Louis, 298

Haire, Mason, 219, 224
Hall, Calvin S., 174, 179
Hall, O. Milton, 250, 255
Hall, William E., 437, 441
Hallowell, Alfred I., 33, 37, 53, 60
Harding, John, 306, 310
Hare, A. Paul, 413, 427
Harlow, Harry F., 140, 143, 324–327, 333
Harms, Irene, 344–345, 353
Harris, Jane S., 385–386, 424, 464, 475
Harris, Mary Ellen, 503, 509
Harris, Theodore L., 359, 378
Hartley, Eugene L., 11, 91, 97, 119, 122, 131, 320, 332, 459, 475
Hartley, Ruth E., 119, 122, 131, 320, 328, 332, 333, 459, 475
Hartman, C. H., 435, 441
Hartman, G. W., 275, 291
Hasan, Khwaja Arif, 137, 143
Hastorf, Albert H., 160, 178, 202, 210
Havighurst, Robert J., 103, 115
Hayakawa, S. I., 464, 475

Health: definitions of, 47–49, 230–241 passim; intimate nature of, 55–56; programs and learning, 380–387; social influences on, 39–40, 49–51, 88; social role and, 129–130; value of, 284–288; value influences on, 261–292 passim
Hearing, 63–64
Hebb, Donald O., 368, 379, 390
Heider, Fritz, 263, 264, 290
Hein, Ted, 172, 179
Heinzelmann, Fred, 396, 425
Henderson, R. L., 390, 424
Heredity, 53–55, 62 ff.; and motivation, 200–201, 208; and perception, 149–151
Heron, Woodburn, 390–391, 425
Herzog, Herta, 465, 475, 491, 506, 510
Hierarchy of needs, 246–248
Hildum, D. C., 434, 440
Hilgard, Ernest R., 150–151, 158, 338, 352, 359, 378, 408, 426
Hochbaum, Godfrey M., 79, 83, 215, 220–221, 223, 224, 329, 333, 391, 395–397, 425, 426
Hoff, Wilbur I., 411, 427
Hollingshead, August B., 104, 115
Homeostasis, 38–39, 201–210 passim
Horney, Karen, 200
Horowitz, Eugene L., 218, 223, 320, 332
Horowitz, Ruth E., 320, 332
Hospital, meanings of, 232–237
Hovland, Carl I., 304, 310, 392, 425, 466, 468, 469, 475, 476, 501–502, 506, 509–510
Hoyt, Cyril J., 76, 83, 214, 223, 502, 509
Hromadka, Gordon V., 79, 83
Huenemann, Ruth, 10, 132
Hughes, J. L., 366, 379
Human nature value orientation, 278–280
Humphrey, Hubert H., 450, 454
Hunt, Joseph McV., 67, 70, 343, 353
Hurwitz, H. M. B., 390, 424
Hutterites, the, 48
Hyman, Herbert, 238, 242

Identity, 218–219. See also Ego
Illness, social definitions of, 47–51 passim
Indices in public health, 103–105
Individual differences, 51–71 passim: in constitution, 68–70; in detecting chronic conditions, 66; in discrimination capacities, 150–151; in diseases and disorders, 62; factors influencing, 53–56; health status

and, 55; in intelligence, 66–68; in kinesthetic sensation, 66; in other societies, 53–54; patterns of, 61–71; in perception, 63–66, 172–175; in perception of bodily change, 66, 156–157; in personality style, 56–57, 174; and problems of generalization, 57–60; in reading of x-rays, 174–175; in response to pain, 156–157; in taste and smell, 65–66; in touch, 65; in vision and hearing, 63–64

Insko, Chester A., Jr., 467, 475
Instincts, 200–201, 202–210 *passim*
Institute for Social Research, 121, 131
Interaction, 30
Interpersonal communication, 511–521
Irwin, Orvis C., 341, 342, 350, 352
Isolation experiments: with animals, 154–156, 346–348; with humans, 391–393
Ittelson, William H., 159–160, 178

JACKSON, J., 514, 521
Jahoda, Marie, 48, 51, 218, 223, 238, 242, 298, 309
Jain sect, 287
James, William, 200, 318, 332
Janet, Pierre, 201
Janis, Irving L., 391–392, 425, 468–469, 475, 476
Johnson, M. L., 162, 178
Jones, A., 390, 425
Jones, Edward E., 305, 310
Jung, Carl G., 200

KAGAN, Jerome, 350, 353
Kalish, Richard A., 288, 292
Katz, Daniel, 296, 307, 309, 310, 508, 510
Kegeles, S. Stephen, 396, 425
Kelley, Earl C., 375, 379, 519, 522
Kelley, Harold H., 392, 425, 468–469, 475, 476
Kelly, George A., 226, 228, 242
Kelman, Herbert C., 410, 427
Kendall, Patricia L., 499, 509
Kermit, Mark L., 172, 179
Keys, Ancel B., 251–253, 255
Kilpatrick, Franklin P., 37, 159–160, 178, 271, 291
Kimball, S. T., 387, 424
Kimble, Gregory A., 359, 367, 378, 379
King, Stanley H., 49, 51, 130, 131
Kirscht, John P., 280, 282, 291, 292, 407, 426
Kish, G. B., 390, 424

Klapper, Joseph T., 466, 475, 499, 501, 509
Klein, Donald C., 75, 83
Kluckhohn, Clyde, 27–28, 95, 97, 263, 265, 290
Kluckhohn, Florence R., 277–278, 291
Knutson, Andie L., 5, 6, 51, 65, 70, 76, 83, 110, 115, 160, 178, 186–187, 192, 193, 214, 223, 244, 250–251, 254, 255, 264, 280, 282, 284, 289, 290, 291, 292, 293, 407, 426, 434, 440, 458, 464, 472, 474, 475, 476, 502, 509, 514, 521
Koch, Sigmund, 359, 378
Kohler, Rika, 305, 310
Kohler, Wolfgang, 184, 192
Koos, Earl L., 49, 51, 408, 426
Kornhauser, Arthur, 276, 291, 457, 474
Korzybski, Alfred, 464, 475
Krasner, Leonard, 430, 433, 434, 440
Krech, David, 98, 100, 115, 244–248 *passim*, 255, 296, 298, 308, 309, 310, 359, 361, 378, 399, 400, 420–421, 426, 427
Kretschmer, E., 68
Kubzansky, Philip E., 390, 425

LANDRETH, Catherine, 206–207, 211, 340–343, 352, 371, 379
LaPierre, Richard T., 306, 310
Larkins, William T., 11
Lazarsfeld, Paul F., 250, 255, 303, 310, 499, 503–504, 508, 509, 510
Lazarus, Richard S., 359, 378
Leadership skills, 56–57
Learning: and anxiety, 391, 414–417; and awareness, 429–433; of concepts, 338–339; cultural theories of, 376; definitions of, 367–372; and deprivation, 334–353 *passim;* and ego-involvement, 410; and experience, 369–370; exploratory behavior in, 399–405; and the growing edge, 423–424; as improvement, 370–372; of inappropriate behaviors, 408–409; and integration, 421–423; of language, 339–343; and maturation, 368–369; and motivation, 389–399; and participation, 409–412; and perception, 151–156, 334–353 *passim,* 388–390, 402–403; of roles, 327–328; of rules, 322; situations in public health, 380–387; and social groups, 412–417; and socialization, 315–333; theories of, 359–379; and thwarting, 405; transfer of, 417–421; of values, 318, 320–323; values and, 372–376

Leeper, Robert W., 491–493, 497
Leventhal, Howard, 396, 425
Levin, Harry, 275, 291, 332, 333
Levine, Jerome M., 305, 310, 362, 378
Levinson, Daniel J., 122, 131
Lewin, Kurt, 138–139, 143, 181–182, 184–185, 192, 264, 290, 372, 379, 413, 427, 471, 476
Lieberman, Seymour, 302, 310
Life, value of, 284–288, 397–398
Life cycle: food and the, 134–135; learning and, 368–369. *See also* Behavioral cycle
Likert, Rensis, 298
Lindemann, Erich, 39, 43, 75, 83
Lindzey, Gardner, 224, 274, 291
Linton, Ralph, 92, 96, 97, 118–119, 130, 131
Lionberger, Herbert F., 424, 427
Lippitt, Ronald, 289, 292
Lippmann, Walter, 176, 179
Lipset, Seymour M., 301, 302, 309
Livingston, William K., 157, 158
Lofquist, Lloyd H., 411, 427
Long, L., 341, 352
Lord, Edith, 328–329, 333
Lumsdaine, Arthur A., 366, 379, 468–469, 475, 476, 501–502, 509
Lund, F. H., 467, 475
Lurie, Louis A., 69, 71
Lynd, Robert S., 158

Maccoby, Eleanor E., 275, 291, 332, 333
MacKinnon, C. Frances, 503, 509
MacKinnon, Donald W., 213, 223
MacLeod, Robert B., 181, 192
Mahrer, A. R., 434, 440
Man-nature value orientation, 280–281
Mangold, Walter, 10
Margolin, Joseph B., 349, 353
Marquis, Donald G., 408, 426
Martiz, Pedro, 191, 193
Maslow, Abraham H., 200, 243–254 *passim*, 255
Mathews, Betty P., 439, 441
Mausner, B., 434, 440
McCarthy, Dorothea A., 341, 343, 350, 352
McClintock, Charles, 307, 310
McDill, Edward L., 301, 309
McDougall, William, 200, 201
McGuire, William, 305, 310
McNeil, Donald R., 308, 310
McPhee, William N., 304, 310
Mead, George, 318, 332
Mead, Margaret, 34, 37, 284, 292, 329–330, 333, 376, 379
Mechanic, David, 130, 131

Mednick, Sarnoff A., 359, 377, 420, 427
Melzack, Ronald, 346–348, 353
Merton, Robert K., 126, 131, 503–504, 505, 509, 510
Metzner, Charles A., 499, 509
Mielke, Robert, 79, 83
Miller, Alan D., 349, 353
Miller, Clyde R., 464, 475
Miller, Norman, 467, 475
Miller, Walter B., 102, 115
Mishler, E., 514, 521
Mitford, Jessica, 288, 292
Morris, Charles, 269, 290
Mosel, James N., 366, 378, 383, 424
Motivation, 197–255: in communication, 511–521 *passim;* in infancy, 205–208; learning and, 389–399; and operant conditioning, 428–429; patterns of, 243–255; a theory of, 208, 225–242; values and, 264–265
Motivation research, 212–223
Motives: biogenic, 203–204; conflicting, 214; indirect measurement of, 217–223; inferring of, 214–215; motive-response relationships, 215–216; problems in definition, 213–214; sociogenic, 203–204; validity of, 217; value quality as, 216–217
Mountin, Joseph W., 270, 279, 290, 357, 358
Mowrer, O. H., 359, 378
Muenzinger, Karl F., 153, 158
Munn, Norman L., 359, 378
Murai, Mary M., 132
Murelius, Olof, 237, 242
Murphy, Gardner, 29, 37, 40, 43, 45, 50–51, 69, 71, 152, 158, 159, 163, 168–169, 178, 201, 204–205, 208, 210, 211, 293, 305, 309, 310, 334, 351, 362, 378
Murphy, Lois, 293, 309
Murray, Edward J., 434, 440
Murray, Henry A., 27, 28, 200, 263, 265, 290
Musgrave, Barbara S., 429, 439
Mussen, Paul H., 223, 350, 353
Myrdal, Gunnar, 289, 292

Nagel, Ernest, 184, 192
National Institute of Mental Health, 344, 348, 349
National Institutes of Health, 121
National Research Council, 141, 143
National Tuberculosis Association, 76, 79
Neal, Helen, 450, 454
Newcomb, Theodore M., 98, 115, 204, 210, 293, 487–489, 497

Nimkoff, Meyer, 203, 210
Nissen, Henry W., 203, 210
Nonverbal communication, 428–441 *passim*, 515–517
Nuthmann, A. M., 436, 441
Nyswander, Dorothy B., 10, 11, 76, 83, 413, 427

OBJECTIVE facts, 40–41, 183–184
Ongerth, Henry J., 65, 70
Operant conditioning, 364–366, 428–441
Orne, Martin T., 437–438, 441
Osgood, Charles E., 429, 439

PACKARD, Vance O., 219, 224
Pain: perception of, 156–157, 188; as subjective state, 41
Parent education, 331–332
Parsons, Talcott, 91, 97, 130, 131
Participation: learning and, 409–412; motivation and, 215–216
Paul, Benjamin D., 95, 97, 156, 158
Pavlov, Ivan P., 200, 359, 364
Payne, Stanley Le Baron, 434, 440
Pearsall, Marion, 387, 424
Perception: and action, 159–160; chimpanzee, studies of, 154–156; and communication, 517–521; constancy in, 162–165; defense mechanisms in, 172–173; definitions of, 147, 149, 159; difficulties in research on, 152; dynamic nature of, 161–162; factors influencing, 171–175; field theory and, 48 ff.; functions of, 159–178 *passim;* and impressions of people, 486–487; indirect nature of, 167; individual differences in, 171–175; in infancy, 334–338; and innate capacities, 150–151; and interpersonal relations, 511–521 *passim;* and learning, 151–156, 334–353 *passim,* 388–390, 402–403; and maturation, 152; of pain, 156–157, 188; personality factors and, 174–175; of physiological change, 156–157; process of, 165–170; sensitivity of process of, 170–171; social, 520–521; stereotyping in, 176–177. *See also* Individual differences
Perceptual act, 169
Perceptual curiosity, 389–391
Personal security-insecurity, 249–251
Personality: constitution and, 68–70; food and, 138; geography and, 32–34; groups and, 35–36, 38–40; perception and, 172–175
Personality style and perception, 174–175

Persuasion, 307–308, 504–506
Piaget, Jean, 338–339, 341, 352
Pierre the Pelican pamphlets, 503
Pineda, Virginia G. de, 280, 292
Pintner, R., 275, 291
Pisoni, Stephanie, 434, 436, 440, 441
Play, 327–328
Polgar, Steven, 79, 83, 238, 242
Pollio, Howard R., 359, 377, 420, 427
Position and status, 117–119
Postman, Leo J., 218, 219, 224
Prasad, B. G., 136–137, 143
Primacy, law of, 467–468
Private world, 180–193: communication and, 518–521; concept of, 180–181; and culture, 96
Professional groups, as reference groups, 109–115
Psychological readiness, 390–399: law of readiness, 363
Psychological set, 162: and communication, 477–478, 506. *See also* Psychological readiness

RAMSEY, Glenn V., 159, 178
Reading disabilities, 348–351
Recency, law of, 467–468
Redlich, Fredrick C., 49, 51, 104, 115
Rees, Linford, 68, 70
Reference groups, 98–115 *passim:* American Public Health Association as an example, 110–115; and attitude formation, 107, 113–114, 237–238; and attitude change, 307–308; communication and, 487–489; definition of, 106–107; and membership groups, 106–115
Relationship value orientation, 283
Riesen, Austin H., 153–155, 158, 207, 211
Robbins, Paul R., 391, 425
Roberts, Beryl J., 10, 161, 178, 408, 426
Robinson, James Harvey, 338, 352
Rockefeller Sanitary Commission, 49, 51
Rogers, Edward S., 10
Rokeach, Milton, 297, 300, 309
Role, 117–130: and attitudes, 302, definitions of, 119–120; and health, 129–130; learning of, 327–328; and rehabilitation, 36; of staff and line, 120–122
Role conflicts, 128–129
Role definition, 122–125
Role dilemmas, 122
Role sets, 126
Role-taking, 126–127
Romano-V., Octavio I., 118–119, 130

Rose, Arnold M., 122, 131
Rosenberg, Milton J., 294, 309
Rosenstock, Irwin M., 396, 425
Roshal, Sol M., 403, 426
Rudin, Stanley A., 157, 158
Rumble strips, 172–173
Rundquist, Edward A., 250, 255
Russell Sage Foundation, 5, 6, 10, 11

SALZINGER, Kurt, 428–430 passim, 434–436 passim, 439, 440, 441
Salzinger, Suzanne, 436, 441
Sanford, Fillmore H., 464–465, 475, 517, 522
Sarbin, Theodore, 122, 131, 438, 441
Sarnoff, Irving, 307, 310
Saunders, Lyle, 95, 97, 279–282 passim, 291, 292
Schachter, Stanley, 480–484 passim, 496, 497, 512, 521
Schiele, Burtrum C., 251–253, 255
Schneider, David M., 27, 28, 263, 265, 290
Schramm, Wilbur, 445, 447, 499, 502, 509
Schwahn, Wilson E., 359, 378
Schwartz, Arnold D., 75, 83
Scott, John P., 368, 379
Sears, Robert R., 275, 291, 332, 333
Seiden, Richard H., 346, 353
Self, 31, 230–242 passim, 318 ff. See also Ego; Identity
Self-action, 30
Self-anchoring scale, 271–273
Self-image, 31, 230 ff., 318 ff.
Selltiz, Claire, 218, 223, 298, 309
Selye, Hans, 69, 71
Senden, M. von, 153, 158
Shapiro, Leona R., 132
Shattuck, Lemuel, 279
Sheffield, Fred D., 468–469, 475, 476, 501–502, 509
Sheldon, W. H., 68
Sherif, Carolyn W., 486, 497
Sherif, Muzafer, 230, 233, 242, 294, 304, 309, 310, 477–478, 485–486, 489, 496, 497
Sherman, Susan Roth, 437, 441
Sherrington, Sir Charles Scott, 41, 43
Shibutani, Tamotsu, 122, 131
Shils, Edward A., 91, 97
Shimberg, Benjamin, 78, 110, 115, 187–188, 193, 264, 290, 385–386, 424, 464, 475
Shneidman, Edwin S., 288, 292
Sigerist, Henry E., 48, 51
Simmel, Arnold, 301, 309
Simmons, Leo W., 69, 71
Simmons, Ozzie G., 95, 97

Skeels, Harold M., 343–345, 353
Skinner, B. F., 208–209, 211, 365, 378, 428–429, 433, 439, 440
Skinner, Mary Lou, 110, 115
Skodak, Marie, 344, 353
Sleeper effect, 466
Sletto, Raymond F., 250, 255
Smell, 65–66
Smith, Charles E., 7, 10, 12
Smith, George H., 219, 224
Smith, Kate, 505
Smith, M. Brewster, 51, 266, 290, 295–302 passim, 309, 321, 332
Smock, Charles D., 422, 427
Snygg, Donald, 181, 192, 230
Social class, 99–106: and caste, 105–106; definitions of, 99–102; implications of, 103; indices of, 103–105; measures of, 103–105
Social comparison theory, 480–481
Social environment, 87–144 passim: definition of, 87–88
Social status: and communications, 513–515; and food, 140–141; and placement, 93–94; and position, 117–119
Socialization, 314–353: definition of, 315; experimental study of, 322–326; parent role in, 331; slow development and, 45–46; of values, 285–286, 320–323. See also Learning
Socializing agents, 316–318, 328–332
Society: characteristics of, 92–94; distinguished from culture, 91–92; placement in, 93–94, 98–115 passim
Solley, Charles M., 152, 158, 159, 168–170, 178
Solomon, Philip, 425
Source credibility, 464–465, 506–509
Spicer, Edward H., 374, 379, 389, 412, 424, 427
Spock, Benjamin, 73
Spoerl, Dorothy T., 275, 291
Spranger, Edward, 273–274, 291
Spranger's value types, 273–274
Srole, Leo, 301, 309
Staats, Arthur W., 436, 441
Stacey, Chalmers L., 224
Stagner, Ross, 157, 158
Starbuck, Nancy, 186, 192
Stauffer, Samuel A., 250, 255
Stendler, Cecilia B., 335, 351
Stereotypes, 176, 452–453, 460
Stiles, Charles W., 49, 51
Stimpson, David V., 293
Stock, Dorothy, 217, 223
Stotland, E., 296, 309
Stress, 68–69, 73, 75, 173

Strodtbeck, Fred L., 277–278, 291
Subjective facts, 40–41, 183–184
Suchman, Edward A., 88, 89
Suci, George J., 429, 439
Swanson, Guy E., 289, 292
Switzer, John, 238, 242

TANNENBAUM, Percy H., 429, 439, 452–453, 454
Taste, 65–66
Taylor, William, 408, 426
Thelen, Herbert A., 217, 223
Thomas, William I., 293, 309
Thompson, William R., 346–348, 353
Thorndike, Edward L., 200, 362–363, 365, 378, 405–406, 426, 428–431 passim, 439, 440
Thurstone, Louis L., 298, 309
Time value orientation, 281–282
Toch, Hans H., 202, 210
Tolman, Edward C., 406–408 passim, 426
Top level bias, 276–277, 456
Touch, 65
Transaction, 29–31
Transfer of learning, 417–421
Trial and error learning, 362–364
Triplett, Richard J., 275, 291
Tropp, A., 514, 521
Tyler, Leona E., 61, 67, 68, 70

UNIQUENESS, 42–60
United States Public Health Service, 10, 11, 76, 79, 301, 357, 450

VALUE orientations, 277–284
Values: in administration, 275–277, 289; American, 268–270; and attitude climate, 487–489; and attitudes, 259, 299; and change, 374; and communication, 456–457, 460–461; definitions, 262–264; family planning, 286; health, 270, 284–288 passim; and health programs, 380–387 passim; held by women, 275; inferred from behavior, 266–267; influences on health, 49–50, 261–289 passim; and learning, 372–376 learning of, 265–266, 320–323; life, 284–288, 397–398; and motivation, 265; prenatal and infant care, 285; of resistance, 374; and social analysis, 289–290
Veblen, Thorstein, 141
Verbal conditioning, 428–441: awareness in, 429–433; and diagnosis, 435–436; and experimental research, 437–438; and opinion surveys, 434–435; and public health, 433–439; and therapy, 433–434. See also Operant conditioning
Vernon, Philip E., 274, 275, 291
Verplanck, W. S., 430, 434, 440
Vision, 63–64
Volkart, Edmund H., 87, 89, 130, 131

WAGMAN, Morton, 307, 310
Walkely, Rosabelle P., 36, 37, 306, 310
Warren, Howard C., 200
Water potability, 65–66
Watson, John B., 200
Weaver, Warren, 58, 60
Weil, Robert J., 48, 51
Weiss, Walter, 466, 475
Welch, Livingston, 340, 341, 350, 352
Welles, Orson, 465, 506
Wessen, A. F., 514, 521
Westie, Frank R., 306, 310
White, David M., 499, 509
White, Robert W., 295–302 passim, 309
Whitehead, Alfred North, 34, 37, 149, 392, 423–424, 425, 427
Whorf, Benjamin L., 34, 37
Wickes, T. A., Jr., 434, 440
Wiebe, Gerhart D., 456, 474, 504, 510
Wiener, Norbert, 39, 43
Wilkinson, H. J., 390, 425
Williams, Robert J., 69, 71
Williams, Robin M., 269, 270, 290
Wilner, Daniel M., 36, 37, 306, 310
Winslow, Charles E., 279
Wolfenstein, Martha, 40, 43
Wolff, Harold G., 69, 71
Women, values of, 275
Work and food, 136–138
Wright, Beatrice A., 411, 427
Wright, Herbert F., 42, 43

X-RAY surveys, 76–79, 219–221, 391–392, 395–397, 502
X-rays, reading of, 174–175

YARROW, Leon J., 343, 353
Yerushalmy, Jacob, 10, 174–175, 179
Yolles, Stanley F., 349, 353
Yoshioka, J. G., 512, 521
Young, Donald, 10
Young, Paul T., 200, 210, 224, 359, 378

ZANDER, Alvin, 387, 413, 424, 427
Zawadzki, Bohan, 250, 255
Zborowski, Mark, 156, 158
Zimmer, Herbert, 390, 425
Znaniecki, Florian, 293, 309
Zolkas, Helen H., 349, 353